Ferguson & Johnson

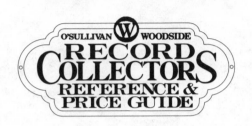

O'SULLIVAN WOODSIDE
RECORD
COLLECTORS
REFERENCE &
PRICE GUIDE

1ST EDITION

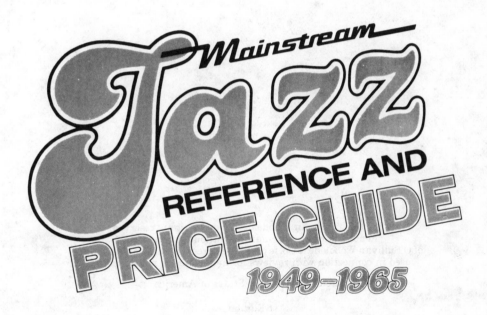

Mainstream Jazz REFERENCE AND PRICE GUIDE 1949-1965

O'SULLIVAN
WOODSIDE
BOOK PUBLISHER

Table of Contents

Dedicated to Linda Ferguson for relentless hours of continued research, support, devotion, love, understanding and for just being my wife and sharing my love of jazz.

C. Ferguson

*In Memory Of
The Late, Great
Herb "Mr. J" Johnson
Jazz Pioneer Of Arizona*

Appreciation

We wish to express our gratitude to the many friends, associates, fellow enthusiasts and collectors who contributed in a great number of ways to the creation of this book. The encouragement, support and varied degrees of assistance have combined and blended to generate the energy necessary to keep the momentum going to bring this guide to what it is. There is no conceivable way to name each and every one of the persons responsible, but we would like to note the few who have been a part from the beginning: Mary "MT" Terrell, William "Bill" Salt, Ruth and Larry Floyd, Vertis King, Jeff of Jeff's Classical Records and Joe of Grass Roots Records.

From a less personal perspective are the recording companies and publishers we have referred to or who have made available upon request the data we needed in our attempt to bring you the most comprehensive information possible. Alphabetically, these companies include:

Aladdin Records
A&M Records
Argo/Cadet Records
Bethlehem Records
Capitol Records
Columbia Records
Commodore Records
Down Beat Magazine, 1952 - 1965
EmArcy Records
Everest Records
Fantasy Records
Leonard Feather's Encyclopedia of Jazz
   Vol. 1 - 1960; Vol. 2 - 1966; Vol. 3 - 1976

Gene Norman Presents Records
Impulse Records
Mercury Records
Metronome Magazine, 1959 - 1961
Panassié and Gauder -
   Guide to Jazz 1956
Prestige Records
RCA Records
Riverside Records
Savoy Records
Schwann Catalogs, 1949 - 1965
United Artists Records
Verve Records

Foreword

To simplify matters before you begin, we would like to give you a few highlights of the format used to list the recordings in this book.

The first listing you will find after the name of a recording is the original release. After this number, date and price you will find any EP (extended play) records that were released with the same subject matter. EP's are listed by record number only and are not listed by title. They can be located under artist and label they were released on. After the EP listing we have included the reissues of the recording along with the price and date only if it is not retitled. If it has been retitled you should undoubtedly find it listed later under the artist. You will also note that we have supplied short label descriptions throughout the book to serve as constant reminders of something directly related to the label it accompanies.

In addition to the above, we would also like to say just a few words regarding obvious qualities to be aware of while you are looking to enhance your collection.

Aside from most anything but their condition, the most valuable recording you can possess is a test pressing; these are the very first cuts of a recording. Disc jockey and signature (autographed) recordings are the next most valuable record to find; however, these will value only slightly more than the original release, which would be the next most valuable. The value of all of the above depends solely upon the condition of the record. A mint condition record is one that obviously has not been played or played very little and shows no signs of adverse handling and should still be in its original cover. A near-mint condition record will show slight signs of use but will allow you to listen to an undisturbed and clear sound when played as the result of not having scratches or surface defects.

A very easy way to determine whether a record is an original or possibly a reissue is the record weight. The older recordings will have a least three times the weight of reissues of later years. Take your time and read the labels carefully. Often times the only clue to a record's time origin is so obscure that it can easily be overlooked.

We have used these guidelines, among many others, to aid in the value determination of the recordings in this book. You may wish to pay more or less than we have indicated, and understandably so. This decision is entirely up to you, but you must keep in mind that a record has little or no material or monetary value if it is in very poor condition.

The very best to you and your collection!

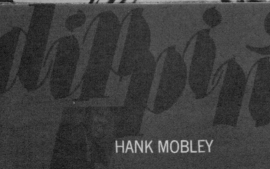

Introduction

The primary purpose of this book is to convey to you, the collector, a comprehensive compilation of our knowledge of jazz music in a combination of aesthetic, historical and monetary values.

It is our intention to reveal all jazz artists within the realm of mainstream, cool and be-bop from 1949 through 1965 that we are aware of, regardless of their degree of significance or impact on the jazz audience. We firmly believe that, as with anything of aesthetic value, a person must acquire a knowledge for the depth and high quality of jazz. It is indeed a privilege to have the opportunity to contribute to the history of this form of art and to give credit due to the many fine musicians who created and maintained its uniqueness.

There are instances of feeling that cannot possibly be put into words that come as a result of finally discovering the eluding record that has been the object of a long and tedious search. We are confident that, as a serious collector, this "wordless" excitement and satisfaction is not completely foreign to you. Coming upon that certain Charlie Parker, Billie Holiday or Lester Young original recording is just the beginning; to listen to a clear, unmarred piece of art coming from the turntable is additionally unbelievable; but, to find that the source of this dream come true has even been autographed, the cover actually touched, is more than one can ever hope for! But it happens, and this is what gives dated, original masterpieces their values. Finding such a recording in such condition allows one to enjoy an undisturbed recreation of the era, decades ago, in which jazz was newborn, exploring and on the verge of establishing ground on which to grow.

Keep in mind that this book is to serve as a record guide and not a historical or biographical layout for each of the artists. You will find a short entry on individuals who may seem more familiar than most, but we have also attempted to bring to light some of those persons whose works are not as well known. In many cases, superb musicians may have only one or a very few recordings to his/her credit but can be found as an outstanding backup on many other well-known cuts with more recognized artists.

Considerable research has gone into the price determination for each of the records listed. There are various points to consider and keep in mind before an appraisal can be made. In all fairness, we have solicited opinions from a variety of collectors and jazz enthusiasts, and the values given are those that we feel are warranted for mint and near-mint condition recordings. However, because this book represents only our knowledgeable price opinion, we certainly realize that it may be justly disputed; and we are open to any and all concerned feedback regarding its content, pro or con.

Please keep in mind as well that we have gathered this information and presented it to you to the best of our ability and in the very best of faith but cannot, unfortunately, fully warrant or guarantee the complete preciseness or accuracy of all data we have conveyed to you. We found many hindrances in our research and discovered that not all of the recording companies and sources of information contacted cared to share their wealth of jazz history. Consequently, you will find that rather than mislead you or give you incorrect information, we have omitted unclear data to prevent confusing you with our "educated guesses." Please inform us of our errors and any inadvertent oversights you may detect. We welcome any additional information or input you may have to offer.

Nat Adderley
Autobiography

NEVER SAY YES • STONY ISLAND • JUNKANOO • LOVE SAMBA • WORK SONG
LITTLE BOY WITH THE SAD EYES • THE OLD COUNTRY • SERMONETTE
NAT ADDERLEY PLAYS THE...

'65
ARRANGED AND CONDUCTED BY
Peter Matz

CANNONBALL
ADDERLEY
Quintet
in chicago

LULLABY OF BIRDL
And Other Famous Hits

THE MASTERSOUNDS

jackie mclean

NEW JAZZ 8212 • ORLEANS

**BLUE
STARS**
of France

Mose Allison

SWINGIN' MACHINE

1398

mildred bailey

sings

"*... and the blues*"

ArGO
JAZZ
720

**LOREZ
ALEXAND**

FOR SWINGERS ON

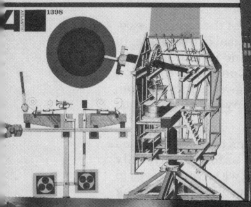

**Pat Bowie
Out of Sight!**

PRESTIGE

RCA
CAMDEN
LONG PLAY 33⅓ RPM

**Basie's
Basement
Count Basie**
AND HIS ORCHESTRA INCLUDING
Jimmy Rushing
Hey, Pretty Baby
Seventh Avenue Express
Walking Slow Behind You
Mister Roberts' Roost
Don't You Want a Man Like Me
South
The Jungle King
Sophisticated Swing
House Rent Boogie
Basie's Basement!
Brand New Wagon

*Pieces of
Eighty-Eight*
**EVANS
BRADSHAW
Trio**

Label Descriptions

The following list should serve as a description guide for identifying most of the labels in this book. Refer to exhibit indicated for visual clarifications.

ARGO - Original label (A1); changed in 1965 (A2); changed again in latter part of 1965 to Cadet Records on dark blue and light blue label with Cadet in pink and white (A3).

ATLANTIC - Originals before the 60's on black label with silver lettering (B1); mono on red and violet label; stereo on green and blue label (B2) both with logo on right side in black square; 1964 had same colors with logo on right side and Atlantic vertically in middle of logo (B3); Atlantic across bottom of logo (B4) will not be listed.

BETHLEHEM - Originals (C1 & C2) are maroon with silver lettering; recordings issued in the 60's are maroon with silver lettering and King at the bottom of the label.

BLUE NOTE - Original blue and white labels are #1500-1542 with Lexington address on label; #1543 with W. 63rd, New York (NY) address on label (D1); #4100 with New York (NY) only on label (D2); later with A Division of Liberty (D3) or A Division of United Artists (D4) on label. The only reason the latter two are listed is because they are still on the original blue and white label.

CAPITOL - Originals of the 50's on green label with logo on top (E1); 1958 black label with logo on left side (E2); 1962 black label with logo on top (E3); 1963 tan and black label with logo on top, a special edition of Capitol "Dimensions In Jazz" (E4) in addition to black label recordings with logo on top.

CLEF - Released by Mercury (Mercury/Clef) as 10" with trumpeter logo; 12" Clef has trumpeter logo (F1); in 1957 Verve bought Clef and originals say Clef Series and have trumpeter logo with Verve Records, Inc. on bottom of label (F2) and Clef Series without the trumpeter logo are reissues.

A1

A2

A3

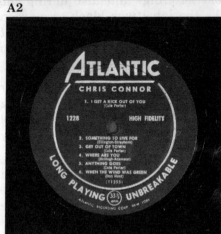

B1

B2

B3

B4

C1

COLUMBIA - Originals from 1954-56 are on red label with gold lettering (G1); originals from 1956-62 are on red label with three black logos on each side (G2); from 1962 on red label with one white logo on each side (G3).

CONTEMPORARY - Original (H1 & H2) mono on yellow label with black lettering; original stereo is black label with gold lettering; later came a light orange label which will not be listed in this book.

DECCA - Original label is black with gold lettering, and also during the 50's the label was black or maroon with silver lettering (I1); in the 60's it changed to black with rainbow strip and Decca through the middle (I2).

EMARCY - Original has drummer logo on top (J1); 1958 is EmArcy Jazz within Mercury logo on top of label (J2); 1965 is a gray label with EmArcy logo forming a circle on label (J3).

FANTASY - Original mono was red label with silver lettering during the 50's (K1); from 1958 and during the 60's stereo was released on blue label with silver lettering.

IMPULSE - All Impulse recordings listed in this book are on orange labels (L1).

LIBERTY - Originals were on green and sometimes blue label with silver lettering (M1).

MAINSTREAM - Originals began in 1965 on black and light blue label with microphone on right side (N1). This label is the only one listed in this book.

MERCURY - Originals released beginning in 1955 on black label with silver lettering (O1). In the 60's it changed to a red label with Mercury man logo on upper left side (O2).

METRO JAZZ - Originals of the 50's on red label with black lettering, Metro Jazz at top, lion head in O of Metro and MGM Records, A Division of Loew's, Inc., on bottom of label (P1); in 1965 Metro only on top of black label with silver lettering and Metro Records, A Division of Metro Goldwyn Mayer, Inc., on bottom (P2).

MGM - 1955 Original label was black and yellow with lion head on top with MGM Records, A Division of Loew's,

C2

D1

D2

D3

D4

E1

E2

E3

E4

F1

F2

G1

G2

G3

H1

H2

Inc., on bottom (Q1); the 60's have lion head on top with multicolored MGM on black label and MGM, A Division of Metro Goldwyn Mayer, Inc., on bottom (Q2).

KING - Originals of the 50's on black label with silver lettering without crown on top (R1); 1960s changed to blue label without crown on top of label.

PACIFIC JAZZ - First 12″ LPs released on black label with silver lettering and Pacific Jazz on top (S1) and all reissues of these recordings from 1955-58 on World Pacific retained same number as on Pacific Jazz; 1958 the label only changed to World Pacific on top of label (S2); in 1960 Pacific Jazz came out again in addition to World Pacific (S3).

PRESTIGE - Originals on yellow label with New York address on top are numbers 7001-7141 (T1); beginning #7142 in 1957-64 on yellow label with Bergenfield address on top of label (T2); in 1964 changed to blue label with logo on right and Bergenfield address on bottom of label (T3).

RIVERSIDE - #12-201 thru 12-242 originals of 1955-56 are on white label (U1); #12-243 is mono on blue label (U2); in 1958 stereo was released on black label; all three labels have two reels and a microphone on the top and Bill Grauer Productions on bottom.

ROULETTE - Originals of the 50's are on white label with multicolored pinwheel (V1); in late 1959 released on light and dark orange checked roulette wheel label (V2).

SAVOY - Originals released on maroon label with musical note in center and silver lettering and are the only ones in this book (W1).

UNITED ARTISTS - Originals from 1958-59 on red label with United Artists on top (X1); 1959 on black label with New York address on bottom and colored circles on top (X2); 1962 on gray label with silhouette of sax player on right side (X3).

VANGUARD - Originals on maroon label with silver lettering are covered in this book (Y1).

VERVE - Original labels have Verve on top and Verve Records, Inc. on

I1

I2

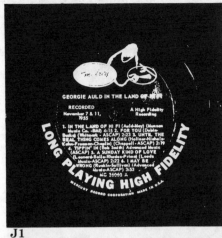

J1

J2

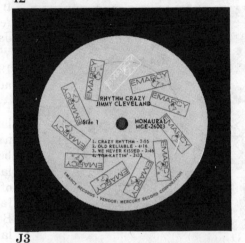

J3

K1

bottom of label (Z1 & Z2); 1962-65 Verve is on top and MGM on bottom of label (Z3); after the 60's Verve is on top and MGM with Sunset address is on bottom but these are not listed in this book.

You will find that several records will have the recording date on them and not the release date. For example, many World Pacific records will show a 1956 date but World Pacific was not actually in existence until 1958 and many will be reissues of Pacific Jazz recordings of the early 50's.

The following is a list of major labels and the dates that they came into existence and were first issued in LP form:

1949 - Columbia, Decca, Mercury, Concert Hall and Allegro.

1950 - Commodore, Atlantic, Continental, Brunswick, Discovery, Imperial, RCA Victor, Savoy, Stinson and REM.

Early 1950's - Aladdin, Bethlehem, Blue Note, Clef, Contemporary, Debut, EmArcy, Fantasy, Hi Lo, Norgran, Pacific Jazz, Prestige and Riverside.

L1

N1

M1

O1

O2

P1

P2

Q1

Q2

R1

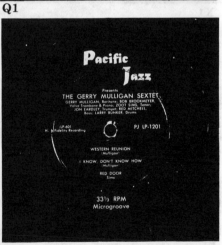

S1

S2

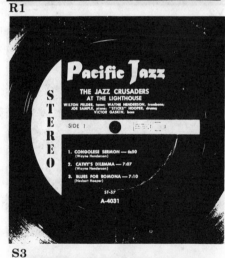

S3

T1

T2

T3

XV

U1

U2

V1

V2

W1

X1

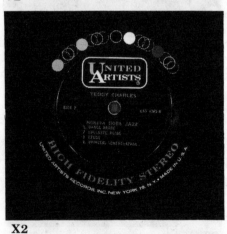

X2

X3

Y1

Z1

Z2

Z3

AHMED ABDUL-MALIK

bass, several instruments
born - 1927 Brooklyn, NY

JAZZ SAHARA — Riverside 12-287/1121 (1958) blue label with Bill Grauer Pro. **$40**.

EAST MEETS WEST — RCA Victor 2015 (1959) dog on top **$40**.

THE MUSIC OF — New Jazz 8266 (1961) **$25**.

SOUNDS OF AFRICA — New Jazz 8282 (1963) **$25**.

SPELL BOUND — Status 8303 (1965) **$20**.

JERRI ADAMS

vocals - born 1930 Cincinnatti, OH

IT'S COOL INSIDE — Columbia 916 (1956) red label with 3 black logos on each side **$45**.

PLAY FOR KEEPS — Columbia 1258 (1959) red label with 3 black logos on each side **$40**.

PEPPER ADAMS

baritone sax - born 1930 Highland Park, IL

A player of all woodwinds, Adams was influenced by Duke Ellington's baritone player, Harry Carney. Considered to be one of the finest baritone sax players, Adams' career began in the early 50's and, in the mid-50's, found him performing with musicians of such notability as Kenny Burrell and Maynard Ferguson. Continuing to date, some of Adams' best pieces can be found on recordings with Donald Byrd on the Blue Note label.

PEPPER ADAMS — Mode 112 (1957) **$60**; *reissued* Interlude 502/1002 (1959) **$45**.

CRITIC'S CHOICE — World Pacific 407 (1958) **$45**.

COOL SOUND — Regent 6066 (1958) green label **$45**.

PEPPER-KNEPPER QUINTET — Metrojazz 1004 (1958) **$40**.

10 TO 4 AT THE FIVE SPOT CAFE/with Donald Byrd — Riverside 12-265/1104 (1958) blue label with Bill Grauer Pro. **$40**.

MOTOR CITY SCENE — Bethlehem 6056 (1960) maroon label **$40**.

OUT OF THIS WORLD/with Donald Byrd — Warwick 2041 (1961) **$50**.

PLAYS THE COMPOSITIONS OF CHARLIE MINGUS — Jazz Workshop 219 (1963) **$35**.

THE SOUL OF JAZZ PERCUSSION — Warwick 5003 (1963) **$35**.

JULIAN "CANNONBALL" ADDERLEY

alto sax - born 1928 Tampa, FL died 1975

Adderley burst on the jazz scene with his own recordings on the Savoy label becoming famous with his on-and-off work with a Miles Davis group which included John Coltrane. "Cannonball" worked with his brother Nat Adderley and other notable sidemen such as Joe Zawinul and Yusef Lateef. One of his most significant hits was *Mercy, Mercy, Mercy*, being adapted in many different musical styles. Adderley continued to work until his death in 1975.

PRESENTING CANNONBALL — Savoy 12018 (1955) maroon label **$60**.

JULIAN CANNONBALL ADDERLEY — EmArcy 36043 (1955) **$45**; EP 1-6144 (1955) **$30**.

CANNONBALL ADDERLEY AND STRINGS — EmArcy 36063 (1955) **$45**; *reissued* Mercury 20652/60652 (1962) black label **$25**.

IN THE LAND OF HI FI — EmArcy 36077 (1956) **$45**.

SOPHISTICATED SWING — EmArcy 36110 (1957) **$40**.

CANNONBALL'S SHARPSHOOTERS — EmArcy 36135 (1958) **$40**; *reissued* Mercury 20531/60208 (1961) black label **$25**.

JUMP FOR JOY — EmArcy 36146 (1958) **$40**; *reissued* Mercury 20530/60207 (1961) black·label **$25**.

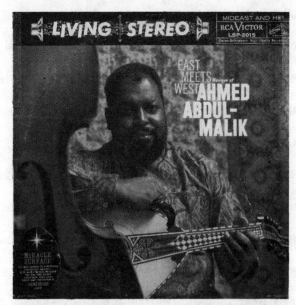

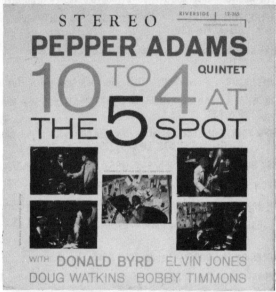

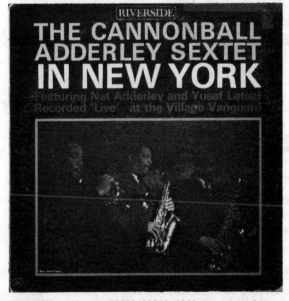

CANNONBALL ENROUTE — Mercury 20616/60616 (1962) black label **$35**.

QUINTET IN CHICAGO/with John Coltrane — Mercury 20449/60134 (1961) black label **$45**.

LUSH SIDE — Mercury 20652/60652 (1962) black label **$25**; *reissue* of EmArcy 36063.

SOMETHIN' ELSE/with Miles Davis — Blue Note 1595 (1958) with NY address on label **$45**; with A Division of Liberty on label **$20**.

PORTRAIT OF CANNONBALL — Riverside 12-269 (1958) blue label with Bill Grauer Pro. **$40**.

THINGS ARE GETTING BETTER/with Milt Jackson — Riverside 12-286/1128 (1958) blue label with Bill Grauer Pro. **$40**.

TAKES CHARGE — Riverside 12-303/1148 (1959) blue label with Bill Grauer Pro. **$35**.

IN SAN FRANCISCO — Riverside 12-311/1157 (1959) blue label with Bill Grauer Pro. **$35**; EP 3211 (1959) **$20**.

THEM DIRTY BLUES — Riverside 322/1170 (1960) blue label with Bill Grauer Pro. **$35**.

QUINTET AT THE LIGHTHOUSE — Riverside 344/9344 (1960) blue label with Bill Grauer Pro. **$35**; 7" 33 1/3 RPM EP R-33454 (1960) **$15**.

AFRICAN WALTZ — Riverside 377/9377 (1961) blue label with Bill Grauer Pro. **$30**; EP 3210 (1961) **$20**.

CHILD'S INTRODUCTION TO JAZZ — Riverside Wonderland 1435 (1961) blue label with Bill Grauer Pro. **$45**.

MOVIN' ALONG — Riverside 342/9342 (1960) blue label with Bill Grauer Pro. **$30**.

AND THE POLL WINNERS — Riverside 355/9355 (1960) blue label with Bill Grauer Pro. **$30**.

MERRY OLDE SOUL — Riverside 366/9366 (1961) blue label with Bill Grauer Pro. **$35**.

QUINTET PLUS — Riverside 388/9388 (1961) blue label with Bill Grauer Pro. **$30**.

KNOW WHAT I MEAN — Riverside 433/9433 (1961) blue label with Bill Grauer Pro. **$30**.

IN NEW YORK/with Yusef Lateef — Riverside 404/9404 (1962) blue label with Bill Grauer Pro. **$35**; EP 3224 (1962) **$25**.

BOSSA NOVA — Riverside 455/9455 (1963) blue label with Bill Grauer Pro. **$25**.

NIPPON SOUL — Riverside 477/9477 (1963) **$25**.

WITH NANCY WILSON — Capitol 1657 (1962) black label with logo on left side **$25**.

LIVE SESSION/with Ernie Andrews — Capitol 2284 (1965) black label with logo on top **$20**.

FIDDLER ON THE ROOF — Capitol 2218 (1965) black label with logo on top **$15**.

DOMINATION — Capitol 2203 (1965) black label with logo on top **$15**.

LIVE — Capitol 2399 (1965) black label with logo on top **$20**.

ROOTS/with Gil Evans Orchestra — Pacific Jazz 40 (1962) **$30**.

CANNONBALL ADDERLEY & JOHN COLTRANE — Limelight 86009/82009 (1964) **$20**; *reissue* of Mercury 20449.

NAT ADDERLEY
trumpet, cornet, composer - born 1931 Tampa, FL

A strong player influenced by Dizzy Gillespie, Clark Terry and Miles Davis, Adderley played with Woody Herman but soon after joined his brother "Cannonball's" group and on to groups of his own and recognition as a composer.

THAT'S NAT — Savoy 12021 (1955) maroon label **$40**.

INTRODUCING NAT ADDERLEY — EmArcy 36091 (1956) **$40**; EP 1-6000 (1956) **$25**.

TO THE IVY LEAGUE FROM NAT — EmArcy 36100 (1956) **$40**.

NATURALLY! — Jazzland 47/947 (1961) **$25**.

IN THE BAG — Jazzland 75/975 (1962) **$25**.

BRANCHING OUT/with Johnny Griffin and The Three Sounds — Riverside 12-285 (1958) blue label with Bill Grauer Pro. **$40**.

MUCH BRASS — Riverside 12-301/1143 (1959) blue label with Bill Grauer Pro. **$35**.

THAT'S RIGHT/with Yusef Lateef — Riverside 12-330/9330 (1960) blue label with Bill Grauer Pro. **$35**.

WORK SONG/with Wes Montgomery — Riverside 12-318/1167 (1960) blue label with Bill Grauer Pro. **$35**.

LITTLE BIG HORN — Riverside 474/9474 (1964) blue label with Bill Grauer Pro. **$25**.

AUTOBIOGRAPHY — Atlantic 1439 (1965) with logo on side **$20**.

TOSHIKO AKIYOSHI
piano - born 1929 Dairen, Manchuria

TOSHIKO'S PIANO — Norgran 22 (1954) 10" **$75**; EP 47, EP 48 (1954) **$30** ea.

THE TOSHIKO TRIO — Storyville 912 (1956) **$50**.

HER TRIO/HER QUARTET/with Boots Mossulli — Storyville 918 (1957) **$45**.

MANY SIDES OF — Verve 8273 (1958) with Verve Records, Inc. on bottom of label **$35**.

AT NEWPORT — Verve 8236 (1958) with Verve Records, Inc. on bottom of label **$35**.

UNITED NOTIONS/with Bobby Jaspar — Metrojazz 1001 (1958) **$40**.

COUNTRY & WESTERN SOUNDS OF JAZZ — Dauntless 4308/6308 (1963) **$25**.

TOSHIKO-MARIANO QUARTET — Candid 8012 (1960) **$40**.

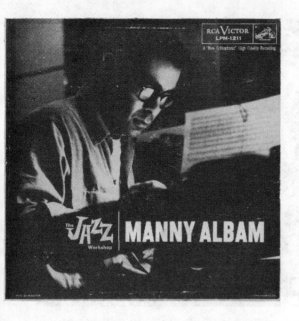

MANNY ALBAM
tenor, baritone saxes, composer - born 1922
Dominican Republic

Known as an arranger for movies and television, Albam's Jazz Workshop on RCA label in the mid-50's displayed his ability to provide a showcase for quality sidemen. Recordings listed below are those within the scope of this book.

THE JAZZ WORKSHOP/with Al Cohn — RCA Victor 1211 (1956) dog on top **$60.**

THE DRUM SUITE/with Ernie Wilkins — RCA Victor 1279 (1956) dog on top **$60**; EPA 826, EPA 827, EPA 828 (1956) **$35 ea.**

I HAD THE CRAZIEST DREAM — RCA Victor 2508 (1961) dog on top **$30.**

AND HIS ORCHESTRA — RCA Victor 2432 (1961) dog on top **$30.**

DOWN BEAT JAZZ CONCERT — Vol 1/with Tony Scott & Paul Horn — Dot 9003/29003 (1958) **$50.**

DOWN BEAT JAZZ CONCERT — Vol 2 — Dot 3188 (1958) **$50.**

JAZZ NEW YORK/with Zoot Sims — Dot 9004/29004 (1958) **$45.**

STEVE'S SONG/with Al Cohn — Dot 9008 (1958) **$45.**

JAZZ GREATS OF OUR TIME — Vol 1 — Coral 57142 (1958) maroon label **$50.**

JAZZ GREATS OF OUR TIME — Vol 2 — Coral 57173 (1958) maroon label **$50.**

WEST SIDE STORY — Coral 57207 (1958) **$35**; *reissued* Vocalion 3678 (1960) **$20**; Decca 4517/74517 (1964) **$15.**

ELLINGTON — Coral 57231 (1958) maroon label **$35.**

THE BLUES IS EVERYBODY'S BUSINESS — Coral 59101 (1958) maroon label **$35.**

JAZZ GOES TO THE MOVIES — Impulse 19 (1962) orange label **$25.**

JOE ALBANY
piano - born 1924 Atlantic City, NJ

THE RIGHT COMBINATION — Riverside 12-270 (1957) blue label with Bill Grauer Pro. **$45.**

LOLA ALBRIGHT
vocals

DREAMSVILLE/with Henry Mancini — Columbia 1327/8133 (1959) red label with 3 black logos on each side **$35.**

MAX ALBRIGHT
drums, vibes - born 1923 Kokomo, IN

To date, Albright is a prolific studio and television drummer with one LP to his credit on the Motif label featuring quality West Coast jazz stars including Buddy Collette and Dave Wells.

MOOD FOR MAX/with Buddy Collette — Motif 502 (1956) **$60.**

JOE ALEXANDER
tenor sax - born Birmingham, AL died 1970

BLUE JUBILEE — Jazzland 23/923 (1960) **$35.**

MONTY ALEXANDER
piano - born 1944 Kingston, Jamaica

MONTY ALEXANDER — Pacific Jazz 86 (1965) **$20.**

SPUNKY — Pacific Jazz 10094/20094 (1965) **$15.**

ROLAND ALEXANDER
tenor, soprano saxes - born 1935 Boston, MA

PLEASURE BENT — New Jazz 8267 (1962) **$35.**

LOREZ ALEXANDRIA

vocals - born 1929 Chicago, IL

A quality jazz vocalist whose influences, namely Ella Fitzgerald, Dinah Washington and Sarah Vaughan, afford Alexandria a great versatility in her songs. Alexandria still records to date and her rarest releases are to be found on King label.

THIS IS LOREZ — King 542 (1958) **$50.**

LOREZ SINGS PREZ — King 565 (1958) **$50.**

SONG EVERYBODY KNOWS — King 676 (1959) **$45.**

THE BAND SWINGS LOREZ SINGS — King 656 (1959) **$45.**

EARLY IN THE MORNING — Argo 663 (1960) **$40.**

SING NO SAD SONGS FOR ME — Argo 682 (1961) **$35.**

DEEP ROOTS — Argo 694 (1962) **$35.**

FOR SWINGERS ONLY — Argo 720 (1963) **$25.**

THE GREAT — Impulse 62 (1964) orange label **$20.**

MORE OF THE GREAT — Impulse 76 (1965) orange label **$20.**

BRYON ALLEN

alto sax - born 1940 Omaha, NE

BRYON ALLEN TRIO — ESP Disk 1005 (1965) **$15.**

*HENRY "RED" ALLEN

trumpet, vocals - born 1908 Algiers, LA died 1967

RIDE, RED, RIDE IN HI-FI/with Coleman Hawkins — RCA Victor 1509 (1957) dog on top **$45.**

---
*The only LP's within the scope of this book.
---

*STEVE ALLEN

piano - born 1921 New York City, NY

STEVE ALLEN'S ALL STARS/with Terry Gibbs - EmArcy 36138 (1958) **$35**; *reissued* Mercury 20518/60195 (1961) **$25.**

STEVE ALLEN/MANNY ALBAM — Dot 3194 (1959) **$30.**

---
*The only LP's within the scope of this book.

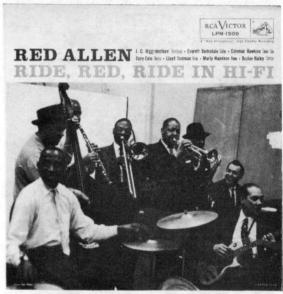

MOSE ALLISON

piano, vocals, composer - born 1927 Tippo, MS

An accomplished jazz pianist who has worked with a variety of major jazz stars, Allison began entertaining the public in the early 50's. He has played backup ivory for names such as Stan Getz and Gerry Mulligan but his most popular work has been his very unique bluesy vocal style.

BACK COUNTRY SUITE — Prestige 7091 (1957) yellow label **$45.**

YOUNG MAN MOSE — Prestige 7137 (1958) yellow label **$45.**

CREEK BANK — Prestige 7152 (1958) yellow label **$45.**

LOCAL COLOUR — Prestige 7121 (1958) yellow label **$40.**

AUTUMN SONG — Prestige 7189 (1959) yellow label **$40.**

RAMBLIN' WITH MOSE — Prestige 7215 (1959) yellow label **$40.**

SING — Prestige 7279 (1963) yellow label **$35.**

TRANSFIGURATION OF HIRAM BROWN — Columbia 1444 (1960) red label with 3 black logos on each side **$35.**

I LOVE THE LIFE I LIVE — Columbia 1565/8367 (1960) red label with 3 black logos on each side **$30.**

TAKES TO THE HILLS — Epic 16031/17031 (1962) **$30.**

I DON'T WORRY ABOUT A THING — Atlantic 1389 (1962) with logo on side **$25.**

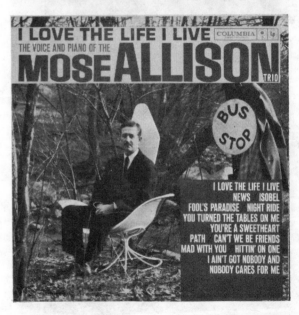

SWINGIN' MACHINE — Atlantic 1398 (1962) with logo on side **$25.**

THE WORD FROM MOSE — Atlantic 1424 (1964) with logo on side **$20.**

*LAURINDO ALMEIDA

guitar, composer - born 1917 Paolo, Brazil

Born in Brazil, Almeida came to America in the late 40's and has worked and recorded with big bands, small groups and as solo. Through his bossa nova style, Almeida has had a continuing affect in blending South American (Brazilian) and North American jazz. The following are within the scope of this book:

LAURINDO ALMEIDA QUARTET/with Bud Shank — Vol 1 — Pacific Jazz 7 (1954) 10" **$50**; EP 410 (1954) **$25**.

LAURINDO ALMEIDA QUARTET/with Bud Shank — Vol 2 — Pacific Jazz 13 (1954) 10" **$50**; EP 4-22 (1954) **$25**; *reissued* World Pacific 1204 (1956) **$35**.

BRAZILIANCE — Vol 1 — World Pacific 1412 (1962) **$25**; *reissue of LP 7 & LP 13 Pacific Jazz 1204.*

BRAZILIANCE — Vol 2 — World Pacific 1419 (1962) **$25**.

BRAZILIANCE — Vol 3 — World Pacific 1425 (1962) **$25**.

LATIN CONTRASTS — World Pacific 1281 (1959) **$30**.

VIVA BOSSA NOVA — Capitol 1759 (1963) black label with logo on top **$15**.

OLE! BOSSA NOVA — Capitol 1862 (1963) black label with logo on top **$15**.

IT'S A BOSSA NOVA WORLD — Capitol 1946 (1963) black label with logo on top **$15**.

DELIGHTFULLY MODERN/with Chico Hamilton — Jazztone 1264 (1958) one side each **$35**.

The only LP's within the scope of this book.

TRIGGER ALPERT

bass, arranger - born 1916 Indianapolis, IN

Alpert is considered to be a fine bassist working most notably in studio, radio and television. His only LP, which is truly a collector's item, featured such great musicians as Zoot Sims and Al Cohn.

TRIGGER HAPPY/with Al Cohn & Zoot Sims — Riverside 12-225 (1956) blue label with Bill Grauer Pro. **$60**; *reissued* Jazzland 11 (1960) **$35**.

GENE AMMONS

tenor sax - born 1925 Chicago, IL died 1974

The son of famous boogie woogie piano player Albert Ammons, Gene was heavily influenced early in his career by such greats as Lester Young and Charlie Parker. Ammons gained recognition playing with the Billy Eckstine Band and later the Woody Herman Band. He continued to contribute his vast series of recordings for nearly 30 years. The most famous of these can be found on the 1950-52 Prestige label when he doubled with another tenor player, Sonny Stitt. After this phase in his musical endeavour, Ammons ventured out on his own to develop his blues style with which he remained until 1974.

GENE AMMONS/with Sonny Stitt — Prestige 107 (1951) 10" **$150**; EP 1316 (1950) **$70**.

GENE AMMONS/with Sonny Stitt — Prestige 112 (1951) 10" **$125**.

GENE AMMONS BAND/with Sonny Stitt — Prestige 127 (1953) 10" **$125**.

GENE AMMONS QUARTET/with Sonny Stitt — Prestige 149 (1953) 10" **$100**.

BATTLE OF SAXES/with Sonny Stitt — Prestige 197 (1954) 10" **$150**.

JAMMIN' IN HI FI — Prestige 7010 (1955) yellow label **$70**; *reissued* Prestige 7176.

HI FI JAM SESSION — Prestige 7039 (1956) yellow label **$60**.

ALL STAR SESSIONS — Prestige 7050 (1956) yellow label **$60**; *reissue of Prestige 107 & 127.*

JAMMIN' WITH GENE — Prestige 7060 (1956) yellow label **$60**.

FUNKY — Prestige 7083 (1957) yellow label **$55**.

WOOFIN' AND TWEETIN' — Prestige 7050 (1960) yellow label **$35**; *reissue of Prestige All Star Sessions 7050.*

THE HAPPY BLUES — Prestige 7039 (1960) yellow label **$35**; *reissue of Prestige Hi Fi Jam Session 7039.*

NOT REALLY THE BLUES — Prestige 7060 (1960) yellow label **$35**; *reissue of Prestige Jammin' With Gene 7060.*

THE BIG SOUND/with John Coltrane — Prestige 7132 (1958) yellow label **$60**.

BLUE GENE — Prestige 7146 (1958) yellow label **$50**.

THE TWISTER — Prestige 7176 (1960) yellow label **$40**; *reissue of Prestige 7010.*

BOSS TENOR — Prestige 7180 (1960) yellow label **$40**.

JUG — Prestige 7192 (1960) yellow label **$35**.

GROOVE BLUES — Prestige 7201 (1961) yellow label **$35**.

UP TIGHT — Prestige 7208 (1961) yellow label **$35**.

MELLOW GRAVY — Prestige 7228 (1962) yellow label **$35**.

SOUL SUMMIT — Prestige 7234 (1962) yellow label **$35**.

TWISTING THE JUG — Prestige 7238 (1962) yellow label **$35**.

BAD BOSSA NOVA — Prestige 7257 (1962) yellow label **$35**.

PREACHIN' — Prestige 7270 (1963) yellow label **$35**.

SOUL SUMMIT — Vol 2 — Prestige 7275 (1964) yellow label **$35**.

LATE HOUR SPECIAL — Prestige 7287 (1964) yellow label **$35**.

ANGEL EYES — Prestige 7369 (1965) blue label **$20**.

VELVET SOUL — Prestige 7320 (1965) blue label **$20**.

WITH OR WITHOUT — EmArcy 26031 (1954) 10" **$90**; EP 1-6053, EP 1-6052 (1954) **$40** ea.

LIGHT, BLUESY AND MOODY — Wing 16156/12156 (1960) **$35**; *reissue* of EmArcy 26031.

GOLDEN SAXOPHONE — Savoy 14033 (1961) maroon label **$25**.

JUGGIN' AROUND — Vee Jay 3024 (1960) **$35**.

BOSS TENORS/with Sonny Stitt — Verve 8426 (1961) **$35**.

BOSS TENORS IN ORBIT/with Sonny Stitt — Verve 8468 (1962) **$25**.

DIG HIM/with Sonny Stitt — Argo 697 (1962) **$35**.

JUST JUG — Argo 698 (1962) **$35**.

GROOVIN' WITH JUG/with Richard "Groove" Holmes — Pacific Jazz 32 (1961) **$35**.

CURTIS AMY

tenor, alto, soprano saxes, flute - born 1929 Houston, TX

THE BLUES MESSAGE/with Paul Bryant — Pacific Jazz 9 (1960) **$40**.

GROOVIN' BLUE/with Frank Butler — Pacific Jazz 19 (1961) **$35**.

MEETIN' HERE/with Paul Bryant — Pacific Jazz 26 (1961) **$35**.

WAY DOWN — Pacific Jazz 46 (1962) **$35**.

TIPPIN' ON THROUGH — Pacific Jazz 62 (1962) **$35**.

KATANGA — Pacific Jazz 70 (1962) **$35**.

THIS IS THE BLUES — Kimberly 2020/11020 (1960) **$25**.

SOUNDS OF HOLLYWOOD — Palomar 24003/34003 (1965) **$15**.

CAT ANDERSON

trumpet - born 1916 Greenville, SC

CAT ON A HOT TIN HORN — EmArcy 36142 (1959) **$40**; *reissued* Mercury 20522/60199 (1961) black label **$30**.

ERNESTINE ANDERSON

vocals - born 1928 Houston, TX

In the early stages of her professional career, Anderson performed as vocalist with Lionel Hampton. Her warm voice and ability to improvise with a strong jazz feeling led to critical acclaim and a series of justifiably important recordings, many on the Mercury label.

HOT CARGO — Mercury 20354 (1958) black label **$45**.

ERNESTINE ANDERSON — Mercury 20400/60074 (1958) black label **$45**.

FASCINATING ERNESTINE — Mercury 20492/60171 (1959) black label **$45**.

MY KINDA SWING — Mercury 20496/60175 (1959) black label **$35**.

MOANIN' MOANIN' MOANIN' — Mercury 20582/60242 (1960) black label **$30**.

ERNESTINE ANDERSON — Mercury 12281/16281 (1964) black label **$20**.

JOHN ANDERSON

trumpet - born 1921 Birmingham, AL

A SWINGIN' GIG/with Buddy Collette — Tampa 2 (1958) **$50**.

MILDRED ANDERSON

vocals

PERSON TO PERSON/with Eddie "Lockjaw" Davis — Prestige/Bluesville 1004 (1960) **$35**.

NO MORE IN LIFE/with Al Sears — Prestige/Bluesville 1017 (1961) **$35**.

EARL ANDERZA

alto sax - born Los Angeles, CA

OUTA SIGHT — Pacific Jazz 65 (1963) **$35**.

ERNIE ANDREWS

vocals - born 1927 Philadelphia, PA

IN THE DARK — Gene Norman Presents 28 (1957) **$45**.

ERNIE ANDREWS — Gene Norman Presents 42 (1959) **$40**.

*ANDY & THE BEY SISTERS
vocals

NOW HEAR/with Jerome Richardson, Kenny Burrell — Prestige 7346 (1965) blue label **$20.**

---

*The only LP's within the scope of this book.

*LOUIS ARMSTRONG
trumpet, vocals - born 1900 New Orleans, LA died 1971

An original jazz giant, Armstrong began decades of recording on 78 RPM discs in 1925. The stature of Armstrong is obviously unquestioned and much of his early work has been rereleased in LP form. His modern jazz recordings, as listed, are those made during the period this book covers. Armstrong's dixieland style will not be included. In the scope of this book are the following:

ELLA AND LOUIS/with Ella Fitzgerald — Verve 4003 (1956) with Verve Records, Inc. on bottom of label **$45;** EP 5007, EP 5008 (1956) **$25** ea.

ELLA AND LOUIS AGAIN/with Ella Fitzgerald — Verve 4006 (1957) with Verve Records, Inc. on bottom of label 2 LP's **$70;** EP 5036, EP 5037, EP 5038 (1957) **$25** ea.

ELLA AND LOUIS AGAIN — Vol 1/with Ella Fitzgerald — Verve 4017 (1957) with Verve Records, Inc. on bottom of label **$40.**

ELLA AND LOUIS AGAIN — Vol 2/with Ella Fitzgerald — Verve 4018 (1957) with Verve Records, Inc. on bottom of label **$40.**

PORGY & BESS/with Ella Fitzgerald — Verve 4011/6040 (1957) 2 LP's with Verve Records, Inc. on bottom of label **$60.**

MEETS OSCAR PETERSON — Verve 8322/6062 (1960) with Verve Records, Inc. on bottom of label **$45.**

WITH DUKE ELLINGTON — Roulette 52074 (1963) with dark and light orange checked roulette wheel label **$25.**

THE GREAT REUNION/with Duke Ellington — Roulette 52103 (1963) with dark and light orange checked roulette wheel label **$25.**

---

*The only LP's within the scope of this book.

BUDDY ARNOLD
tenor sax, clarinet - born 1926 New York City, NY

WAILING — ABC Paramount 114 (1956) **$50.**

HARRY ARNOLD
composer - born 1920 Halsingborg, Sweden

BIG BAND + QUINCY JONES = JAZZ — EmArcy 36139/S80006 (1956) **$35.**

MYSTERY BAND — Jazztone 1270 (1958) **$35.**

GREAT BIG BAND AND FRIENDS — Jazzland 65/965 (1961) **$25.**

I LOVE HARRY ARNOLD AND ALL THAT JAZZ — Atco 33-120 (1960) **$25.**

DOROTHY ASHBY
harp, piano - born 1932 Detroit, MI

JAZZ HARPIST — Regent 6039 (1957) green label **$35.**

HIP HARP — Prestige 7140 (1958) yellow label **$35.**

IN A MINOR GROOVE — New Jazz 8209 (1958) **$35.**

SOFT WINDS — Jazzland 61/961 (1961) **$20.**

DOROTHY ASHBY — Argo 690 (1962) **$20.**

*GEORGE AULD
tenor, alto, soprano saxes - born 1919 Toronto, Ontario, Canada

Auld is a saxophone player who achieved initial renown with swing and big bands and one of the few who made the transition to the more modern styles. Auld's works covered in this perspective are:

CONCERT IN JAZZ — Apollo 102 (1951) 10" **$80;** *reissued* Grand Award 33-316 (1956) **$35.**

QUINTET — Roost 403 (1952) 10" **$80;** EP 307 **$35.**

THAT'S AULD — Discovery 3007 (1950) 10" **$80.**

TENDERLY — Coral 56060 (1952) 10" **$50;** EP 81052 (1952) **$20;** 7" 4 record box set 9-8060 (1952) **$20.**

MANHATTAN — Coral 56085 (1952) 10" **$50.**

JAZZ CONCERT — Allegro 3102 (1955) **$45.**

IN THE LAND OF HI FI WITH — EmArcy 36060 (1956) **$35.**

DANCING IN THE LAND OF HI FI — EmArcy 36090 (1956) **$35.**

JUMPIN' BANDS — Savoy 12098 (1957) **$35;** *reissue* of Discovery 3007.

GEORGE AULD/THE MELLOWLARKS — Top Rank 306/606 (1959) **$30.**

GOOD ENOUGH TO KEEP — Top Rank 333/633 (1959) **$30.**

HERE'S TO THE LOSERS/with Frank Rosolino — Philips 200-116 (1963) **$20.**

PLAYS THE WINNERS/with Frank Rosolino — Philips 600-096 (1963) **$20.**

---

*The only LP's within the scope of this book.

CLAIRE AUSTIN
vocals

WHEN YOUR LOVER HAS GONE/with Barney Kessel — Contemporary 5002 (1957) yellow label **$50.**

AUSTRALIAN JAZZ QUARTET

AUSTRALIAN JAZZ QUARTET — Bethlehem 1031 (1955) 10" $45; *reissued* Bethlehem 6002 (1956) $30.

AUSTRALIAN JAZZ QUARTET — Bethlehem 6003 (1956) $40.

AT THE VARSITY DRAG — Bethlehem 6012 (1957) $40; EP 131 (1957) $25; EXLP-2 (1956) $25.

PLUS ONE — Bethlehem 6015 (1956) $40.

PLAYS ROGERS & HAMMERSTEIN — Bethlehem 6022 (1957) $40.

FREE STYLE — Bethlehem 6029 (1958) $35.

THREE PENNY OPERA — Bethlehem 6030 (1958) $35.

ROY AYERS

vibes - born 1940 Los Angeles, CA

WEST COAST VIBES/with Curtis Amy — United Artists 3325/6325 (1964) $20.

ALBERT AYLER

tenor, soprano saxes - born 1936 Cleveland, OH

SPIRITUAL UNITY — ESP Disk 1002 (1964) $20.

BELLS — ESP Disk 1010 (1965) $20.

MY NAME IS — Fantasy 6016 (1965) $20.

HARRY BABASIN

bass, cello - born 1921 Dallas, TX

JAZZ PICKERS/with Terry Gibbs — Mode 119 (1957) $45.

DON BAGLEY

bass - born 1927 Salt Lake City, UT

BASICALLY BAGLEY — Dot 3070/25070 (1958) $40.

JAZZ ON THE ROCKS — Regent 6061 (1957) green label $45.

THE SOFT SELL — Dot 9007/29007 (1959) $40.

BENNIE BAILEY

trumpet - born 1925 Cleveland, OH

BIG BRASS — Candid 8011/9011 (1961) $35.

THE MUSIC OF QUINCY JONES — Argo 668 (1961) $35.

DAVE BAILEY

drums - born 1926 Portsmouth, VA

GETTIN' INTO SOMETHING — Epic 16011/17011 (1960) $35.

ONE FOOT IN THE GUTTER — Epic 16008/17008 (1960) $35.

TWO FEET IN THE GUTTER — Epic 16021/17021 (1961) $35.

REACHING OUT — Jazztime 003 (1961) $45.

BUSH — Jazzline 33-01 (1961) $45.

MILDRED BAILEY

vocals - born 1907 Tekoa, WA died 1951

MILDRED BAILEY SERENADE — Columbia 6094 (1950) 10" $60.

SINGS — Allegro 3119 (1951) 10" $60.

SONGS — Allegro 4007 (1952) 10" $50.

SONGS — Allegro 4040 (1952) 10" $50.

THE ROCKIN' CHAIR LADY — Decca 5387 (1953) 10" $45; 7" box set 4 records - Decca 9-296 (1953) $25.

ME AND THE BLUES — Regent 6032 (1957) green label $45.

MILDRED BAILEY — Royale EP 164 (1955) $20.

BLUES BY — Columbia EP B-1617 (1953) $20.

M.B. — Savoy 12219 (1964) maroon label $20.

GREATEST PERFORMANCES — Columbia C3L-22 (1962) red with 3 black logo's on each side of label 3 LP box set with 16 page booklet $75.

*PEARL BAILEY

vocals - born 1918 Newport News, VA

ENTERTAINS — Columbia 6099 (1953) 10" $50.

DEFINITIVE — Columbia 985 (1957) red with 3 black logos on each side of label $35; EP 2570 (1957) $15.

I'M WITH YOU — Coral 56078 (1953) 10" $50.

SAY SI SI — Coral 56068 (1953) 10" $45.

BIRTH OF THE BLUES — Coral 57037 (1957) $35.

CULTURED PEARL — Coral 57162 (1958) $30.

INTOXICATING — Mercury 20277 (1958) black label $35.

THE ONE & ONLY — Mercury 20187 (1957) black label $35.

GEM — Vocalion 3621 (1958) $30.

---

*The only LP's within the scope of this book.

CHET BAKER

trumpet, fluegelhorn and occasional vocals born 1929 Yale, OK

...aker displays an immediately recognizable style which began to ...ain him attention on the West Coast in the early 50's. He continues ...orking today although he has experienced significant periods of ...activity over the years. Of special note to collectors, pay particular ...tention to some of Baker's best recordings found on Pacific Jazz ...d World Pacific.

...IET BAKER QUARTET — Pacific Jazz 3 (1953) 10" **$95**; EP 4-4; EP 4-14 (1953) **$35** ea.; *reissued* Pacific Jazz 1206 (1955).

...IET BAKER QUARTET/with Russ Freeman — Pacific Jazz 6 (1953) 10" **$95**; EP 4-8; EP 4-9 (1953) **$35** ea.; *reissued* World Pacific 1206 (1958).

...ISEMBLE — Pacific Jazz 9 (1954) 10" **$90**; EP 4-15 **$30**.

...IET BAKER SINGS — Pacific Jazz 11 (1954) 10" **$90**; Pacific Jazz 1222 (1956) **$60**; *reissued* World Pacific 1222 (1958) **$50**.

...IET BAKER SEXTET — Pacific Jazz 15 (1954) 10" **$90**.

...IET BAKER GROUP — Pacific Jazz 1206 (1955) **$85**; EP 4-30 (1955) **$30**.

...IET BAKER SINGS AND PLAYS — World Pacific 1202 (1958) **$85**; EP 4-30 (1955) **$30**.

... EUROPE — Pacific Jazz 1218 (1955) **$85**; EP 4-47 **$30**; *reissued* World Pacific 1218 (1958) **$50**.

...ZZ AT ANN ARBOR — Pacific Jazz 1203 (1955) **$90**; *reissued* World Pacific 1203 (1958) **$50**.

...E TRUMPET ARTISTRY OF — Pacific Jazz 1206 (1955) **$90**; *reissued* World Pacific 1206 (1958) **$50** (*reissue of LP 3 & 6*).

...G BAND — Pacific Jazz 1229 (1956) **$85**; *reissued* World Pacific 1229 (1958) **$50**.

...UNION/with Gerry Mulligan — World Pacific 1007 (1958) **$60**; *reissued* Pacific Jazz 47 (1962) **$35**.

PLAYBOYS/with Art Pepper — Pacific Jazz 1234 (1956) **$85**.

CHET BAKER/RUSS FREEMAN — Pacific Jazz 1232 (1956) **$85**; *reissued* World Pacific 1232 (1958) **$85**.

THE JAMES DEAN STORY — World Pacific 2005 (1958) **$100**; *reissued* Kimberly LP 2016/11016 (1960) **$40**.

PICTURE OF HEALTH — Pacific Jazz 18 (1962) **$35**; *reissue* of Pacific Jazz 1234.

CHET BAKER AND CREW — Pacific Jazz 1224 (1956) **$85**; *reissued* World Pacific 1224/1004 (1957) **$50**.

CHET BAKER AND STRINGS — Columbia 549 (1954) **$80**; *reissued* Harmony 7320 (1962) **$25**.

IT COULD HAPPEN TO YOU — Riverside 12-278/1120 (1958) blue label with Bill Grauer Pro. **$40**.

IN NEW YORK/with Johnny Griffin — Riverside 281/1119 (1958) blue label with Bill Grauer Pro. **$40**.

CHET/with Pepper Adams and Herbie Mann — Riverside 12-299/1135 (1959) blue label with Bill Grauer Pro. **$40**.

PLAYS THE BEST OF LERNER & LOEWE/with Zoot Sims & Pepper Adams — Riverside 12-307/1152 (1959) blue label with Bill Grauer Pro. **$40**.

CHET BAKER ORCHESTRA — Jazzland 11 (1961) **$30**.

CHET BAKER SEXTET — Jazzland 18 (1961) **$30**.

THE MOST IMPORTANT JAZZ ALBUM — Colpix 476 (1964) **$20**.

SINGS AND PLAYS — Limelight 82003/86003 (1965) **$20**.

BAKER'S HOLIDAY — Limelight 86019/82019 (1965) **$20**.

RONNIE BALL
piano - born 1927 Birmingham, England

ALL ABOUT RONNIE — Savoy 12075 (1957) maroon label **$45**.

BILL BARRON
tenor, soprano saxes, flute, composer - born 1927 Philadelphia, PA

Considered to be an educator in music, Barron worked with his own group recording on the Savoy label in the early to mid-60's. Prior to this, he could be found performing with artists such as Philly Joe Jones and Cecil Taylor.

TENOR STYLINGS — Savoy 12160 (1961) maroon label **$35**.

MODERN WINDOWS — Savoy 12163 (1962) maroon label **$35**.

HOT LINE — Savoy 12183 (1964) maroon label **$30**.

MOTIVATION — Savoy 12303 (1965) maroon label **$25**.

NOW HEAR THIS — Audio Fidelity 6123 (1964) **$30**.

WEST SIDE STORY BOSSA NOVA — Dauntless 6312 (1963) **$35**.

COUNT BASIE
piano, organ, composer, leader - born 1904
Red Bank, NJ died 1984

Organist and pianist whose fame began in the mid-30's, Basie has worked in every imaginable context including, in part, big band; small groups; and trios while enjoying the accompaniment of some of the most respected sidemen and vocalists in the business. While all old Basie recordings have value, some highlights for collectors would be those on Clef and Verve labels. Basie's well deserved reputation as one of the giants of jazz will continue indefinitely despite his death this year.

COUNT BASIE & HIS ORCHESTRA — Clef 120 (1952) 10" **$70**; EP C 131, EP C 132, (1952) **$35** ea.

COUNT BASIE BIG BAND — Clef 148 (1952) 10" **$70**; EP C 195, EP C 196 (1952) **$35** ea.

COUNT BASIE SEXTET — Clef 164 (1952) 10" **$70**; EP C 185, EP C 186 (1952) **$35** ea.

DANCE SESSION #1 — Clef 626 (1953) **$60**; EP C 220, EP C 221, EP C 222 (1953) **$30** ea.

DANCE SESSION #2 — Clef 647 (1954) **$60**; EP C 338, EP C 339 (1954) **$30** ea.

BASIE JAZZ "BASIEANA" — Clef 633 (1953) **$60**; EP C 251, EP C 252 **$30** ea.

BASIE — Clef 666 (1954) **$60**; EP C 364 (1954) **$30**.

COUNT BASIE SWINGS/JOE WILLIAMS SINGS — Clef 678 (1955) **$50**; EP C 375, EP C 372 (1955) **$30** ea.; *reissued* Verve 8063 (1957) & 8488 (1962).

COUNT BASIE SEXTET/QUINTET — Clef 685 (1956) **$50**; *reissue* of records off other Clef LP's.

SWINGIN' COUNT — Clef 706 (1956) **$50**; *reissue* of records off other Clef LP's.

BASIE ROARS AGAIN — Clef 723 (1956) **$50**; *reissue* of records off other Clef LP's.

COUNT BASIE & HIS ORCHESTRA — Clef 729 (1956) **$50**; *reissue* of records off other Clef LP's.

COUNT BASIE — Clef 724 (1956) **$50**; *reissue* of records off other Clef LP's.

JAZZ ROYALTY/with Earl Hines — EmArcy 26023 (1954) 10" **$80**.

TIN ROOF BLUES — EmArcy 26012 (1954) 10" **$50**.

BASIN STREET SIX — Circle 403 (1951) 10" **$50**.

BASIE & LESTER YOUNG — Jazz Panorama 1803 (1952) 10" **$80**.

AND HIS KANSAS CITY SEVEN — Mercury 25015 (1950) 10" **$50**.

AMERICA'S MUSIC — Mercury 25111 (1951) 10" **$50**.

AT THE PIANO — Decca 5111 (1950) 10" **$50**.

AND HIS ORCHESTRA — Decca 8049 (1953) 10" **$50**; EP 2067, EP 2068, EP 2069 (1953) **$25** ea.

THE OLD COUNT & THE NEW COUNT BASIE — Epic 1021 (1954) 10" **$60**.

ROCK THE BLUES — Epic 1117 (1954) 10" **$50**.

LESTER LEAP IN — Epic 3107 (1955) **$60**; EP 7017 (1955) **$35**.

LET'S GO TO PREZ — Epic 3168 (1955) **$60**.

BASIE'S BACK IN TOWN — Epic 3169 (1955) **$60**; EP 7029 (1955) **$35**.

BASIE'S BEST — Brunswick 58019 (1954) 10" **$45**.

DANCE PARADE — Columbia 6079 (1950) 10" **$50**; EP B 2100 (1950) **$25**.

BLUES BY BASIE — Columbia 901 (1956) red label with 3 black logos on each side **$45**.

CLASSICS — Columbia 754 (1956) **$45**; EP B 2555 (1956) red label with 3 black logos on each side **$15**; *reissued* Harmony 7229 (1960) **$25**.

ONE O'CLOCK JUMP — Columbia 997 (1956) red label with 3 black logos on each side **$40**.

THE GREATEST/with Joe Williams — Verve 2016/6006 (1956) with Verve Records, Inc. on bottom of label **$50**; EP 5105, EP 5106 (1956) **$25** ea.

BASIE RIDES AGAIN — Verve 8108 (1957) with Verve Records, Inc. on bottom of label **$40**; *reissue* of Clef 729.

APRIL IN PARIS — Verve 8012 (1957) with Verve Records, Inc. on bottom of label **$40**. Ⓐ

BASIE ROARS AGAIN — Verve 8018 (1957) with Verve Records, Inc. on bottom of label **$40**; *reissue* of Clef 723.

COUNT BASIE SWINGS/JOE WILLIAMS SINGS — Verve 8063 (1956) with Verve Records, Inc. on bottom of label **$45**; *reissued* Verve 8488 (1962) **$30**; are *reissues* of Clef 678.

THE COUNT — Verve 8070 (1957) with Verve Records, Inc. on bottom of label **$35**; *reissue* of Clef 120.

THE BAND OF DISTINCTION — Verve 8103 (1957) with Verve Records, Inc. on bottom of label **$35**; *reissue* of Clef 666.

KING OF SWING — Verve 8104 (1957) with Verve Records, Inc. on bottom of label **$35**; *reissue* of Clef 724.

BASIE IN LONDON — Verve 8199 (1957) with Verve Records, Inc. on bottom of label **$30**.

AT NEWPORT — Verve 8243/6024 (1958) with Verve Records, Inc. on bottom of label **$30**.

AT NEWPORT/with Joe Williams — Verve 8244 (1958) with Verve Records, Inc. on bottom of label **$35**; *reissued* Verve 8560/68560 (1963) **$20**.

ONE O'CLOCK JUMP/with Ella Fitzgerald & Joe Williams — Verve 8288 (1958) with Verve Records, Inc. on bottom of label **$35**.

HALL OF FAME — Verve 8291 (1959) with Verve Records, Inc. on bottom of label **$25**.

ESSENTIAL — Verve 8407 (1962) with MGM on bottom of label **$25**.

WITH JOE WILLIAMS — Roulette 52033 (1959) **$35.**

DANCE WITH BASIE — Roulette 52036 (1959) **$20.**

BASIE/ECKSTINE, INC. — Roulette 52029 (1959) **$25.**

NOT NOW, I'LL TELL YOU WHEN — Roulette 52044 (1960) **$20.**

JUST THE BLUES/with Joe Williams — Roulette 52054 **$35**; EP 1029 (1960) **$15.**

STRING ALONG WITH BASIE — Roulette 52051 (1961) **$20.**

BENNY CARTER'S KANSAS CITY SUITE — Roulette 52056 (1961) **$25.**

BASIE AT BIRDLAND — Roulette 52065 (1961) **$20.**

BEST — Roulette 52081 (1962) **$20.**

BEST — Vol 2 — Roulette 52089 (1962) **$20.**

THE LEGEND — Roulette 52086 (1962) **$20.**

IN SWEDEN — Roulette 52099 (1962) **$25**; EP 1049 (1962) **$10.**

EASIN' IT — Roulette 52106 (1962) **$20.**

WORLD — Roulette 52111/2/3 (1962) 3 LP box set **$45.**

COUNT BASIE — RCA Victor 1112 (1954) 10" **$60**; EP A 420 (1954) dog on top **$30.**

THE COUNT — Camden 395 (1958) **$35.**

BASIE'S BASEMENT — Camden 497 (1959) **$35.**

A NIGHT AT COUNT BASIE'S — Vanguard 8508 (1957) **$35.**

KANSAS CITY SEVEN — Impulse 15 (1962) orange label **$20.**

BASIE'S BEST — American Recording Society G422 (1957) **$30.**

BASSO/VALDAMBRINI OCTET
Gianni Basso, tenor sax - born 1931 Asti, Italy
Oscar Valdambrini, trumpet, fluegelhorn - born 1924
Turin, Italy

JAZZ FESTIVAL, MILAN — Verve 20009 (1960) **$40.**

NEW SOUND FROM ITALY — Verve 20011 (1960) **$40.**

BILLY BAUER
guitar - born 1915 New York City, NY

LET'S HAVE A SESSION — Ad Lib 5501 (1955) 10" **$60.**

PLECTRIST — Norgran 1082 (1956) 10" **$60**; *reissued* Verve 8172 (1957) **$45.**

AARON BELL
bass, piano, trumpet, tuba, composer - born 1922
Muskogee, OK

Bell is a highly respected bass player who played with Duke Ellington in 1960-62 and known primarily as a sideman. Recordings of greatest rarity are those found on the Lion label.

AFTER THE PARTY'S OVER — RCA Victor 1876 (1959) dog on top **$25.**

JAZZ ALL THE WAY — RCA Victor EP 4239 (1959) dog on top **$15.**

MUSIC FROM PETER GUNN — Lion 70112 (1959) **$35.**

77 SUNSET STRIP — Lion 70111 (1959) **$35.**

VICTORY AT SEA — Lion 70113 (1959) **$35.**

THREE SWINGING BELLS — Herold 0100 (1956) **$25.**

CHARLES BELL
piano - born 1933 Pittsburgh, PA

ANOTHER DIMENSION — Atlantic 1400 (1963) with logo on side **$20.**

IN CONCERT — Gateway 7015 (1964) **$15.**

THE CHARLES BELL CONTEMPORARY JAZZ QUARTET — Columbia 1582/8382 (1961) red label with black logo's on each side **$20.**

LIL OL' GROOVEMAKER — Verve 8549 (1963) with MGM on bottom of label **$20.**

ON MY WAY — Verve 8511/68511 (1963) with MGM on bottom of label **$20.**

MORE HITS OF 50's & 60's — Verve 8563/68563 (1963) with MGM on bottom of label **$15.**

BASIELAND — Verve 8597/68597 (1964) with MGM on bottom of label **$20.**

VERVE'S CHOICE BEST — Verve 8596/68596 (1965) with MGM on bottom of label **$15.**

PICKS THE WINNERS — Verve 8616/68616 (1964) with MGM on bottom of label **$15.**

BASIE (E=Mc2) — Roulette 52003 (1958) **$35.**

MEMORIES AD LIB — Roulette 52021 (1958) **$35.**

BASIE PLAYS HEFTI — Roulette 52011 (1958) **$25.**

SING ALONG WITH BASIE/with Lambert, Hendricks & Ross and Joe Williams — Roulette 52018 (1959) **$40**; EP 1008 (1960) **$25.**

THE ATOMIC MR. BASIE — Roulette 52003 (1958) **$35**; EP 1309 (1958) **$15.**

BREAKFAST DANCE & BARBECUE — Roulette 52028 (1959) **$30**; EP 1011 (1959) **$15.**

CHAIRMAN OF THE BOARD — Roulette 52032 (1959) **$30**; EP 1004 (1959) **$15.**

ONE MORE TIME — Roulette 52024 (1959) **$30**; EP 1013 (1959) **$15.**

AL BELLETTO

alto, baritone saxes, clarinet - born 1928 New Orleans, LA

HALF & HALF — Capitol 751 (1956) **$35**; EP 1-751, EP 2-751, EP 3-751 (1956) green label **$15 ea.**

KENTON PRESENTS JAZZ — Capitol 6506 (1954) 2 EP set green label **$25**.

WHISPER NOT — Capitol 901 (1957) green label **$35**.

SOUNDS & SONGS — Capitol 6514 (1954) 2 EP set green label **$25**.

THE BIG SOUND — King 716 (1961) **$20**.

LOUIS BELLSON

drums, composer - born 1924 Rockfalls, IL

One of the best big band drummers, Bellson worked with Benny Goodman, Dorsey Brothers, Harry James and Duke Ellington just to mention only the most famous. His own recordings feature him in many different settings but look especially for his early works on the Norgran label.

AMAZING ARTISTRY — Norgran 7 (1954) 10" **$100**; EP 10 (1954) **$35**.

WITH WARDELL GRAY — Norgran 14 (1954) 10" **$150**; EP 23 (1954) **$50**.

JOURNEY INTO LOVE — Norgran 1007 (1955) **$70**.

QUINTET/with Zoot Sims — Norgran 1011 (1955) **$125**; EP 70, EP 71, EP 72, EP 73 (1955) **$45 ea.**

THE DRIVING — Norgran 1020 (1955) **$60**; EP 107 (1955) **$20**.

SKIN DEEP — Norgran 1046 (1955) **$60**.

LOUIS BELLSON — Capitol H348 (1954) 10" **$85**.

JUST JAZZ ALL STARS/with Wardell Gray — Capitol 348 (1953) 10" **$100**; EP CCF 348 (1953) green label 3 record set **$40**.

CONCERTO FOR DRUMS — Verve 8016 (1957) **$50**; *reissue of Norgran 1011.*

SKIN DEEP — Verve 8137 (1957) with Verve Records, Inc. on bottom of label **$45**; *reissue of Norgran 1046.*

HAWK TALKS — Verve 8186 (1957) with Verve Records, Inc. on bottom of label **$45**.

DRUMORAMA — Verve 8193 (1957) with Verve Records, Inc. on bottom of label **$45**.

AT THE FLAMINGO — Verve 8256 (1958) with Verve Records, Inc. on bottom of label **$45**.

LET'S CALL IT SWING — Verve 8258 (1958) with Verve Records, Inc. on bottom of label **$45**.

MUSIC, ROMANCE & ESPECIALLY LOVE — Verve 8280 (1959) with Verve Records, Inc. on bottom of label **$40**.

DRUMMER'S HOLIDAY — Verve 8354 (1959) with Verve Records, Inc. on bottom of label **$40**.

BRILLIANT BELLSON SOUND — Verve 2123/6093 (1960) with Verve Records, Inc. on bottom of label **$35**.

SWINGS JULE STYNE — Verve 2131/6138 (1960) with Verve Records, Inc. on bottom of label **$35**.

BIG BAND JAZZ AT THE SUMMIT — Roulette 52087 (1962) **$25**.

THE MIGHTY TWO/with Gene Krupa — Roulette 52098 (1963) **$25**.

AROUND THE WORLD IN PERCUSSION — Roulette 65002 (1965) **$25**.

BETTY BENNETT

vocals - born 1926 Lincoln, NE

Gained a good reputation and considerable experience as a band vocalist with such jazz artists as Woody Herman, Stan Kenton and Georgie Auld. Bennett's recordings number few but are quite popular collectables.

SINGS PREVIN ARRANGEMENTS — Trend 1006 (1954) 10" **$80**.

NOBODY ELSE BUT ME/with Bob Cooper — Atlantic 1226 (1956) black label **$60**; EP 572, EP 573 (1956) **$30 ea.**

BLUE SUNDAY — Kapp 1052 (1956) **$50**.

I LOVE TO SING — United Artists 3070/6070 (1959) **$45**.

MAX BENNETT

bass - born 1928 Des Moines, IA

MAX BENNETT SEPTET — Bethlehem 48 (1956) **$35**.

PLAYS — Bethlehem 50 (1956) **$35**.

WALTER BENTON

tenor sax - born 1930 Los Angeles, CA

OUT OF THIS WORLD — Jazzland 28/928 (1961) **$35**.

MILT BERNHART

trombone - born 1926 Valparaiso, IN

MODERN BRASS — RCA Victor 1123 (1955) dog on top **$50**.

THE SOUND OF BERNHART — Decca 9214 (1959) **$40**.

LEONARD BERNSTEIN

piano, composer - born 1918 Lawrence, MA

WHAT IS JAZZ — Columbia 919 (1956) red label with 3 black logos on each side **$50**; red label with 1 white logo on each side **$20**.

BILL BERRY

trumpet, fluegelhorn - born 1930 Benton Harbor, MI

JAZZ: & SWINGING PERCUSSION — Directional Sound 5002 (1963) **$35**.

CHU BERRY
tenor sax - born 1910 Wheeling, VA died 1941

Berry's style and smooth, mellow sound elected him as another jazz music greats. Working most often as a sideman his own few albums are much sought after. Berry's greatest decade was the 30's when he joined up with names like Gene Krupa and Roy Eldridge.

MEMORIAL — Commodore 20024 (1954) 10" **$90**.

CHU BERRY — Commodore 30017 (1959) **$45**.

PREZ & CHU: TOPS ON TENOR/with Lester Young — Jazztone 1218 (1956) one side only **$45**.

SITTIN' IN — Mainstream 6038/50038 (1965) **$25**.

CHU — Epic 3124 (1956) **$45**.

EDDIE BERT
trombone - born 1922 Yonkers, NY

EDDIE BERT — Discovery EP 20 (1953) **$35**.

QUINTET — Discovery 3020 (1953) **$60**.

ENCORE — Savoy 12019 (1955) maroon label **$50**.

MUSICIAN OF THE YEAR — Savoy 12015 (1955) maroon label **$50**.

ALL STARS — Jazztone 1223 (1956) **$35**.

BIRDLAND DREAMBAND — Vol 1 — Vik 1070 (1957) **$35**.

BIRDLAND DREAMBAND — Vol 2 — Vik 1077 (1957) **$35**.

LET'S DIG BERT — Transworld 208 (1955) **$50**.

LIKE COOL — Somerset 5200 (1958) **$35**.

*HAROLD BETTERS
trombone

MEETS SLIDE HAMPTON — Gateway 7009 (1964) **$35**.

---

*The only LP's within the scope of this book.

WALTER BISHOP, JR.
piano - born 1927 New York City, NY

SPEAK LOW — Jazztime 002 (1961) **$25**.

SALLIE BLAIR
vocals

SQUEEZE ME — Bethlehem 6009 (1957) maroon label **$45**.

BETTY BLAKE
vocals

SINGS IN A TENDER MOOD — Bethlehem 6058 (1956) maroon label **$45**.

ART BLAKEY
drums - born 1919 Pittsburgh, PA

A very strong leader among musicians, Blakey began as a sideman in the early bop years. His versatile personality enabled him to start a group called The Jazz Messengers which has experienced an uninterrupted history to date. The continually evolving personnel of this group has given jazz literally dozens of the finest musicians of today. Blakey's especially valued works are found on early Blue Note 10 inch LP's.

ART BLAKEY JAZZ MESSENGERS — Blue Note 5010 (1952) 10" **$90**.

A NIGHT AT BIRDLAND — Vol 1 — Blue Note 5037 (1954) 10" **$90**; *reissued* Blue Note 1521 (1956) with NY address on label **$40**; with A Division of Liberty on label **$20**.

A NIGHT AT BIRDLAND — Vol 2 — Blue Note 5038 (1954) 10" **$90**; *reissued* Blue Note 1522 (1956) with NY address on label **$40**; with A Division of Liberty on label **$20**.

AT THE CAFE BOHEMIA — Vol 1 — Blue Note 1507 (1955) with NY address on label **$60**; with A Division of Liberty on label **$20**.

AT THE CAFE BOHEMIA — Vol 2 — Blue Note 1508 (1955) with NY address on label **$60**; with A Division of Liberty on label **$20**.

ORGY IN RHYTHM — Vol 1 — Blue Note 1554 (1957) with NY address on label **$60**; with A Division of Liberty on label **$20**.

ORGY IN RHYTHM — Vol 2 — Blue Note 1555 (1957) with NY address on label **$60**; with A Division of Liberty on label **$20**.

MOANIN' — Blue Note 4003 (1958) with NY address on label **$50**; with A Division of Liberty on label **$20**.

HOLIDAY FOR SKINS — Vol 1 — Blue Note 4004 (1958) with NY address on label **$50**; with A Division of Liberty on label **$20**.

HOLIDAY FOR SKINS — Vol 2 — Blue Note 4005 (1958) with NY address on label **$50**; with A Division of Liberty on label **$20**.

AT THE JAZZ CORNER OF THE WORLD — Vol 1 — Blue Note 4015 (1959) with NY address on label **$45**; with A Division of Liberty on label **$20**.

AT THE JAZZ CORNER OF THE WORLD — Vol 2 — Blue Note 4016 (1959) with NY address on label **$45**; with A Division of Liberty on label **$20**.

THE BIG BEAT — Blue Note 4029 (1960) with NY address on label **$40**; with A Division of Liberty on label **$20**.

A NIGHT IN TUNISIA — Blue Note 4049 (1960) with NY address on label **$40**; with A Division of Liberty on label **$20**.

MEET YOU AT THE JAZZ CORNER OF THE WORLD — Vol 1 — Blue Note 4054 (1960) with NY address on label **$40**; with A Division of Liberty on label **$20**.

MEET YOU AT THE JAZZ CORNER OF THE WORLD — Vol 2 — Blue Note 4055 (1960) with NY address on label **$40**; with A Division of Liberty on label **$20**.

THE FREEDOM RIDER — Blue Note 4156 (1961) with NY on label **$35**; with A Division of Liberty on label **$20**.

MOSAIC — Blue Note 4090 (1961) with NY on label **$35**; with A Division of Liberty on label **$20**.

BUHAINA'S DELIGHT — Blue Note 4104 (1961) with NY on label **$35**; with A Division of Liberty on label **$20**.

INDESTRUCTIBLE — Blue Note 4193 (1962) with NY on label **$30**; with A Division of Liberty on label **$20**.

THE AFRICAN BEAT — Blue Note 4097 (1962) with NY on label **$30**; with A Division of Liberty on label **$20**.

FREE FOR ALL — Blue Note 4170 (1964) with NY on label **$25**; with A Division of Liberty on label **$20**.

JAZZ MESSENGERS WITH MONK — Atlantic 1278 (1957) black label **$40**; with logo on side (1962) **$25**.

LES LIAISONS DANGEREUSES — Epic 16022/17022 (1961) **$35**; reissued Fontana 27539/67539 (1965) **$20**.

PARIS CONCERT — Epic 16009 (1960) **$40**.

IN PARIS — Epic 16017/17017 (1961) **$35**.

CU-BOP WITH SABU — Jubilee 1049 (1957) **$40**; reissued Josie 3501 (1963) **$25**.

JAZZ MESSENGERS/ELMO HOPE — Pacific Jazz 33 (1957) **$60**.

RITUAL — Pacific Jazz 402 (1957) **$60**; EP 4-54; EP 4-73; EP 4074 (1957) **$30** ea.; reissued World Pacific 1257 (1959) **$45**.

PLAYS LERNER AND LOEWE — Vik 1103 (1957) **$60**.

NIGHT IN TUNISIA — Vik 1115 (1957) **$60**; reissued RCA Victor 2654 (1963) dog on top **$30**.

GOLDEN BOY — Colpix 478 (1965) gold label **$20**.

MIDNIGHT SESSION — Elek 120 (1957) **$50**; reissued Savoy 12171.

ART BLAKEY'S BIG BAND/with John Coltrane — Bethlehem 6027 (1957) maroon label **$50**.

CARAVAN — Riverside 438/9438 (1962) blue label with Bill Grauer Pro. **$30**.

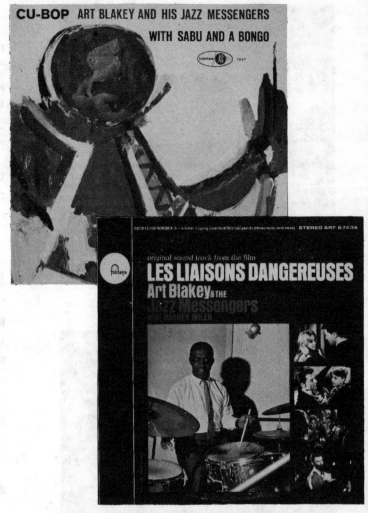

UGETSU — Riverside 464/9464 (1963) blue label with Bill Grauer Pro. **$25**.

3 BLIND MICE — United Artists 14002/15002 (1962) maroon label **$30**.

THE JAZZ MESSENGERS — Savoy 12171 (1964) maroon label **$25**; reissue of Elek 120.

A JAZZ MESSAGE — Impulse 45 (1963) orange label **$30**.

ART BLAKEY JAZZ MESSENGERS — Impulse 7 (1961) orange label **$35**. (A)

S MAKES IT — Limelight 82001/86001 (1965) **$25**.

SOUL FINGER — Limelight 86019/82019 (1965) **$20**.

BLAKEY — EmArcy 26030 (1954) 10" **$90**; EP 1-6151; EP 1-6050 (1954) **$45** ea.

ART BLAKEY — EmArcy EP 1-6007 (1954) **$45**.

THE JAZZ MESSENGERS — Columbia 897 (1956) with 3 black logos on each side of label **$60**.

HARD BOP — Columbia 1040 (1957) with 3 black logos on each side of label **$60**.

DRUM SUITE — Columbia 1002 (1957) with 3 black logos on each side of label **$60**.

TOUGH — Cadet 4049 (1965) **$15**; reissue of Pacific Jazz 402.

PAUL BLEY
piano - born 1932 Montreal, Quebec, Canada

ENTERTAINS — Columbia 6099 (1950) 10" **$60**.

IMPROVISATIONS: INTRODUCING/with Charlie Mingus — Debut 7 (1954) 10" **$70**.

PAUL BLEY — EmArcy 26006 (1954) 10" **$70**; EP 1-6001 (1954) **$35**; reissued EmArcy 36092 (1956) **$35**.

SOLEMN MEDITATION — Gene Norman Presents 31 (1957) **$35**.

FOOTLOOSE — Savoy 12182 (1964) maroon label **$20**.

BLUE STARS
(of France)
*Fats Sadi, Christian Chevallier, Roger Guerin,
Jean Mercadier, Christiane Legrand,
Jeanine DeWaleyne, Nadine Young, Blossom Dearie*
_LLABY OF BIRDLAND — EmArcy 36067 (1956) drummer logo **$50**.

WILLIE BOBO
*bongos, congas, drums - born 1934 New York, NY
died 1983*
_BO'S BEAT — Roulette 52097 (1963) with dark and light orange checked roulette wheel label **$15**.
_T'S GO BOBO — Roulette 52727 (1964) with dark and light orange checked roulette wheel label **$15**.
_ANISH GREASE — Verve 8631 (1965) with MGM on bottom of label **$15**.

GEORGE BOHANON
*trombone, tenor, piano, bass, flute - born 1937
Detroit, MI*
_LD BOHANON — Workshop 214 (1963) **$25**.

EDDIE BONNEMERE
piano - born 1921 New York City, NY
EDDIE BONNEMERE — Prestige 7354 (1965) blue label **$20**.
PIANO BON BONS BY BONNEMERE — Roost 2236 (1959) **$40**.
THE SOUND OF MEMORY — Roost 2241 (1960) **$40**.

CLAUDE BOLLING
piano - born 1930 Cannes, France
FRENCH JAZZ — Bally 12003 (1956) **$45**.
ROLLING WITH BOLLING — Omega 6 (1957) **$40**.

BERYL BOOKER
piano - born 1922 Philadelphia, PA
One of the very few female jazz musicians of the time, Booker performed as pianist for many notable vocalist such as Dinah Washington. Unfortunately, Booker was never widely recognized for her talents.
BERYL BOOKER/DON BYAS — Discovery 3022 (1953) 10" **$90**.
BERYL BOOKER TRIO — Discovery 3021 (1953) 10" **$60**.
GIRL MET A PIANO — EmArcy 26007 (1954) 10" **$50**; EP 1-6013; EP 1-6014 (1954) **$20** ea.
BERYL BOOKER — Cadence 1000 (1955) 10" **$45**.

PAT BOWIE
vocals - born Evanston, IL
OUT OF SIGHT/with Ray Bryant — Prestige 7385 (1965) blue label **$35**.
FEELIN' GOOD/with Charles McPherson — Prestige 7437 (1965) blue label **$35**.

ROCKY BOYD
tenor sax
EASE IT/with Kenny Dorham — Jazztime 001 (1961) **$45**.

EVANS BRADSHAW
piano - born 1933 Memphis, TN
LOOK OUT FOR/with Philly Joe Jones — Riverside 12-263 (1958) blue label with Bill Grauer Pro. **$35**.
PIECES OF 88 — Riverside 12-296/1136 (1959) blue label with Bill Grauer Pro. **$35**.

*RUBY BRAFF
trumpet - born 1927 Boston, MA
AND FRIENDS — Storyville 324 (1954) 10" **$60**; *reissued* Storyville 908 (1956).
HUSTLIN' AND BUSTLIN' — Storyville 908 (1956) **$50**.
SWINGS — Bethlehem 1005 (1954) 10" **$60**; *reissued* Bethlehem 5 (1955).
OMNIBUS — Bethlehem 5 (1955) **$35**.
THE BEST OF — Bethlehem 6043 (1960) maroon label **$30**.
RUBY BRAFF/with Dave McKenna — ABC Paramount 141 (1956) **$40**.
BRAFF! — Epic 3377 (1957) yellow label **$40**.
HI FI SALUTE TO BUNNY/with Dick Hafer — RCA Victor 1510 (1957) dog on top **$60**.
EASY NOW/with Roy Eldridge — RCA Victor 1966 (1959) dog on top **$60**.
INVENTIONS IN JAZZ/with Ellis Larkins — Vanguard 8019 (1954) 10" **$50**; *reissued* Vanguard 8516.
INVENTIONS IN JAZZ/with Ellis Larkins — Vanguard 8020 (1954) 10" **$50**; *reissued* Vanguard 8516.
SPECIAL/with Samuel Margous — Vanguard 8504 (1955) maroon label **$35**.
TWO BY TWO/with Ellis Larkins — Vanguard 8507 (1955) maroon label **$35**.

POCKETFULL OF DREAMS/with Ellis Larkins — Vanguard 8516 (1955) maroon label **$35.**

BUCK MEETS RUBY/with Buck Clayton — Vanguard 8517 (1956) **$35.**

SWING WITH — Jazztone 1210 (1956) **$35.**

GOES GIRL CRAZY/with Al Cohn — Warner Brothers 1273 (1959) **$50.**

BLOWING AROUND THE AROUND/with Galbraith — United Artists 3045/6045 (1959) **$50.**

RUBY BRAFF/MARSHALL BROWN SEXTET — United Artists 4093/5093 (1960) **$40.**

*The only LP's within the scope of this book.

GEORGE BRAITH
tenor, soprano saxes - born 1939 Bronx, NY

SOUL STREAM — Blue Note 4161/84161 (1964) with NY on label **$35;** with A Division of Liberty on label **$20.**

TWO SOULS IN ONE — Blue Note 4184/84184 (1964) with NY on label **$35;** with A Division of Liberty on label **$20.**

BRASIL '65
vocal group

IS HERE — Capitol 2294 (1965) logo on top **$25.**

IN PERSON AT EL MATADOR — Atlantic 8112 (1965) logo on side **$20.**

BUDDY BREGMAN
composer - born 1930 Chicago, IL

SWINGIN' STANDARDS — World Pacific 1263 (1959) **$45.**

SWINGIN' KICKS — Verve 2042 (1957) with Verve Records, Inc. on bottom of label **$45.**

BIG BUDDY IN HiFi — Verve 2094 (1957) with Verve Records, Inc. on bottom of label **$45.**

RONNELL BRIGHT
piano - born 1930 Chicago, IL

BRIGHT FLIGHT — Vanguard 8512 (1957) **$35.**

BRIGHT'S SPOT — Regent 6041 (1957) green label **$35.**

BOB BROOKMEYER
trombone, piano, composer - born 1929 Kansas City, KS

A great jazz player and the only major proponent of the valve trombone. Much of his earlier recording was done on World Pacific and Pacific Jazz labels which represent good examples of his work and are of significant value. Brookmeyer is best known for his work with Chet Baker and Gerry Mulligan although the on-and-off contributions he made to the Thad Jones-Mel Lewis Orchestra should also be noted.

FEATURING AL COHN — Storyville 305 (1954) 10" **$125;** EP 405; EP 406 (1954) **$50 ea.**

TONIGHT'S JAZZ TODAY/with Zoot Sims — Storyville 907 (1956) **$90.**

WHOOEEE/with Zoot Sims — Storyville 914 (1956) **$90.**

BOB BROOKMEYER QUARTET — Pacific Jazz 16 (1954) 10" **$100;** EP 4-25 (1954) **$45.**

TRADITIONALISM REVISITED/with Jimmy Giuffre — World Pacific 1233 (1958) **$60.**

THE STREET SWINGERS/with Jimmy Raney — World Pacific 1239 (1958) **$60.**

WITH PHIL URSO — Savoy 15041 (1954) 10" maroon label **$95.**

WITH RHYTHM SECTION — Clef 644 (1955) **$80;** EP 321; EP 322; EP 323 (1955) **$35 ea;** *reissued* Verve 8111 (1957).

BOB BROOKMEYER/with Jimmy Raney — Prestige 214 (1955) 10" **$100;** *reissued* Prestige 7066 (1956) & New Jazz 8294 (1963).

THE DUAL ROLE OF — Prestige 7066 (1956) yellow label **$70;** *reissue* of Prestige 214.

REVELATION — New Jazz 8294 (1963) **$45;** *reissue* of Prestige 214.

BROOKMEYER/with Al Cohn & Nick Travis — Vik 1071 (1957) **$60.**

KANSAS CITY REVISITED/with Al Cohn — United Artists 4008/5008 (1959) red label **$45.**

THE IVORY HUNTERS/with Bill Evans — United Artists 4044/5044 (1959) re[d] label **$60.**

STRETCHING OUT/with Zoot Sims — United Artists 4023/5023 (1959) red lab[el] **$60.**

JAZZ IS A KICK/with Curtis Fuller — Mercury 20600/60600 (1960) black labe[l] **$45.**

PORTRAIT OF THE ARTIST — Atlantic 1320 (1960) logo on side **$40.**

THE MODERNITY OF — Verve 8111 (1957) with Verve Records, Inc. on bottom o[f] label **$50;** *reissue* of Clef 644.

7 X WILDER — Verve 8413/68413 (1961) with MGM on bottom of label **$35.**

GLOOMY SUNDAY — Verve 8455/68455 (1962) with MGM on bottom of label **$25**

THE BLUES HOT & COLD/with Jimmy Rowles — Verve 8385/68385 (1961) wit[h] MGM on bottom of label **$35.**

TROMBONE JAZZ SAMBA — Verve 8494 (1962) with MGM on bottom of label **$20**

AND FRIENDS/with Stan Getz — Columbia 2237/9037 (1965) with 1 white log[o] on each side of label **$20.**

TONIGHT/with Clark Terry — Mainstream 56043/6043 (1965) **$20.**

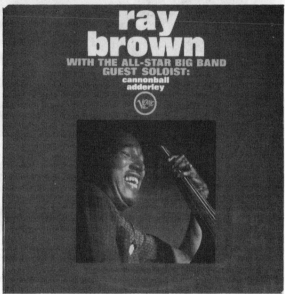

CLIFFORD BROWN
trumpet - born 1930 Wilmington, DE died 1956

Brown was, and still is, considered to have been a bright young jazz star who played with some of the best jazz musicians including Max Roach, Miles Davis and Lionel Hampton. Brown provided some great music in his short career which ended in his death in an auto accident at the age of only 25. This situation is unfortunately repeated all too often in music for various reasons and results in an easily documented career and highly sought after recordings. It is believed that, if not for his untimely death, Brown would most definitely be a leader in trumpet artistry. Labels of note for Brown would be Blue Note and EmArcy.

NEW STAR ON THE HORIZON — Blue Note 5032 (1953) 10" **$150**; *reissued* Blue Note 1526 (1957).

CLIFFORD BROWN QUARTET — Blue Note 5047 (1954) 10" **$125**.

MEMORIAL ALBUM — Blue Note 1526 (1956) with NY address on label **$60**; with A Division of Liberty on label **$20**.

ENSEMBLE/with Zoot Sims — Pacific Jazz 19 (1954) 10" **$125**; EP 4-27 (1954) **$45**; *reissued* Pacific Jazz 1214.

JAZZ IMMORTAL/with Zoot Sims — Pacific Jazz 1214 (1956) **$60**; *reissued* Pacific Jazz 3 (1960) **$45**.

SWEDISH ALL STARS/with Art Farmer — Prestige 167 (1954) 10" **$125**; EP 1353 (1954) **$45**.

MEMORIAL — Prestige 7055 (1957) yellow label **$65**; *reissue* of Prestige 167.

CLIFFORD BROWN & MAX ROACH — EmArcy 26043 (1954) 10" **$100**; EP 1-6074; EP 1-6075 (1954) **$40** ea.; *reissued* EmArcy 36036 (1955) **$50**.

BROWN & ROACH, INC. — EmArcy 36008 (1955) **$70**; EP 1-6111; EP 1-6112; EP 1-6113 (1955) **$35** ea.

CLIFFORD BROWN ALL STARS — EmArcy 36102 (1955) **$70**.

AND STRINGS — EmArcy 36005 (1955) **$60**; EP 1-6102; EP 1-6100 (1955) **$30**.

A STUDY IN BROWN — EmArcy 36037 (1955) **$70**.

AT BASIN STREET — EmArcy 36070 (1955) **$70**.

REMEMBER CLIFFORD — Mercury 20827/60827 (1963) **$30**. (A)

CLIFFORD BROWN & MAX ROACH — Gene Norman Presents 7 (1954) 10" **$90**; EP 5 (1954) **$35**.

IN CONCERT/with Max Roach — Gene Norman Presents 18 (1955) **$70**.

DONNA BROOKS
vocals

I'LL TAKE ROMANCE — Dawn 1105 (1956) **$45**.

DONNA BROOKS — Bethlehem BEP 104 (1955) **$25**.

JOHN BENSON BROOKS
piano - born 1917 Houlton, ME

FOLK JAZZ U.S.A. — Vik 1083 (1957) **$45**.

THE ALABAMA CONCERT — Riverside 276/1123 (1959) blue label with Bill Grauer Pro. **$40**.

ROY BROOKS
drums - born 1938 Detroit, MI

BEAT — Workshop 220 (1963) **$25**.

TINA BROOKS
tenor sax

BACK TO THE TRACKS — Blue Note 4052 (1960) with NY address on label **$65**; with A Division of Liberty on label **$20**.

TRUE BLUE — Blue Note 4041 (1960) with NY address on label **$65**; with A Division of Liberty on label **$20**.

RAY BROWN
bass - born 1926 Pittsburgh, PA

Much in demand since his teens during the early 50's, Ray Brown has worked in nearly every context imaginable and yet has only a handful of recordings under his own name which are all undoubtedly collectables. Pay particular attention to his work when with Oscar Peterson during the 60's.

BASS HIT — Verve 8022 (1957) **$60**.

THIS IS RAY BROWN — Verve 8290 (1959) **$45**.

JAZZ CELLO — Verve 8390/68390 (1960) **$40**.

ALL-STAR BIG BAND — Verve 8444/68444 (1962) **$40**.

MUCH IN COMMON — Verve 8580/68580 (1964) **$30**.

BROWN & JACKSON/with Milt Jackson — Verve 8615/68615 (1964) **$30**.

RUTH BROWN
vocals - born 1928 Portsmouth, VA

A gospel upbringing combined with a unique style, Brown's early recordings were in the rhythm and blues flavor. Subsequent maturity and opportunity in the early 60's afforded her quality jazz recordings on the following label:

RUTH BROWN '65 — Mainstream 6034 (1965) **$25**.

TED BROWN
tenor sax - born 1927 Rochester, NY

FREE WHEELING/with Art Pepper & Warne Marsh — Vanguard 8515 (1956) **$50**.

DAVE BRUBECK
piano, composer - born 1920 Concord, CA

One of the most popular jazz musicians extending even to the non-jazz public whose early work on Fantasy featured, among others, Cal Tjader on drums in a trio context. His pairing with altoist Paul Desmond began in 1949 and continued through the 60's revealing some of his best and most popular collectable music.

TRIO — Fantasy 3-1 (1951) 10" **$60**; EP 4001, EP 4002 (1949) **$25** ea.; *reissued* Fantasy 3-204 (1956) **$45**.

TRIO — Fantasy 3-2 (1951) 10" **$60**; EP 4005, EP 4006 (1950) **$25** ea.; *reissued* Fantasy 3-205 (1956) **$45**.

OCTET — Fantasy 3-3 (1951) 10" **$80**; EP 4019, EP 4020 (1949) **$30** ea; *reissued* Fantasy 3-239 (1956) **$50**; *reissued* Fantasy 3239/8094 (1962) **$35**.

QUARTET/with Paul Desmond — Fantasy 3-5 (1951) 10" **$90**; EP 4065 (1951) **$40**; *reissued* Fantasy 3-229 (1956) **$50**.

QUARTET/with Paul Desmond — Fantasy 3-7 (1951) 10" **$90**; EP 4066 (1951) **$40**; *reissued* Fantasy 3-230 (1956) **$50**.

JAZZ AT STORYVILLE — Fantasy 3-8 (1952) 10" **$80**; EP 4011, EP 4012 (1952) **$30** ea.; *reissued* Fantasy 2340 (1957) **$45**; *reissued* Fantasy 8080 (1962) **$25**.

JAZZ AT THE BLACK HAWK — Fantasy 3-10 (1953) 10" **$60**; EP 4014, EP 4053 (1953) **$30** ea.; *reissued* Fantasy 3-210 (1956) **$45**; *reissued* Fantasy 3298 (1962) **$30**.

JAZZ AT OBERLIN — Fantasy 3-11 (1953) 10" **$60**; EP 4007, EP 4013, EP 4062 (1952) **$30** ea.; *reissued* Fantasy 3245 (1957) **$45**; *reissued* Fantasy 8069 (1962) **$25**.

JAZZ AT COLLEGE OF PACIFIC — Fantasy 3-13 (1953) 10" **$60**; EP 4054, EP 4055 (1953) **$30** ea.; *reissued* Fantasy 3-223 (1956) **$45**.

JAZZ AT WILSHIRE-EBELL — Fantasy 3249 (1957) **$45**; EP 4066; EP 4065 (1953) **$30** ea.; *reissued* Fantasy 8095 (1962) **$25**.

PLAYS SOLO — Fantasy 3259 (1962) **$30**.

RE-UNION — Fantasy 3268/8007 (1962) **$45**.

BRUBECK A LA MODE — Fantasy 3301/8047 (1962) **$30**.

NEAR-MYTH/BRUBECK-SMITH — Fantasy 3319/8063 (1962) **$25**; *reissue of* Fantasy 3-11.

BRUBECK-TJADER — Vol. 1 — Fantasy 3331/8073 (1962) **$25** *reissue of* Fantasy 3-1.

BRUBECK-TJADER - Vol. 2 — Fantasy 3332/8074 (1962) **$25**; *reissue of* Fantasy 3-2.

JAZZ IMPRESSIONS OF THE U.S.A. — Columbia 932 (1957) red label with 3 black logos on each side **$45**.

JAZZ GOES TO COLLEGE — Columbia 566 (1954) red label with Columbia at top only in gold; (1956) red label with 3 black logos on each side **$60**; ea. EP B 1940, EP B 1943 (1954) **$25** ea.

AT STORYVILLE 1954 — Columbia 590 (1955) red label with 3 black logos on each side **$50**; EP B 1834, EP B 1894 (1955) **$25** ea.

BRUBECK TIME — Columbia 622 (1955) red label with 3 black logos on each side **$50**; EP B 1946, EP B 1947, EP B 1967 (1955) **$25** ea.

JAZZ RED HOT & COOL — Columbia 699 (1955) red label with 3 black logos on each side **$50**; EP B 2552 **$25**.

BRUBECK PLAYS BRUBECK — Columbia 878 (1956) **$35**.

AT NEWPORT/JAY & KAI — Columbia 932 (1956) one side Brubeck the other Jay & Kai - red label with 3 black logos on each side **$40**.

JAZZ GOES TO JUNIOR COLLEGE — Columbia 1034 (1957) red label with 3 black logos on each side **$45**.

DAVE DIGS DISNEY — Columbia 1059/8090 (1957) red label with 3 black logos on each side **$45**.

IN EUROPE — Columbia 1168/8128 (1958) red label with 3 black logos on each side **$40**.

NEWPORT 1958 — Columbia 1249/8082 (1958) red label with 3 black logos on each side **$40**.

JAZZ IMPRESSIONS OF EURASIA — Columbia 1251/8058 (1958) red label with 3 black logos on each side **$40**.

TIME OUT — Columbia 1397/8192 (1960) red label with 3 black logos on each side **$35**.

GONE WITH THE WIND — Columbia 1347/8156 (1959) red label with 3 black logos on each side **$35**.

THE RIDDLE — Columbia 1454 (1960) red label with 3 black logos on each side **$25**.

SOUTHERN SCENE — Columbia 1439/8235 (1960) red label with 3 black logos on each side **$25**.

WEST SIDE STORY — Columbia 1466/8257 (1960) red label with 3 black logos on each side **$25**.

BRUBECK & RUSHING/with Jimmy Rushing — Columbia 1553/8353 (1960) red label with 3 black logos on each side **$35**.

TONIGHT ONLY/with Carman McRae — Columbia 1609 (1961) red label with 3 black logos on each side **$30**.

COUNT DOWN TIME IN OUTER SPACE — Columbia 1775/8575 (1962) red label with 3 black logos on each side **$20**.

TIME FURTHER OUT — Columbia 1690/8490 (1961) red label with 3 black logos on each side **$20**.

BRANDENBERG GATE: REVISITED — Columbia 1963/8763 (1962) red label with 1 white logo on each side **$20**.

BOSSA NOVA U.S.A. — Columbia 1998/8798 (1963) red label with 1 white logo on each side **$20.**

TIME CHANGES — Columbia 2127/8927 (1964) red label with 1 white logo on each side **$15.**

JAZZ IMPRESSIONS OF JAPAN — Columbia 2212/9012 (1964) red label with 1 white logo on each side **$15.**

AT CARNEGIE HALL — Columbia C2L 26/C2S 826 (1963) red label with 1 white logo on each side - 2 LP's **$25.**

JAZZ IMPRESSIONS OF NEW YORK — Columbia 2275/9075 (1965) red label with 1 white logo on each side **$15.**

ANGEL EYES — Columbia 2348/9148 (1965) red label with 1 white logo on each side **$15.**

DAVE BRUBECK/PAUL DESMOND QUARTET/CAL TJADER QUARTET — Crown 5406 (1964) with picture of Brubeck on album cover **$20.**

DAVE BRUBECK QUARTET/with Paul Desmond and Cal Tjader — Crown 288 (1962) **$10.**

THE GREATS/with Paul Desmond — Crown 361 (1963) **$15.**

JOY BRYAN
vocals

JOY BRYAN SINGS — Mode 108 (1957) **$60.**

CLORA BRYANT
trumpet, vocals - born Texas

GIRL WITH A HORN/with Walter Benton — Mode 106 (1957) **$80.**

PAUL BRYANT
organ - born 1933 Long Branch, NJ

THE BLUES MESSAGE/with Curtis Amy — Pacific Jazz 9 (1960) **$40.**

BURNIN' — Pacific Jazz 12 (1961) **$35.**

MEETIN' HERE/with Curtis Amy — Pacific Jazz 26 (1961) **$35.**

SOMETHING'S HAPPENING/with Plas Johnson — Fantasy 3357/8357 (1964) **$25.**

RAY BRYANT
piano, composer - born 1931 Philadelphia, PA

Bryant's good reputation as a solid, swinging jazz pianist led him to work with many big names in jazz and, eventually, as leader on albums under, among others, New Jazz and Epic labels.

MEET BETTY CARTER AND — Epic 3202 (1956) **$60.**

TRIO — Epic 3279 (1956) **$40.**

ALONE WITH THE BLUES — Prestige/New Jazz 8213 (1962) **$25.**

PLAYS — Signature 6008 (1960) **$35.**

LITTLE SUSIE — Columbia 1449/8244 (1960) red label with 3 black logos on each side **$30.**

MADISON TIME — Columbia 1476/8276 (1960) red label with 3 black logos on each side **$30.**

CON ALMA — Columbia 1633/8433 (1961) red label with 3 black logos on each side **$30.**

DANCING THE BIG TWIST — Columbia 1746/8546 (1962) red label with 3 black logos on each side **$25.**

HOLLYWOOD JAZZ BEAT — Columbia 1867/8667 (1962) red label with 3 black logos on each side **$25.**

RUSTY BRYANT
tenor, alto saxes - born 1929 Huntington, VA

AMERICA'S GREATEST JAZZ — Dot 3353/25353 (1961) **$20.**

PLAYS JAZZ — Dot 3079 (1958) **$50.**

ALL NIGHT LONG — Dot 3006 (1956) **$50.**

MILT BUCKNER
piano, organ, leader - born 1915 St. Louis, MO died 1977

PIANO — Savoy 15023 (1955) 10" maroon label **$45.**

SEND ME SOFTLY — Capitol 938 (1958) green label **$35.**

ROCKIN' WITH MILT — Capitol 642 (1955) green label **$40.**

ROCKIN' HAMMOND — Capitol 722 (1956) green label **$40.**

MIGHTY HIGH — Argo 660 (1960) **$25.**

PLEASE MR. ORGAN PLAYER — Argo 670 (1961) **$25.**

MIDNIGHT MOOD — Argo 702 (1963) **$25.**

JACK BURGER
drums, bongos

THE END ON BONGO'S/with Buddy Collette — Hi Fi 804 (1962) **$25.**

SASCHA BURLAND
guitar, vocals - born 1927 New York City, NY

SWINGIN' THE JINGLES — Riverside 7515 (1961) red label **$45.**

THE NUTTY SQUIRRELS — Hanover 8014 (1960) **$35.**

RALPH BURNS
piano, composer, arranger - born 1922 Newton, MA

Burns worked primarily as an arranger and composer. Good examples of his creativity are Jazz At The Philharmonic and Studio Five dates. He toured with Woody Herman's group and soon thereafter began working with radio and television scores.

FREE FORMS — Clef 115 (1953) 10" **$60**; EP C 136, EP 137 (1953) **$20** ea.

JAZZ RECITAL — Clef 718 (1956) **$40**; *reissue* of Clef 115.

AMONG THE JATP'S — Norgran 1028 (1955) **$80**; EP 128, EP 129, EP 130, EP 131 (1955) **$25** ea.; *reissued* Verve 8121 (1957) **$45**.

WHERE THERE'S BURNS THERE'S FIRE — Warwick 5001 (1961) **$35**.

SPRING SEQUENCE — Period 1105 (1955) 10" **$50**; *reissued* Jazztone 1228 (1958) **$35**.

BIJOU — Period 1109 (1955) 10" **$50**; *reissued* Bethlehem 68 (1957) **$35**.

WITH BEVERLY KENNEY — Roost 2212 (1956) **$40**.

JAZZ STUDIO FIVE — Decca 8235 (1956) black label with silver lettering **$40**.

THE MASTERS REVISITED — Decca 8555 (1957) black label with silver lettering **$40**.

PORGY & BESS — Decca 9215/79215 (1958) black label with silver lettering **$30**.

VERY WARM FOR JAZZ — Decca 9207 (1958) black label with silver lettering **$50**.

KENNY BURRELL
guitar - born 1931, Detroit, MI

A Detroit native beginning his career as a sideman with a strong bop background. His keen abilities have allowed him to make recordings in many contexts and with some of the best sidemen and leaders. You will discover that Prestige and Blue Note labels represent some of his best recordings.

INTRODUCING — Blue Note 1523 (1956) with NY address on label **$50**; with A Division of Liberty on label **$20**.

KENNY BURRELL — Blue Note 1543 (1957) with NY address on label **$45**; with A Division of Liberty on label **$20**.

BLUE LIGHTS - Vol 1/with Tina Brooks — Blue Note 1596 (1958) with NY address on label **$45**; with A Division of Liberty on label **$20**.

BLUE LIGHTS - Vol 2/with Tina Brooks — Blue Note 1597 (1958) with NY address on label **$45**; with A Division of Liberty on label **$20**.

ON VIEW AT THE FIVE SPOT/with Tina Brooks — Blue Note 4021 (1959) with NY address on label **$45**; with A Division of Liberty on label **$20**.

MIDNIGHT BLUE — Blue Note 4123 (1963) with NY on label **$35**; with A Division of Liberty on label **$20**.

KENNY BURRELL — Prestige 7088 (1957) **$45**; *reissued* Prestige 7308 (1964).

BLUE MOODS — Prestige 7308 (1964) yellow label **$20**.

TWO GUITARS/with Jimmy Raney — Prestige 7119 (1958) yellow label **$50**.

BLUESY BURRELL/with Coleman Hawkins — Moodsville 29 (1963) **$35**.

KENNY BURRELL/JOHN COLTRANE — New Jazz 8276 (1958) **$45**.

CRASH/with Jack McDuff — Prestige 7347 (1964) blue label **$20**.

SOUL CALL — Prestige 7315 (1964) yellow label **$35**.

WEAVER OF DREAMS — Columbia 1703/8503 (1961) red label with 3 black logos on each side **$35**.

LOTSA BOSSA NOVA — Kapp 1326/3326 (1962) **$20**.

GUITAR FORMS — Verve 8612/68612 (1965) with MGM on bottom of label **$20**.

BLUE BASH — Verve 8552/68552 (1963) with MGM on bottom of label **$25**.

NIGHT AT THE VANGUARD — Argo 655 (1959) **$35**.

GARY BURTON
vibes, composer - born 1943 Anderson, IN

Influenced greatly by Bill Evans, Burton began as a young sideman for Stan Getz in 1964. While maintaining the basis and quality of his music Burton has gone on through many changes while developing his own unique style.

NEW VIBE MAN IN TOWN — RCA Victor 2420 (1962) dog on top **$25**.

WHO IS GARY BURTON? — RCA Victor 2665 (1963) dog on top **$25**.

SOMETHING'S COMING — RCA Victor 2880 (1964) dog on top **$20**.

THE GROOVY SOUND OF MUSIC — RCA Victor 3360 (1965) dog on top **$20**.

JOE BURTON
piano - born 1918 Chicago, IL

An example of an accomplished piano player whose works have become collectable due in large measure to their scarcity. Credited to Burton are recordings on Coral and Regent labels.

QUARTET — Trend EP 501 (1951) **$40**.

SESSION — Coral 57098 (1957) **$45**.

HERE I AM IN LOVE AGAIN — Coral 57175 (1957) **$40**.

JAZZ PRETTY — Regent 6036 (1957) green label **$45**.

SUBTLE SOUND — Joday 1000 (1963) **$20**.

JAKI BYARD
piano, composer - born 1922 Worcester, MA

HERE'S JAKI — New Jazz 8256 (1961) **$35**.

HI FLY — New Jazz 8273 (1962) **$35**.

OUT FRONT — Prestige 7379 (1965) blue label **$20**.

DON BYAS
tenor sax - born 1912 Muskogee, OK died 1972

Byas was a hard swinging, big toned and highly respected tenor player. He was known as a sideman primarily, gaining recognition with Count Basie. Consequently, the few albums he made as a leader, on many different labels, are of great value.

WITH BERYL BOOKER — Discovery 3022 (1954) 10" **$90**.

LAURA — Norgran 12 (1954) 10" **$85**.

TENOR SAXOPHONE CONCERTO — Dial 216 (1951) 10" **$125.**

TENOR SAX SOLOS — Atlantic 117 (1952) 10" **$90.**

TENOR SAX SOLOS — Savoy 15013 (1955) 10" maroon label **$60.**

DON BYAS SAX — Savoy 9007 (1950) 10" maroon label **$80.**

JAZZ: FREE & EASY — Regent 6044 (1957) green label **$45.**

HOLIDAY IS SAX/with Coleman Hawkins — EmArcy 26026 (1954) 10" **$85.**

FAVORITES — Seeco 35 (1955) 10" **$60.**

JAZZ FROM SAINT GERMAIN DES PRES — Verve 8119 (1957) one side only **$45.**

APRIL IN PARIS — Battle 6121 (1963) **$25.**

BILLY BYERS

trombone - born 1927 Los Angeles, CA

BILLY BYERS - JOE NEWMAN SEXTET/EDDIE BERT SEPTET EAST COAST SOUNDS — Jazztone 1276 (1959) **$35.**

*CHARLIE BYRD

guitar, composer - born 1925 Suffolk, VA

The blending of a strong classical guitar background and a good swinging style, Charlie Byrd's early recordings on Offbeat and Riverside labels established him as a true jazz master. Listed here are his releases which are in the scope of this particular book.

JAZZ AT THE SHOW BOAT - Vol 1 — Offbeat 3001 (1959) **$40.**

JAZZ AT THE SHOW BOAT - Vol 2 — Offbeat 3005 (1959) **$40.**

JAZZ AT THE SHOW BOAT - Vol 3 — Offbeat 3006 (1959) **$40.**

CHARLIE'S CHOICE — Offbeat 3007 (1960) **$40.**

JAZZ RECITAL — Savoy 12099 (1958) maroon label **$45.**

BOSSA NOVA PELOS PASSAROS — Riverside 436/9436 (1962) blue label with Bill Grauer Pro. **$35.**

BYRD'S WORD — Riverside 448/9448 (1962) blue label with Bill Grauer Pro. **$35.**

BYRD IN THE WIND — Riverside 449/9449 (1962) blue label with Bill Grauer Pro. **$35.**

BYRD AT THE GATE — Riverside 467/9467 (1963) blue label with Bill Grauer Pro. **$30.**

ONCE MORE — Riverside 454/9454 (1963) blue label with Bill Grauer Pro. **$30.**

*The only LP's within the scope of this book.

DONALD BYRD

trumpet, fluegelhorn - born 1932 Detroit, MI

An outstanding example of exceptional talent coming from Detroit, Byrd earned this early reputation from his work with Art Blakey's Jazz Messengers. Noteworthy for collectors are some of his earlier efforts as a leader in the Jazz Lab series with Gigi Gryce. Byrd has performed with a vast assortment of top drawer musicians on numerous recording labels.

BYRD'S EYE VIEW/with Hank Mobley — Transition 4 (1956) **$70.**

BYRD JAZZ/with Yusef Lateef — Transition 5 (1956) **$70.**

BYRD BLOWS ON BEACON HILL — Transition 17 (1956) **$60.**

BYRD'S WORD/with Frank Foster — Savoy 12032 (1955) maroon label **$45.**

JAZZ EYES — Regent 6056 (1957) green label **$60.**

MOTOR CITY SCENE/with Pepper Adams — Bethlehem 6056 (1960) **$40.**

THREE TRUMPETS/with Art Farmer & Idrees Sulieman — Prestige 7092 (1956) yellow label **$75.**

TWO TRUMPETS/with Art Farmer — Prestige 7062 (1956) yellow label **$75.**

YOUNGBLOODS/with Phil Woods — Prestige 7080 (1956) yellow label **$70.**

MODERN JAZZ PERSPECTIVES — Columbia 1058 (1958) red label with 3 black logos on each side **$50.**

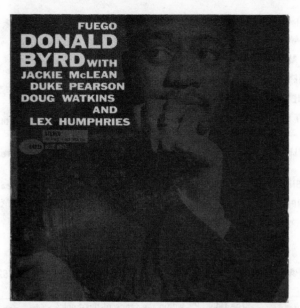

JAZZ LAB - Vol 1/with Gigi Gryce — Columbia 998 (1957) red label with 3 black logos on each side **$50.**

JAZZ LAB - Vol 2/with Gigi Gryce — Columbia 1058 (1957) red label with 3 black logos on each side **$50.**

JAZZ LAB/with Gigi Gryce — Jubilee 1059 (1957) **$50.**

JAZZ LABORATORY/with Gigi Gryce — Verve 8238 (1958) with Verve Records, Inc. on bottom of label one side only **$40.**

UP UP UP/with Stanley Turrentine — Verve 8609/68609 (1964) with MGM on bottom of label **$25.**

OFF TO THE RACES/with Jackie McLean — Blue Note 4007 (1959) with NY address on label **$40**; with A Division of Liberty on label **$20.**

BYRD IN HAND/with Charlie Rouse — Blue Note 4019 (1959) with NY address on label **$40**; with A Division of Liberty on label **$20.**

BYRD IN FLIGHT/with Jackie McLean — Blue Note 4048 (1961) with NY address on label **$35**; with A Division of Liberty on label **$20.**

FUEGO/with Jackie McLean — Blue Note 4026/84026 (1960) with NY address on label **$40**; with A Division of Liberty on label **$20.**

AT THE HALF NOTE CAFE - Vol 1/with Pepper Adams — Blue Note 4060/84060 (1961) with NY address on label **$35**; with A Division of Liberty on label **$20.**

AT THE HALF NOTE CAFE - Vol 2/with Pepper Adams — Blue Note 4061/84061 (1961) with NY address on label **$35**; with A Division of Liberty on label **$20.**

CAT WALK/with Pepper Adams — Blue Note 4075/84075 (1961) with NY address on label **$35**; with A Division of Liberty on label **$20.**

ROYAL FLUSH/with Pepper Adams — Blue Note 4101/84101 (1961) with NY address on label **$35**; with A Division of Liberty on label **$20.**

FREE FORM/with Wayne Shorter — Blue Note 4118/84118 (1962) with NY on label **$25**; with A Division of Liberty on label **$15.**

NEW PERSPECTIVE/with Hank Mobley — Blue Note 4124/84124 (1963) with NY on label **$25**; with A Division of Liberty on label **$15.**

I AM TRYIN' TO GET HOME — Blue Note 4188/84188 (1965) with NY on label **$25**; with A Division of Liberty on label **$15.**

JACKIE CAIN AND ROY KRAL

Jackie - vocals - born 1928 Milwaukee, WI
Roy - vocals, piano - born 1921 Chicago, IL

JACKIE CAIN AND ROY KRAL — Brunswick 54026 (1955) **$70.**

JACKIE CAIN AND ROY KRAL — Storyville 322 (1955) 10" **$70**; *reissued* Storyville 915 (1956) **$50.**

PRESENTS JACKIE AND ROY — Storyville 904 (1956) **$50.**

SING BABY SING — Storyville 915 (1956) **$50**; *reissue* of Storyville 322.

GLORY OF LOVE — ABC Paramount 120 (1956) **$40.**

BITS AND PIECES — ABC Paramount 163 (1957) **$40.**

FREE AND EASY — ABC Paramount 207 (1958) **$35.**

IN THE SPOTLIGHT — ABC Paramount 267 (1959) **$35.**

JACKIE CAIN AND ROY KRAL — Regent 6057 (1957) green label **$35.**

SWEET AND LOW DOWN — Columbia 1469/8260 (1960) red label with 3 black logos on each side **$35.**

DOUBLE TAKE — Columbia 1704/8504 (1962) red label with 3 black logos on each side **$30.**

LIKE SING — Columbia 1934 (1962) red label with 3 black logos on each side **$30.**

BY JUPITER GIRL CRAZY — Roulette 25278 (1964) checked roulette label **$30.**

*AL CAIOLA
guitar - born 1920 Jersey City, NJ

CLEOPATRA AND ALL THAT JAZZ/with Clark Terry — United Artists 3299/6299 (1962) black label **$25.**

---

*The Only LP's within the scope of this book.

RED CALLENDER
tuba, bass - born 1918 Richmond, VA

CALLENDER SPEAKS LOW/with Buddy Collette — Crown 5012 (1957) black label with liner notes on back of album cover **$30.**

SWINGIN' SUITE/with Buddy Collette — Modern 1201 (1956) **$30;** *reissued* Crown 5025 (1957) white label **$25.**

THE LOWEST/with Buddy Collette — Metrojazz 1007 (1959) **$25.**

CANADIAN ALL STARS

CANADIAN ALL STARS — Discovery 3025 (1954) 10" **$30;** EP 16 (1954) **$15.**

CANDIDO
congas drums - born 1921 Regal Havana, Cuba

CANDIDO/with Al Cohn — ABC Paramount 125 (1956) **$45.**

THE VOLCANIC/with Art Farmer — ABC Paramount 180 (1957) **$40.**

IN INDIGO — ABC Paramount 236 (1958) **$35.**

LATIN FIRE/with Phil Woods — ABC Paramount 286 (1959) **$35.**

CONGA SOUL/with Jimmy Cleveland — Roulette 52078 (1962) checked roulette label **$25.**

CANDOLI BROTHERS
Conte - trumpet; Pete - trumpet

THE BROTHERS CANDOLI — Dot 3062 (1957) red label **$45.**

BELL, BOOK AND CANDOLI — Dot 3168 (1959) black label **$35.**

TWO FOR THE MONEY — Mercury 20515/60191 (1960) black label **$25.**

THE BROTHERS CANDOLI — Warner Brothers 1462 (1962) **$25.**

CONTE CANDOLI
trumpet - born 1927 Mishawaka, IN

SINCERELY CONTE — Bethlehem 1016 (1954) 10" **$60;** EP 118 (1954) **$25;** *reissued* Bethlehem 9 (1955).

WEST COASTING WITH/with Stan Levey — Bethlehem 9 (1955) maroon label **$40.**

CONTE CANDOLI — Bethlehem 30 (1956) maroon label **$40.**

QUARTET — Mode 109 (1957) **$40;** *reissued* Premier 2009.

VINCE GUARALDI/CONTE CANDOLI QUARTET — Premier 2009 (1963) **$30.**

MUCHO CALOR/with Art Pepper — Andex 3002 (1957) **$30.**

LITTLE BAND BIG JAZZ/with Buddy Collette — Crown 190 (1960) red vinyl, black label with liner notes on back of album cover **$25.**

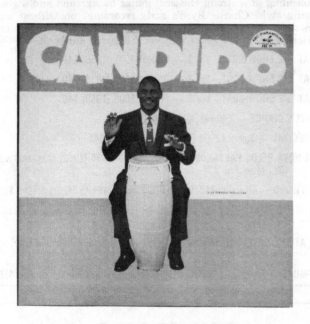

PETE CANDOLI
trumpet - born 1923 Mishawaka, IN

PETE CANDOLI — Capitol EP 1-538 (1953) **$20.**

PETE CANDOLI/with Conte Candoli — Dot 3204 (1959) **$30.**

FOR PETE'S SAKE — Kapp 1230/3230 (1963) **$20.**

PETE CANDOLI — Somerset 17200 (1963) **$15.**

HARRY CARNEY
baritone sax - born 1910 Boston, MA died 1974

WITH STRINGS/with Louis Bellson — Clef 640 (1954) **$80;** EP 288, EP 290 (1954) **$30** ea.; *reissued* Verve 2028.

MOODS FOR GIRL AND BOY — Verve 2028 (1956) with Verve Records, Inc. on bottom of label **$60.**

GEORGIA CARR
vocals - born Los Angeles, CA

SONGS BY A MOODY MISS — Tops 1617 (1958) **$30.**

GEORGIA CARR — Vee Jay 1105 (1964) **$20.**

HELEN CARR
vocals
DOWN IN THE DEPTHS ON THE 90TH FLOOR — Bethlehem 1027 (1954) 10" **$60.**

WHY DO I LOVE YOU — Bethlehem 45 (1956) maroon label **$40.**

HELEN CARR — Bethlehem EP 114 (1954) **$25.**

BARBARA CARROLL
piano - born 1925 Worchester, MA
BARBARA CARROLL TRIO — Discovery EP 4 (1949) **$20.**

PIANO PANORAMA — Atlantic 132 (1952) 10" **$50**; EP 503 (1952) **$20**; reissued 1271 (1958).

LADIES IN JAZZ/with Mary Lou Williams — Atlantic 1271 (1958) black label one side of LP is Mary Lou Williams **$35.**

BARBARA CARROLL TRIO — RCA Victor 1001 (1953) dog on top **$35.**

HAVE YOU MET MISS CARROLL? — RCA Victor 1137 (1956) dog on top **$30**; EP 663 (1956) **$10**; EP 1137, 2 records (1956) dog on top **$20.**

WE JUST COULDN'T SAY GOODBYE — RCA Victor 1296 (1956) dog on top **$30.**

IT'S A WONDERFUL WORLD — RCA Victor 1396 (1957) dog on top **$30.**

LULLABIES IN RHYTHM — RCA Victor 1023 (1955) dog on top **$35.**

BARBARA CARROLL — RCA Victor EP 604 (1954) **$20.**

BARBARA CARROLL — RCA Victor EP 656 (1955) **$20.**

FUNNY FACE — Verve 2063 (1956) with Verve Records, Inc. on bottom of label **$30.**

GEORGE AND IRA GERSHWIN — Verve 2092 (1958) with Verve Records, Inc. on bottom of label **$20.**

BARBARA — Verve 2095 (1958) with Verve Records, Inc. on bottom of label **$20.**

BARBARA CARROLL TRIO — Livingston 1081 (1953) 10" **$50.**

JOE CARROLL
vocals - born 1919 Philadelphia, PA
JOE CARROLL — Prestige EP 1302 (1952) **$35.**

JOE CARROLL/with Ray Bryant — Epic 3272 (1956) **$50.**

MAN WITH THE HAPPY SOUND — Charlie Parker 802 (1962) **$25.**

BENNY CARTER
alto sax, trumpet, clarinet, composer/arranger
born 1907 New York City, NY
Arriving on the scene in the 30's, Carter's work with big bands was widespread enough to allow him to form his own group which he kept together on and off for a number of years. His subsequent career was exercised mainly in California with groups of all sizes in addition to movie and television work during the 50's and 60's.

THE URBANE — Norgran 10 (1953) 10" **$80**; EP 17, EP 18 (1953) **$30** ea.; reissued Norgran 1070 (1956); reissued Verve 8160 (1957).

THE FORMIDABLE — Norgran 21 (1953) 10" **$80**; EP 45, EP 46 (1953) **$30** ea.; reissued Norgran 1058 (1956); reissued Verve 8148 (1957).

COSMOPOLITE — Clef 141 (1953) 10" **$80**; reissued Norgran 1070 (1956) **$50**; reissued Verve 8160 (1957) **$40.**

ALONE TOGETHER/with Oscar Peterson — Norgran 1058 (1956) **$50**; reissued Verve 8148 (1957) **$40.**

NEW JAZZ SOUNDS — Norgran 1044 (1954) **$70**; reissued Verve 8137 (1957) **$40.**

PLAYS PRETTY — Norgran 1015 (1955) **$60**; EP 87, EP 88 (1955) **$25** ea.; reissued Verve 2025 (1957).

MOONGLOW — Verve 2025 (1957) with Verve Records, Inc. on bottom of label **$40**; reissue of Norgran 1015.

JAZZ GIANT — Contemporary 3555/7028 (1959) yellow label **$45.**

SWINGIN' THE TWENTIES — Contemporary 3561/7561 (1959) yellow label **$45.**

THE URBANE JAZZ OF/with Roy Eldridge — American Recording Society 413 (1956) **$60**; reissued Verve 8202 (1957) **$40.**

THE FABULOUS — Audio Lab 1505 (1959) **$40.**

ASPECTS — United Artists 4017/5017 (1959) **$35**; reissued United Artists 4080/5080. (1961).

JAZZ CALENDAR — United Artists 4080/5080 (1961) **$25**; reissue of United Artists 4017/5017.

CAN CAN AND ANYTHING GOES — United Artists 3055/6055 (1959) **$35**; reissued United Artists 4073/5073 (1961) **$25.**

SAX A LA CARTER — United Artists 4094/5054 (1962) **$25.**

BBB & CO. — Swingville 2032 (1962) **$45.**

FURTHER DEFINITIONS — Impulse 12 (1962) orange label **$25.**

IN PARIS — 20th Century Fox 3134 (1963) **$25.**

BETTY CARTER
vocals - born 1930 Flint, MI
Early work with Lionel Hampton and later appearances with Miles Davis were good opportunities to demonstrate her unique vocal talents which feature a strong rythmic approach and extensive wordless vocals. Carter has produced many recordings on various labels and is still touring and recording today.

MEET/with Ray Bryant — Epic 3202 (1956) **$60.**

THE MODERN SOUND OF — ABC Paramount 363 (1960) **$50.**

RAY CHARLES AND BETTY CARTER — ABC Paramount 385 (1961) **$40.**

'ROUND MIDNIGHT — Atco 33-152 (1963) **$50.**

INSIDE — United Artists 3379/6379 (1963) **$50.**

RON CARTER

bass, cello - born 1937 Ferndale, MI

WHERE?/with Eric Dolphy — New Jazz 8265 (1961) **$35**.

AL CASEY

guitar - born 1915 Louisville, KY

BUCK JUMPIN' — Swingville 2007 (1960) **$35**.

AL CASEY QUARTET — Moodsville 12 (1960) **$35**.

PAGE CAVANAUGH

piano, vocals - born 1922 Cherokee, KS

FATS SENT ME/with Plas Johnson — Capitol 879 (1957) **$35**.

SERGE CHALOFF

baritone sax - born 1924 Boston, MA died 1957

Having been termed one of the best bop baritonists and a musicians musician, Chaloff is recognized for his ability to employ the entire range of his horn whether it was up tempo or the softer sound. He performed with such artists as George Auld and Woody Herman with a Charlie Parker influenced style. His self-taught talent gained him several awards during his short but successful career. Pay particular attention to his Blue Serge LP featuring Philly Joe Jones on drums which unfolded one of Chaloff's all time greats, The Goof & I.

NEW STARS, NEW SOUNDS/with Oscar Pettiford — Mercer 1003 (1951) 10" **$100**.

SERGE CHALOFF/with Boots Mussulli — Storyville 310 (1954) 10" **$80**.

THE FABLE OF MABEL/with Charlie Mariano — Storyville 317 (1954) **$80**; EP 26, EP 27 (1954) **$35** ea.

BOSTON BLOW-UP/with Boots Mussulli — Capitol 6510 (1955) green label **$70**.

BLUE SERGE — Capitol 742 (1956) green label **$70**.

PAUL CHAMBERS

bass - born 1935 Pittsburgh, PA died 1969

Chambers exhibited exceptional ability at an early age which led him to combo work around Detroit with Kenny Burrell and others. Worked with Miles Davis from 1955 to 1963, and has several albums with him as leader with various Miles Davis sidemen and other personnel. All of his recorded work is excellent, exemplifying his pizzicato and arco (bow) techniques to good effect.

CHAMBERS' MUSIC A JAZZ DELEGATION FROM THE EAST/with John Coltrane — Jazz West 7 (1956) **$80**; *reissued* Score 4033 (1958) **$50**; *reissued* Imperial 12182/9182 (1961) **$35**.

WHIMS OF CHAMBERS/with John Coltrane — Blue Note 1534 (1957) with NY address on label **$50**; with A Division of Liberty on white and blue label **$20**.

PAUL CHAMBERS QUINTET/with Clifford Jordon — Blue Note 1564 (1957) with NY address on label **$50**; with A Division of Liberty on white and blue label **$20**.

BASS ON TOP/with Kenny Burrell — Blue Note 1569 (1957) with NY address on label **$40**; with A Division of Liberty on white and blue label **$20**.

GO!/with Cannonball Adderley — Vee Jay 1014 (1960) maroon label **$45**; *reissued* Vee Jay 1014 (1960) black label **$35**; *reissued* in part Vee Jay 2501 (1965) **$15**.

1ST BASSMAN/with Yusef Lateef — Vee Jay 3012 (1960) maroon label **$45**; *reissued* Vee Jay 3012 (1960) black label **$35**; *reissued* in part Vee Jay 2501 (1965) **$15**.

EDDIE CHAMBLEE

tenor sax - born 1920 Atlanta, GA

CHAMBLEE MUSIC — EmArcy 36124 (1958) **$45**; *reissued* Mercury 60127 (1959) black label **$35**.

DOODIN' — EmArcy 36131 (1958) **$45**; *reissued* Mercury 80007 (1960) black label **$35**.

EDDIE CHAMBLEE — Prestige 7321 (1964) yellow label **$35**; *reissued* Prestige 7321 (1964) blue label **$25**.

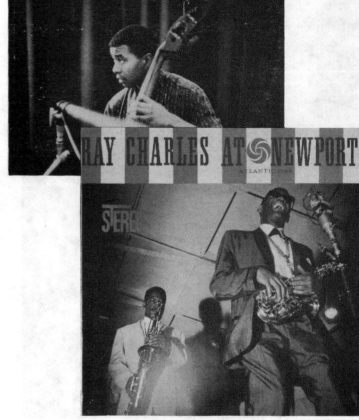

*RAY CHARLES

piano, organ, vocals, composer, alto sax - born 1932 Albany, GA

Early trio work reveals the Nat Cole influence in Ray's vocals and instrumentals. He put together his first band in 1954 backing Ruth Brown and went on to exceptional but nonjazz popularity with vocal hits in blues, rock and roll, gospel and country and western idioms. Charles continued to record big band jazz with highly respected jazz musicians such as Hank Crawford and on occasional collaborations as Soul Meeting with Milt Jackson and the LP Genius + Soul = Jazz featuring him on the organ.

THE GREAT — Atlantic 1259 (1957) black label **$50**; EP 597 (1957) **$20**; *reissued* Atlantic 1259 (1959) with logo on right side **$35**.

AT NEWPORT — Atlantic 1289 (1958) black label **$50**; *reissued* Atlantic 1289 (1959) with logo on right side **$35**.

SOUL MEETING/with Milt Jackson — Atlantic 1360 (1961) with logo on right side **$35**.

SOUL BROTHERS/with Milt Jackson — Atlantic 1279 (1958) black label **$50**; EP 614 (1958) **$20**; *reissued* Atlantic 1279 (1959) with logo on right side **$35**.

THE GENIUS AFTER HOURS — Atlantic 1369 (1961) with logo on right side **$35**.

THE GENIUS OF — Atlantic 1312 (1959) with logo on right side **$35**.

GENIUS + SOUL = JAZZ — Impulse 2 (1961) orange label **$35**.

ARTISTRY OF — Baronet 111 (1962) **$20** (*reissue* of his trio days).

THE INCOMPARABLE — Strand 1086 (1961) **$20** (*reissue* of his trio days).

RAY CHARLES AND BETTY CARTER — ABC Paramount 385 (1961) **$40**.

*The only LP's within the scope of this book.

TEDDY CHARLES
vibes, composer - born 1928 Chicopee Falls, MA

An advocate of the jazz style termed "third stream", Charles studied percussion during the late 40's and began playing professionally with names such as Benny Goodman and Chubby Jackson. The 50's found him joining Oscar Pettiford, Anita O'Day and Roy Eldridge, just to name a few. He continued studying, writing and recording to develop his "New Directions" project and established groups of his own while, at the same time, working for various recording companies and eventually organizing one of his own. Charles is considered to be an exceptional and original writer and musician who holds various awards for his creative pieces.

TEDDY CHARLES TRIO — Prestige 132 (1952) 10" **$50**.

NEW DIRECTIONS - Vol 1/with Jimmy Raney — Prestige 143 (1952) **$70**; EP 1350 (1952) **$35**.

NEW DIRECTIONS - Vol 2/with Hall Overton — Prestige 150 (1952) 10" **$50**.

NEW DIRECTIONS - Vol 3/with Shorty Rogers — Prestige 164 (1953) 10" **$70**; reissued Prestige 7078 (1957).

NEW DIRECTIONS - Vol 4/with Shorty Rogers — Prestige 169 (1954) 10" **$60**; reissued Prestige 7028 (1956).

TEDDY CHARLES/with Bob Brookmeyer — Prestige 178 (1954) 10" **$80**; reissued Prestige 7066 (1957).

N.D. QUARTET — New Jazz 1106 (1954) 10" **$90**; reissued Prestige 206 (1955) 10" **$70**; reissued Prestige 7078 (1957).

COLLABORATION WEST — Prestige 7028 (1956) yellow label **$50**; reissued Prestige 7028 (1964) blue label with logo on right side **$25**.

EVOLUTION — Prestige 7078 (1957) yellow label **$50**; reissued Prestige 7078 (1964) blue label with logo on right side **$25**.

TENTET — Atlantic 1229 (1956) black label **$50**; reissued with logo at right side (1961) **$25**.

WORD FROM BIRD — Atlantic 1274 (1958) black label **$50**; reissued with logo at right side (1961) **$25**.

VIBE-RANT — Elektra 136 (1957) **$50**.

THREE FOR DUKE — Jubilee 1047 (1957) **$45**; reissued Josie 3505 (1963).

PLAYS DUKE ELLINGTON — Josie 3505 (1963) **$30**; reissue of Jubilee 1047.

A SALUTE TO HAMP — Bethlehem 6032 (1958) maroon label **$45**.

ON CAMPUS/with Zoot Sims — Bethlehem 6044 (1960) maroon label **$50**.

METRONOME PRESENTS JAZZ IN THE GARDEN — Warwick 2033 (1960) **$50**.

RUSSIA GOES JAZZ/with Jimmy Giuffre — United Artists 3365/6365 (1964) black label **$35**.

BUDDY CHILDERS
trumpet - born 1926 St. Louis, MO

Childers began his musical career with Stan Kenton with which he remained from 1942 - 54. During this time he ventured out to team up with Les Brown and Benny Carter among others. Toured with Charlie Barnet in the mid-50's which resulted in his best LP, Buddy Childers Quartet, on the Liberty label.

SAM SONGS/with Herbie Stewart — Liberty 6009 (1956) blue label **$45**.

QUARTET — Liberty 6013 (1956) blue label **$45**.

CHARLIE CHRISTIAN
guitar - born 1919 Dallas, TX died 1942

Became famous with Benny Goodman's Sextet in 1939-41 and most especially for what was then a unique style of playing single note melodies and solos in addition to more traditional chord work. One of the early experimenters in New York City working with the new approach which would become known as be-bop, Christian was often credited along with Charlie Parker, Dizzy Gillespie and Thelonious Monk with being one of the important early contributors to that particular style.

MEMORABLE SESSIONS WITH — Blue Note 5026 (1953) 10" **$60**.

JAZZ IMMORTAL — Esoteric 1 (1953) 60; reissued Esoteric 548 (1956).

JAZZ IMMORTAL 1941 — Counterpoint 548 (1956) **$40**; reissue of Esoteric 1.

WITH THE BENNY GOODMAN SEXTET — Columbia 652 (1955) with 3 black logos on each side **$40**.

JUNE CHRISTY
vocals - born 1925 Springfield, IL

Christy earned notable recognition with the Stan Kenton Big Band in the mid-40's. She married the tenor saxman of the group, Bob Cooper, who has since backed, arranged and composed for her on most of her top recordings. Her throaty handling of ballads gained her the nickname "Misty", while her quality presentation of her trademark jump tunes created carefree and happy listening. June has not been given all due recognition but nonetheless has won several awards for her vocals.

SOMETHING COOL — Capitol H516 (1954) 10" **$60**; reissued Capitol T516 (1955) green label with white and blue LP cover **$40**; reissued Capitol T516 (1960) black label with logo on left side and cover in color **$25**.

DUET/with Stan Kenton — Capitol 656 (1955) green label **$45**; EP 1-656, EP 2-656, EP 3-656 **$20** ea.; reissued Capitol 656 (1960) black label with logo on left side **$25**.

THE MISTY MISS CHRISTY — Capitol T725 (1955) green label **$40**; EP 1-725, EP 2-725, EP 3-725 **$15** ea.; reissued Capitol T725 (1960) black label with logo on left side **$25**.

JUNE FAIR AND WARMER — Capitol T833 (1957) green label **$40**; reissued Capitol T833 (1960) black label with logo on left side **$25**.

GONE FOR THE DAY — Capitol T902 (1957) green label **$40**; reissued Capitol T902 (1960) black label with logo on left side **$25**.

JUNE'S GOT RHYTHM — Capitol 1076 (1958) black label **$35**; reissued Capitol 1076 (1962) black label with logo on top **$25**.

THE SONG IS JUNE! — Capitol 1114 (1959) black label with logo on left side **$30**.

RECALLS THOSE KENTON DAYS — Capitol 1202 (1959) black label with logo on left side **$30**; *reissued* Capitol 1202 (1962) black label with logo on top **$20**.

BALLADS FOR NIGHT PEOPLE/with Bob Cooper — Capitol 1308 (1959) black label with logo on left side **$45**; *reissued* Capitol 1308 (1962) black label with logo on top **$35**.

THE COOL SCHOOL — Capitol 1398 (1959) black label with logo on left side **$45**; *reissued* Capitol 1398 (1962) black label with logo on top **$35**.

OFF BEAT — Capitol 1498 (1959) black label with logo on left side **$35**; *reissued* Capitol 1498 (1962) black label with logo on top **$25**.

DO RE MI/with Bob Cooper — Capitol 1586 (1961) black label with logo on left side **$45**; *reissued* Capitol 1586 (1962) black label with logo on top **$35**.

THAT TIME OF THE YEAR (Christmas Album) — Capitol 1605 (1961) black label with logo on left side **$45**; *reissued* Capitol 1605 (1962) black label with logo on top **$35**.

BIG BAND SPECIALS — Capitol 1845 (1962) black label with logo on top **$25**.

THE INTIMATE — Capitol 1953 (1962) black label with logo on top **$25**.

GET HAPPY — Capitol EP 1-448 (1952) **$20**.

DOTTIE CLARK
vocals

I'M LOST — Mainstream 6006 (1965) **$25**.

SONNY CLARK
piano - born 1931 Herminie, PA died 1963

Clark performed and recorded with many big name jazz artists throughout his career. Considered to be a smooth-playing, top-notch pianist, he began as a young man with Oscar Pettiford later to form his own trio and gig around the San Francisco area in the early 50's. Around 1954 he joined up with Buddy De Franco and, in the late 50's, sessioned with The Lighthouse All Stars and Dinah Washington. Sonny died of a heart attack in 1963 but left behind him a distinct impression on the jazz world.

DIAL S FOR SONNY/with Hank Mobley — Blue Note 1570 (1957) with NY address on label **$50**; with A Division of Liberty on label **$20**.

SONNY CLARK TRIO — Blue Note 1579/81579 (1958) with NY address on label **$35**; with A Division of Liberty on label **$20**.

COOL STRUTTIN'/with Jackie McLean — Blue Note 1588/81588 (1958) with NY address on label **$50**; with A Division of Liberty on label **$20**.

SONNY'S CRIB/with John Coltrane — Blue Note 1576/81576 (1957) with NY address on label **$60**; with A Division of Liberty on label **$20**.

LEAPIN' & LOPIN'/with Charlie Rouse — Blue Note 4091/84091 (1961) with NY address on label **$40**; with A Division of Liberty on label **$20**.

SONNY CLARK TRIO — Time 70010 (1960) **$60**; *reissued* Time 52101/2101 (1962) **$40**.

BUCK CLARKE
congos

COOL HANDS/with Charles Hampton — Offbeat 3003 (1960) **$45**.

DRUM SUM/with Charles Hampton — Argo 4007 (1960) **$35**.

SOUNDS/with Charles Hampton — Argo 4021 (1961) **$35**.

KENNY CLARKE
drums, composer - born 1914 Pittsburgh, PA

Credited in his time with developing a new style of drumming to accompany the be-bop sound. He changed the emphasis from the "hi hat" or "sock cymbal" to the "top" or "ride" cymbal using the bass drum and snare to accent and punctuate the melody. His ability to play the much faster tempos (tempi, actually) associated with the then new style made him a true innovator. Most of his work since the 50's has been in Europe and most especially, with big bands in the 60's.

QUINTET/with Milt Jackson — Savoy 15051 (1954) 10" **$50**; *reissued* Savoy 12006 (1955) maroon label **$45**.

SEXTET/with Frank Wess — Savoy 15033 (1955) 10" **$60**; *reissued* Savoy 12006 (1955) maroon label **$45**.

BOHEMIA AFTER DARK/with Cannonball Adderley — Savoy 12017 (1955) maroon label **$60**.

KENNY CLARKE/ERNIE WILKINS — Savoy 12007 (1955) maroon label **$60**.

KLOOK'S CLIQUE/with Donald Byrd — Savoy 12065 (1956) maroon label **$50**.

JAZZ IS UNIVERSAL — Atlantic 1401 (1962) with logo on right side **$35**.

CLARKE/BOLAND BIG BAND — Atlantic 1404 (1962) with logo on right side **$30**.

NOW HEAR OUR MEANIN' — Columbia 2314/9114 (1965) with one white logo on each side **$20**.

JAMES CLAY
tenor sax, flute - born 1935 Dallas, TX

TENORMAN — Jazz West 8 (1956) **$85**.

THE SOUND OF THE WIDE OPEN SPACES — Riverside 12-327/1178 (1960) blue label with Bill Grauer Pro. **$35**.

A DOUBLE DOSE OF SOUL — Riverside 349/9349 (1961) blue label with Bill Grauer Pro. **$35**.

*BUCK CLAYTON
trumpet, composer - born 1911 Parsons, KS

THE HUCKLEBUCK AND ROBBINS NEST — Columbia 546 (1954) red label with Columbia in gold **$70**; *reissued* with 3 black logos on each side **$60**; EP B1836 (1953) **$20**.

HOW HIGH THE FI — Columbia 567 (1954) red label with Columbia in gold **$50**; *reissued (1956) with 3 black logos on each side* **$40**; EP B1958 (1954) **$20**.

CAT MEETS CHICK/with Jimmy Rushing and Ada Moore — Columbia 778 (1956) with 3 black logos on each side **$40**.

JAZZ SPECTACULAR/with Frankie Lane, J.J. Johnson and Kai Winding — Columbia 808 (1956) with 3 black logos on each side $40; EP 8081 (1956) $20.

ALL THE CATS JOIN IN/with Coleman Hawkins — Columbia 882 (1956) with 3 black logos on each side $40.

SONGS FOR SWINGERS/with Buddy Tate — Columbia 1320 (1959) with 3 black logos on each side $35.

BUCK & BUDDY/with Buddy Tate — Swingville 2017 (1960) $30.

BLOW THE BLUES/with Buddy Tate — Swingville 2030 (1962) $30.

---

*The only LP's within the scope of this book.

JIMMY CLEVELAND
trombone - born 1926 Wartrace, TN

A mainstream style which has prompted considerable controversy and varied interpretations among critics gained Cleveland entry into the jazz spotlight. He is a quality trombonist who should rightfully be rated alongside masters such as J.J. Johnson and Kai Winding and has recorded and performed as sideman with many top drawer musicians. Cleveland has free-lanced and performed in musicals, soundtracks and television productions and continues to do so today. His own LP's can be found on the Mercury/EmArcy label but he has played as sideman on many.

INTRODUCING — EmArcy 36066 (1955) $45.

CLEVELAND STYLE — EmArcy 36126 (1958) $35; *reissued* Mercury 20553/60121 (1961) black label $25.

A MAP OF CLEVELAND — Mercury 20442/60117 (1959) black label $35.

RHYTHM CRAZY — EmArcy 26003/66003 (1965) gray label with EmArcy emblems in a circle $25.

*ROSEMARY CLOONEY
vocals - born 1930 Maysville, KY

BLUE ROSE/with Duke Ellington — Columbia 872 (1956) with 3 logos on each side $45.

SWING AROUND ROSIE — Coral 57266/757266 (1958) maroon label $35.

---

*The only LP's within the scope of this book.

ARNETT COBB
tenor sax - born 1918 Houston, TX

A good tenorman whose sporadic appearances have established him a place in the jazz world. He began his professional career in 1933 with Frank Davis but is probably better known for this works with Lionel Hampton during the 40's. Became quite popular for a time in the 50's and into the 60's. A serious illness and auto accident set him

back at different times for some while but Cobb continues to perform publicly to date.

SWINGIN' WITH — Apollo 105 (1952) 10" $80.

BLOW ARNETT BLOW/with Eddie Lockjaw Davis — Prestige 7151 (1959) yellow label $40; *reissued* Prestige 7151 (1964) blue label with logo on right side $25.

SMOOTH SAILING — Prestige 7184 (1959) yellow label $50; *reissued* Prestige 7184 (1964) blue label with logo on right side $25.

PARTY TIME — Prestige 7165 (1961) yellow label $45; *reissued* Prestige 7165 (1964) blue label with logo on right side $25.

MORE PARTY TIME — Prestige 7175 (1960) yellow label $45; *reissued* Prestige 7175 (1964) blue label with logo on right side $25.

MOVIN' RIGHT ALONG — Prestige 7216 (1961) yellow label $35; *reissued* Prestige 7216 (1964) blue label with logo on right side $25.

SIZZLIN' — Prestige 7227 (1961) yellow label $35; *reissued* Prestige 7227 (1964) blue label with logo on right side $25.

BALLADS BY COBB — Moodsville 14 (1961) $25.

AL COHN
tenor, baritone saxes, composer
born 1925 Brooklyn, NY

A man of many talents, Cohn is best known for his endeavors as a tenorman with a great ability towards composing and musical arrangements. During the 40's he could be found working with Woody Herman and the renowned band The Four Brothers which included Zoot Sims, Drew More and Allen Eager. He left the music business for a short while in the early 50's but was soon back to play on many recordings and to compose and arrange for various television and radio shows. Later he toured and recorded with Zoot Sims and evidence of this great teamwork can be found on the LP You 'N Me. Some of his other fine contributions are on the Mercury and Coral labels.

AL COHN QUINTET — Progressive 3002 (1953) 10" $90.

AL COHN QUINTET — Progressive 3004 (1953) 10" $90.

AL COHN QUINTET — Progressive 1003 (1954) 10" $90.

EAST COAST - WEST COAST SCENE — RCA Victor 1020 (1954) dog on top $95 (one side of LP is Shorty Rogers); EP 1020 (1954) $35.

MR. MUSIC — RCA Victor 1024 (1954) dog on top $75.

THE NATURAL SEVEN — RCA Victor 1116 (1955) dog on top $60.

FOUR BRASS ONE TENOR — RCA Victor 1161 (1955) dog on top $60.

THAT OLD FEELING — RCA Victor 1207 (1956) dog on top $60.

THE BROTHERS/with Bill Perkins — RCA Victor 1162 (1956) dog on top $60.

FROM A TO Z/with Zoot Sims — RCA Victor 1282 (1956) dog on top $60.

SON OF DRUM SUITE — RCA Victor 2312 (1960) dog on top **$50.**

THE SAX SECTION — Epic 3278 (1956) yellow label **$60.**

COHN ON THE SAXOPHONE — Dawn 1110 (1956) **$50.**

QUINTET — Coral 57118 (1957) maroon label **$50.**

AL AND ZOOT/with Zoot Sims — Coral 57171 (1957) maroon label **$50.**

EITHER WAY/with Zoot Sims — Fred Miles Presents 1 (1960) **$50.**

YOU 'N ME/with Zoot Sims — Mercury 20606 (1960) **$45.**

AL COHN'S TONES — Savoy 12048 (1956) **$45;** *reissue* of Progressive 3002 and 3004.

A NIGHT AT THE HALF NOTE/with Zoot Sims and Phil Woods — United Artists 4040/5040 (1959) **$45.**

JERRY COKER
tenor sax, arranger - born 1932 South Bend, IN

MODERN MUSIC — Fantasy 3-214 (1956) **$30.**

COZY COLE
drums - born 1909 East Orange, NJ died 1981

COZY COLE/with Illinois Jacquet — Audition 33-5943 (1955) **$50.**

COZY COLE AND HIS ALL-STARS — Paris 122 (1958) **$45.**

AFTER HOURS — Grand Award 33-334 (1955) **$45;** EP 2035 (1955) **$20.**

COZY'S CARAVAN/EARL'S BACKROOM — Felsted 7002 (1959) **$45.**

HOT AND COZY/with Hot Lips Page — Continental 16007 (1962) **$30.**

A COZY CONAPTION OF CARMEN — Charlie Parker 403 (1962) **$25.**

IT'S A COZY WORLD — Coral 57457/757457 (1962) **$25.**

DRUM BEAT DANCING FEET — Coral 57423/757423 (1962) **$25.**

COZY COLE — King 673 (1959) **$35.**

JOHNNY COLE
trumpet

THE WARM SOUND — Epic 16015 (1961) **$35.**

LITTLE JOHNNY C — Blue Note 4144/84144 (1962) with NY on label **$30;** with A Division of Liberty on label **$20.**

*NAT KING COLE
vocals, piano - born 1917 Montgomery, AL died 1965

Straighten Up and Fly Right got the Nat King Cole Trio off to an overwhelming start and set him as the primary artist on the Capitol label in 1943. Needless to say, within a few years he drifted into the more commercial "popular" music of the time and also into motion picture roles and a television series of his own. Although he is best known for his singing, Cole has achieved success as a pianist and received many awards to document his talent. Albums listed in this book reflect his jazz background which is certainly the smaller portion of his musical career. Cole died of cancer in 1965.

AT THE PIANO — Capitol H156 (1952) 10" **$50.**

TRIO — Capitol H177 (1952) 10" **$50;** EP 177 (1952) **$25.**

TRIO — Capitol H220 (1952) 10" **$50;** EP 220 (1952) **$25.**

PENTHOUSE SERENADE — Capitol H332 (1953) 10" **$50;** EP 1-332, EP 2-332 (1953) **$25** ea.; *reissued* Capitol T332 (1955) green label **$35.**

INSTRUMENTAL CLASSICS — Capitol T592 (1955) green label **$45.**

THE PIANO STYLE OF — Capitol T682 (1956) green label **$45.**

AFTER MIDNIGHT — Capitol 782 (1958) green label **$45;** EP 1-782, EP 2-782, EP 3-782, EP 4-782 (1958) **$15** ea.

ST. LOUIS BLUES — Capitol 993 (1958) green label **$45;** *reissued* Capitol 993 (1960) black label with logo on left side **$35.**

NAT KING COLE TRIO/with Lester Young — Score 4019 (1957) **$60;** *reissued* Crown 412 (1964) white label **$20.**

---

*The only LP's within the scope of this book.

EARL COLEMAN
vocals - born 1925 Port Huron, MI

RETURNS — Prestige 7045 (1956) yellow label **$70;** *reissued* Prestige 7045 (1964) blue label with logo on right side **$25.**

GLORIA COLEMAN
organ

SOUL SISTERS/with Pola Roberts — Impulse 47 (1963) orange label **$35.**

ORNETTE COLEMAN
alto sax, composer - born 1930 Fort Worth, TX

SOMETHING ELSE — Contemporary 3551/7551 (1959) yellow label **$35.** Ⓐ

CHANGE OF THE CENTURY — Atlantic 1327 (1960) with logo on right side **$35.**

THE SHAPE OF JAZZ TO COME — Atlantic 1317 (1960) with logo on right side **$35.**

THIS IS OUR MUSIC — Atlantic 1353 (1960) with logo on right side **$30.**

FREE JAZZ — Atlantic 1364 (1961) with logo on right side **$25.**

ORNETTE — Atlantic 1378 (1961) with logo at right side **$25.**

ORNETTE ON TENOR — Atlantic 1394 (1962) with logo at right side **$25.**

AT TOWN HALL 1962 — ESP 1006 (1965) **$20.**

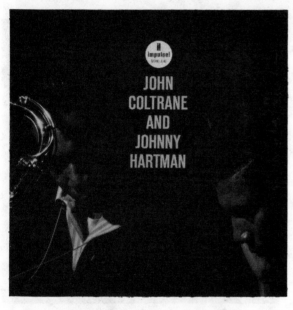

BUDDY COLLETTE
saxes, flute, clarinet, composer - born 1921
Los Angeles, CA

TANGANYIKA — Dig 101 (1956) **$50.**

STAR STUDDED CAST — Tampa 34 (1957) **$35.**

MAN OF MANY PARTS — Contemporary 3522 (1956) yellow label **$45.**

NICE DAY WITH — Contemporary 3531 (1957) yellow label **$40.**

CALM COOL & COLLETTE — ABC Paramount 179 (1957) **$35.**

BUDDY'S BEST — Dooto 245 (1957) **$45.**

EVERYBODY'S BUDDY — Challenge 603 (1957) **$35.**

JAZZ LOVES PARIS — Specialty 5002 (1958) **$35.**

MODERN INTERPRETATIONS OF PORGY AND BESS — Interlude 505/1005 (1957) **$40.**

FLUTE FRATERNITY/with Herbie Mann — Interlude 503/1003 (1957) **$45.**

SWINGIN' SHEPARDS — EmArcy 36133 (1958) **$35.**

SWINGIN' SHEPARDS AT THE CINEMA — Mercury 20447/60132 (1959) **$30.**

AL "JAZZBO" COLLINS
EAST COAST JAZZ SCENE — Coral 57035 (1956) maroon label **$60.**

DICK COLLINS
trumpet, composer - born 1924 Seattle, WA

KING RICHARD THE SWING HEARTED/with Al Cohn — RCA Victor 1027 (1955) dog on top **$45.**

HORN OF PLENTY — RCA Victor 1019 (1955) dog on top **$45.**

JOYCE COLLINS
piano, vocals - born 1930 Battle Mountain, NV

GIRL HERE PLAYS MEAN PIANO — Jazzland 22/922 (1960) **$25.**

JOHN COLTRANE
tenor, soprano saxes - born 1926 Hamlet, NC died 1967

Beginning on tenor in the 40's Coltrane worked with big name groups like those of Dizzy Gillespie, Johnny Hodges and Earl Bostic, during which time he developed his own sound and style. Beginning in 1955 with Miles Davis, Coltrane was inspired and encouraged by the freedom of the group and the music they were creating to experiment with new approaches. This resulted in more intense and lengthy solos or, so-called, "sheets of sound" and set the pattern for much of the remainder of his career. Each significant change in this style resulted in considerable popular and critical reaction, both pro and con. He left Davis for a while in 1957 during which time some memorable music was made and recorded with Thelonious Monk. He rejoined Davis in 1958, staying until 1960 in a band that included saxophonist "Cannonball" Adderley. During that time he began playing soprano sax which he found gave him "another voice." On his departure from Davis in 1960 he recorded My Favorite Things on soprano sax; the song and LP received considerable attention and resulted in a storm of controversy regarding his style, ability and integrity.

Coltrane was fascinated by the Eastern Indian approach to music and that, along with the modes he had explored with Miles, were the areas he chose to work in for the remainder of his career. With increasing intensity approaching religous fervor, he played more and longer on recording after recording. A good example of this is the LP Cosmic Music on Coltrane Records. Of notable exceptions are the Impulse LPs which revealed he had not forgotten his roots as on Ballads with McCoy Tyner. However, except for those occasional pauses, Coltrane's course was set with personnel changes in 1965 and he continued to explore and experiment until his death in 1967.

TWO TENORS/with Hank Mobley — Prestige 7043 (1956) yellow label **$80;** *reissued* Prestige 7043 (1964) blue label with logo on right side **$35.**

COLTRANE — Prestige 7105 (1957) yellow label **$80;** *reissued* Prestige 7105 (1964) blue label with logo on right side **$25.**

WITH THE RED GARLAND TRIO — Prestige 7123 (1958) yellow label **$70;** *reissued* Prestige 7123 (1964) titled Traneing In.

TRANEING IN — Prestige 7123 (1964) blue label with logo on right side **$35;** *reissued* Prestige 7651 (1969) blue label with logo on top **$20.**

SOULTRANE — Prestige 7142 (1958) yellow label **$60;** *reissued* Prestige 7142 (1964) blue label with logo on right side **$25.**

CATTIN'/with Paul Quinichette — Prestige 7158 (1958) yellow label **$60;** *reissued* Prestige 7158 (1964) blue label with logo on right side **$25.**

WHEELIN' AND DEALIN'/with Frank Wess — Prestige 7131 (1958) yellow label **$70.**

LUSH LIFE — Prestige 7188 (1959) yellow label **$60;** *reissued* Prestige 7188 (1964) blue label with logo on right side **$25.**

SETTIN' THE PACE — Prestige 7213 (1961) yellow label **$45;** *reissued* Prestige 7213 (1964) blue label with logo on right side **$25.**

STANDARD COLTRANE — Prestige 7243 (1962) yellow label **$40;** *reissued* Prestige 7243 (1964) blue label with logo on right side **$25.**

STARDUST — Prestige 7268 (1963) yellow label **$35;** *reissued* Prestige 7268 (1965) blue label with logo on right side **$25.**

DAKAR — Prestige 7280 (1964) yellow label **$35;** *reissued* Prestige 7280 (1965) blue label with logo on right side **$25.**

BAHIA — Prestige 7353 (1965) blue label with logo on right side **$25.**

BLACK PEARLS — Prestige 7316 (1965) blue label with logo on right side **$25**.

COLTRANE TIME — United Artists 14001/15001 (1962) with gray label and silhouette of saxophonist **$35**.

GIANT STEPS — Atlantic 1311 (1959) with logo on the right side **$40**.

COLTRANE JAZZ — Atlantic 1354 (1960) with logo on the right side **$35**.

MY FAVORITE THINGS — Atlantic 1361 (1961) with logo on the right side **$35**.

BAGS AND TRANE/with Milt Jackson — Atlantic 1368 (1961) with logo on the right side **$35**.

OLE COLTRANE — Atlantic 1373 (1962) with logo on the right side **$25**.

PLAYS THE BLUES — Atlantic 1382 (1962) with logo on the right side **$35**.

COLTRANE SOUND — Atlantic 1419 (1963) with logo on the right side **$25**.

THE AVANT GARDE/with Don Cherry — Atlantic 1451 (1966) **$25**.

THELONIOUS MONK/JOHN COLTRANE — Jazzland 46/946 (1961) **$35**.

AFRICA/BRASS — Impulse 6 (1961) orange label **$30**.

LIVE AT THE VILLAGE VANGUARD — Impulse 10 (1962) orange label **$30**.

COLTRANE — Impulse 21 (1962) orange label **$30**.

DUKE ELLINGTON AND JOHN COLTRANE — Impulse 30 (1963) orange label **$45**.

BALLADS — Impulse 32 (1963) orange label **$45**.

JOHN COLTRANE AND JOHNNY HARTMAN — Impulse 40 (1963) orange label **$45**.

IMPRESSIONS — Impulse 42 (1963) orange label **$25**.

LIVE AT BIRDLAND — Impulse 50 (1963) orange label **$25**.

CRESCENT — Impulse 66 (1964) orange label **$25**.

LOVE SUPREME — Impulse 77 (1965) orange label **$35**. (A)

QUARTET PLAYS — Impulse 65 (1965) orange label **$25**.

COSMIC MUSIC — Coltrane Records 4950 (1966) **$100**.

COSMIC MUSIC — Coltrane Records 5000 (1966) **$100**.

NOTE: Both Cosmic Music LP's are on Coltrane's private label and are extremely rare. The address to Coltrane Recording Corp. is on the label.

CHRIS CONNOR
vocals - born 1927 Kansas City, MO

Ms. Connor's professional life began in the early 50's as a vocalist for Bob Brookmeyer and later the Stan Kenton band. Her deep, rich voice won her positive acclaim with the jazz audiences as well as jazz critics and eventually settled her into recording dates on the Bethlehem label. The intriguing quality and flexibility in her style carried Chris to her own place in the music world as an unquestioned jazz vocalist.

SINGS LULLABYS OF BIRDLAND — Bethlehem 1001 (1954) 10" **$80**; EP 101A, EP 101B (1954) **$35** ea.; *reissued* Bethlehem 6004 (1957) maroon label **$45**.

SINGS LULLABYS FOR LOVERS — Bethlehem 1002 (1954) 10" **$80**; EP 102A, EP 102B (1954) **$35** ea.; *reissued* Bethlehem 6004 (1957) maroon label **$45**.

THIS IS CHRIS — Bethlehem 20 (1955) maroon label **$45**; EP 129, EP 130, EP 126 (1955) **$35** ea.

CHRIS — Bethlehem 56 (1956) maroon label **$45**; EP 127 (1955) **$25**.

BETHLEHEM GIRLS/with Carmen McRae and Julie London — Bethlehem 6006 (1956) maroon label **$35** (4 songs by each vocalist).

HE LOVES ME, HE LOVES ME NOT — Atlantic 1240 (1957) black label **$45**; *reissued* with logo on right side (1960) **$25**.

I MISS YOU SO — Atlantic 8014 (1956) black label **$50**; EP 580 (1956) **$35**; *reissued* with logo at right side (1960) **$25**.

A JAZZ DATE WITH — Atlantic 1286 (1957) black label **$45**; EP 615 (1956) **$30**; *reissued* with logo at right side **$25**.

SINGS THE GEORGE GERSHWIN ALMANAC OF SONGS — Atlantic 2-601 (1957) black label 2 LP's **$80**; EP 593, EP 594, EP 595, EP 596 (1956) **$25** ea.

CHRIS CRAFT — Atlantic 1290 (1958) black label **$45**; *reissued* with logo on right side (1961) **$25**.

SINGS BALLADS OF THE SAD CAFE — Atlantic 1307 (1959) with logo on right side **$35**.

CHRIS IN PERSON — Atlantic 8040 (1959) with logo on right side **$35**.

WITCHCRAFT — Atlantic 8032 (1959) with logo on right side **$35**.

CHRIS CONNOR — Atlantic 1228 (1956) black label **$50**; EP 577 (1956) **$35**; *reissued* (1960) with logo on right side **$25**.

A PORTRAIT OF CHRIS — Atlantic 8046 (1960) with logo on right side **$35**.

DOUBLE EXPOSURE/with Maynard Ferguson — Atlantic 8049 (1961) with logo on right side **$35**.

FREE SPIRITS — Atlantic 8061 (1962) with logo on right side **$35**.

TWO'S COMPANY/with Maynard Ferguson — Roulette 52068 (1958) white label with multicolored pinwheel **$45**.

AT THE VILLAGE GATE — FM 300 (1963) **$50**.

A WEEKEND IN PARIS — FM 312 (1964) **$50**.

GENTLE BOSSA NOVA — ABC Paramount 529 (1965) **$25**.

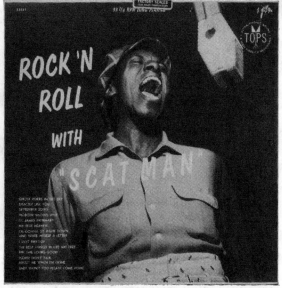

EDDIE COSTA
piano, vibes - born Atlas, PA
QUINTET — Mode 118 (1957) **$60**; *reissued* Interlude 508/1008 (1958) **$45**.

THE HOUSE OF BLUE LIGHTS — Dot 25206/3206 (1958) **$50**.

EDDIE COSTA/VINNIE BURKE TRIO — Jubilee 1025 (1956) **$45**.

AT NEWPORT/with Dick Johnson and Rolf Kuhn — Verve 8237 (1957) **$35**.

CURTIS COUNCE
bass - born 1926 Kansas City, MO died 1963
THE CURTIS COUNCE GROUP/with Jack Sheldon — Contemporary 3526 (1957) yellow label **$50**.

YOU GET MORE BOUNCE/with Carl Perkins — Contemporary 3539 (1957) yellow label **$45**.

CARL'S BLUES — Contemporary 3574 (1960) yellow label **$45**.

HANK CRAWFORD
*tenor, alto, baritone saxes, piano, composer
born 1934 Memphis, TN*
MORE SOUL — Atlantic 1356 (1961) with logo on right side **$35**.

THE SOUL CLINIC — Atlantic 1376 (1961) with logo on right side **$45**.

FROM THE HEART — Atlantic 1387 (1962) with logo on right side **$35**.

SOUL OF THE BALLAD — Atlantic 1405 (1963) with logo on right side **$35**.

TRUE BLUE — Atlantic 1423 (1964) with logo on right side **$30**.

DIG THESE BLUES — Atlantic 1436 (1965) with logo on right side **$20**.

SONNY CRISS
alto sax - born 1927 Memphis, TN
SONNY CRISS — Clef EP 115 (1949) **$35**.

CRISS CROSS — Imperial 9205/12205 (1962) **$40**.

GO MAN! — Imperial 9020 (1956) **$50**.

JAZZ U.S.A. — Imperial 9006 (1956) **$50**.

PLAYS COLE PORTER — Imperial 9024 (1956) **$50**.

"SCATMAN" CROTHERS
vocals, born 1910 Terre Haute, IN
ROCK 'N ROLL WITH "SCATMAN" — Tops 1511 (1956) **$35**; *reissued* Craftsman 8036 (1960).

GONE WITH — Craftsman 8036 (1960) **$20**; *reissue* of Tops 1511.

MIKE CUOZZO
tenor sax - born 1925, Newark, NJ
MIGHTY MIKE — Savoy 12051 (1956) maroon label **$35**.

MIKE CUOZZO — Jubilee 1027 (1956) **$35**.

TED CURSON
trumpet - born 1935 Philadelphia, PA
PLENTY OF HORN — Old Town 2003 (1961) **$60**.

FIRE DOWN BELOW — Prestige 7263 (1963) yellow label **$25**; *reissued* Prestige 7263 blue label (1964) with logo on right side **$15**.

NOW HEAR THIS/with Bill Barron — Audio Fidelity 6123 (1964) **$30**.

*KING CURTIS
*saxophones, composer - born 1935 Fort Worth, TX
died 1971*
SOUL MEETING/with Nat Adderley — Prestige 7222 (1962) yellow label **$45**.

NEW SCENE OF/with Nat Adderley — New Jazz 8237 (1960) **$45**.

AZSURE — Everest 5121/1121 (1960) **$35**.

*The only LP's within the scope of this book.

BOB COOPER
*tenor sax, oboe, arranger, composer
born 1925 Pittsburgh, PA*

s is the story with many young and talented jazz artists, Cooper
ade his debut with Stan Kenton in the mid-40's. He married singer
une Christy in 1946 and began composing and playing backup for
er. Cooper favored saxmen Sonny Stitt and Zoot Sims and has
layed with numerous jazz stars in many parts of the world. It should
e noted that he was the only person to master the oboe in a jazz style
the perfection he did. Beginning in 1954 Cooper joined up with the
umsey's Lighthouse All Stars to remain for sometime. Aside from
is, Cooper concentrated a considerable amount of this time to
mposing and arranging often times for motion pictures and
levision.

ENTON PRESENTS JAZZ — Capitol 6501 (1954) 10" **$80**; EP 6501 (1954) 2
records **$40**; *reissued* Capitol 6501 (1960) black label with logo on left
side **$40**.

IFTING WINDS — Capitol 6513 (1955) green label **$80**; EP 1-6513, EP 2-6513,
EP 3-6513 (1955) **$20** ea.; *reissued* Capitol 6513 (1960) black label
with logo on left side **$40**.

OP! — Contemporary 3544/7012 (1958) yellow label **$50**.

RI MI/with June Christy — Capitol 1586 (1961) black label with logo on left
side **$45**; *reissued* Capitol 1586 (1963) black label with logo on top **$35**.

BOB CORWIN
piano - born 1933 Hollis, L.I., NY
ARTET — Riverside 12-220 (1956) **$35**.

JOE DALEY

tenor sax, clarinet, flute, composer - born 1918
Salem, OH

AT NEWPORT '63 — RCA Victor 2763 (1963) dog on top **$35.**

TADD DAMERON

piano, composer - born 1917 Cleveland, OH died 1965
Early in his career, Dameron became valuable for his arranging capabilities and, as a result, worked with many name groups through the 70's such as Dizzy Gillespie, Miles Davis and later, Milt Jackson and Sonny Stitt. Dameron was most important for his early and effective integration of be-bop elements into big band style.

TADD DAMERON — Prestige 159 (1953) 10" **$80;** EP 1353 (1953) **$35;** *reissued* Prestige 7055 (1956) yellow label **$45.**

FONTAINEBLEAU/with Kenny Dorham — Prestige 7037 (1956) yellow label **$65;** *reissued* Prestige 1607 (1964) **$25.**

MATING CALL/with John Coltrane — Prestige 7070 (1956) yellow label **$75;** *reissued* 7247 (1962) yellow label **$45.**

CLASSICS IN MODERN JAZZ — Vol 2 — Jazzland 68/968 (1962) **$35.**

CLASSICS IN MODERN JAZZ — Jazzland 50/950 (1962) **$35.**

THE MAGIC TOUCH — Riverside 419 (1962) **$35.**

BARBARA DANE

vocals, guitar - born 1927 Detroit, MI

TROUBLE IN MIND — San Francisco 33014 (1957) **$50;** *reissued* Barbary Coast 33014 (1959) **$45.**

LIVIN' WITH THE BLUES/with Earl "Fatha" Hines — Dot 3177/25177 (1959) black label with tri-colored Dot **$45.**

ON MY WAY — Capitol 1758 (1961) black label with logo on left side **$35.**

ALICE DARR

vocals

I ONLY KNOW HOW TO CRY/with Mundell Lowe — Charlie Parker 811 (1962) **$35.**

BOB DAVIS

piano - born 1927 Minneapolis, MN

JAZZ IN ORBIT — Stepheny 4000 (1958) **$35.**

JAZZ FROM THE NORTH COAST/with Bob Crea — Zephyr 12001 (1959) **$50.**

EDDIE "LOCKJAW" DAVIS

tenor - born 1921 New York City, NY

After teaching himself to play tenor, Davis was soon playing with several name bands in the early 40's. The late 40's found him established with his own group and in the 50's he began working and recording with the Count Basie Band. In the late 50's Davis again formed and fronted his own group featuring organist Shirley Scott but rejoined Basie during the mid-60's.

GOODIES/with Bill Doggett — Roost 422 (1954) 10" **$80;** *reissued* Roost 2227 (1958) **$45.**

TRIO/with Shirley Scott — Roost 2227 (1958) **$45.**
  (Note: this LP has same No. as Bill Doggett LP but is different).

MODERN JAZZ EXPRESSION — King 506 (1958) **$45;** EP 372 (1958) **$20.**

JAZZ WITH A HORN — King 526 (1958) **$45.**

JAZZ WITH A BEAT — King 566 (1958) **$45.**

BIG BEAT JAZZ — King 599 (1959) **$40.**

UPTOWN — King 606 (1959) **$40.**

BEST OF — Bethlehem 6069 (1960) **$35;** *reissue* of his King record days.

COUNT BASIE PRESENTS — Roulette 52007 (1958) white label with multicolored pinwheel **$45;** *reissued* Roulette 52007 (1960) light & dark orange label with checked roulette wheel **$35.**

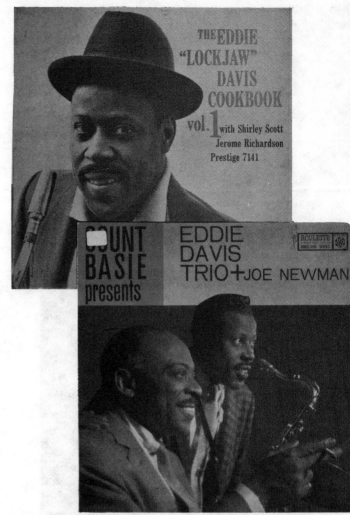

TRIO — Roulette 52019 (1958) white label with multicolored pinwheel **$45;** *reissued* Roulette 52019 (1960) light & dark orange label with checked roulette wheel **$35.**

COOKBOOK — Vol 1 — Prestige 7141 (1958) yellow label **$50;** (Note: this LP has 2 different covers: one he is resting chin on hand; the second is with hat and sax).

COOKBOOK — Vol 2 — Prestige 7161 (1959) yellow label **$50;** (Note: this LP has 2 different covers: one he is with a sax; the second is with hat).

COOKBOOK — Vol 3 — Prestige 7219 (1962) yellow label **$35.**

JAWS IN ORBIT — Prestige 7171 (1959) yellow label **$40.**

BACALAO — Prestige 7178 (1963) yellow label **$40.**

BATTLE STATIONS/with Johnny Griffin — Prestige 7282 (1963) yellow label **$50.**

TRANE WHISTLE/with Eric Dolphy and Jerome Richardson — Prestige 7206 (1961) **$75.**

GOIN' TO THE MEETING — Prestige 7242 (1962) yellow label **$35.**

JAWS — Prestige 7154 (1959) yellow label **$40.**

THE TENOR SCENE — Prestige 7191 (1961) yellow label **$45.**

MIDNIGHT SHOW — Prestige 7330 (1965) blue label with logo on right side **$25.**

LATE SHOW — Prestige 7357 (1965) blue label with logo on right side **$25.**

TOUGH TENORS/with Johnny Griffin — Jazzland 31/931 (1960) **$40.**

LOOKIN' AT MONK/with Johnny Griffin — Jazzland 39/939 (1961) **$35.**

BLUES UP & DOWN/with Johnny Griffin — Jazzland 60/960 (1961) **$35.**

TOUGH TENOR FAVORITES/with Johnny Griffin — Jazzland 76/976 (1962) **$35.**

AFRO-JAWS — Riverside 373/9373 (1961) **$30.**

JAWBREAKERS/with Harry "Sweets" Edison — Riverside 430/9430 (1962) **$40.**

MISTY/with Shirley Scott — Moodsville 30 (1963) **$30.**

JOHNNY "SCAT" DAVIS
vocals

JOHNNY "SCAT" DAVIS — King 626 (1959) King without crown on top of label **$35**.

MILES DAVIS
trumpet, fluegelhorn, composer, leader - born 1926
Alton, IL

Miles began playing trumpet in St. Louis at a very young age and, by the time he was a teen, had established himself in local bands. When the Billy Eckstine Band arrived in town, he sat in with them and was encouraged by Charlie Parker and Dizzy Gillespie to continue his music. To no surprise, Miles soon went to New York to study at Julliard and quickly left that scene for 52nd Street and a job with Charlie Parker. For the remainder of the 40's he worked with a variety of name bands before becoming the nominal leader of a nine piece band of unusual instrumentation with arrangements by Gil Evans and Gerry Mulligan. This band made only two public appearances and a short series of recordings on Capitol and, while not a commercial success, was definitely the beginning of the new "cool" style so closely associated with Miles.

Since that time Miles has always been a leader. His groups and their recordings and appearances have, for over three decades, had a significant following of jazz fans as well as a profound effect on other jazz musicians. His popularity and influence stem from his work with the finest of his contemporaries and from his timing and ability to pick out the very best of young musicians to accompany him on his continuing evolution in styles. Throughout the 50's and 60's Miles Davis continued to change . . . each change bringing new music, new musicians and yet remaining essentially, identifiably, Miles Davis.

JERU — Capitol H459 (1954) 10" **$125**; EP 1-459, EP 2-459, EP 3-459 (1954) **$35** ea.; *reissued* Capitol T-762 (1956).

BIRTH OF THE COOL — Capitol T-762 (1956) green label **$75**; *reissue* of Capitol H459.

MILES DAVIS/with Sonny Rollins — Prestige 124 (1952) 10" **$100**; EP 1339, EP 1349 (1952) **$35** ea.; *reissued* in part Prestige 7012 (1956) titled Dig.

BLUE PERIOD — Prestige 140 (1953) 10" **$100**; EP 1361, EP 1355 (1953) **$35** ea.; *reissued* in part Prestige 7012 (1956) titled Dig.

COMPOSITIONS OF AL COHN/with Al Cohn and Zoot Sims — Prestige 154 (1953) 10" **$125**; *reissued* Prestige 7168 (1960) titled Early Miles.

MILES DAVIS QUARTET — Prestige 161 (1953) 10" **$100**; EP 1360 (1953) **$35**; *reissued* in part Prestige 7054 (1956) titled Blue Haze.

SEXTET/with Lucky Thompson — Prestige 182 (1954) 10" **$100**; EP 1358, EP 1357 (1954) **$30** ea.; *reissued* Prestige 7076 (1957) titled Walkin'.

SOLAR/with Horace Silver — Prestige 185 (1954) 10" **$100**.

THE MUSINGS OF MILES — Prestige 7007 (1955) yellow label with NY address **$85**; (this LP was before they packaged in Bergenfield, NJ).

DIG — Prestige 7012 (1956) yellow label **$85**; *reissued* of Prestige 140 10".

MILES — Prestige 7014 (1956) yellow label **$85**; *reissued* Prestige 7254 (1962) yellow label titled Original Quintet.

MILES DAVIS AND HORNS — Prestige 7025 (1956) yellow label **$85**; *reissued* Prestige 7168 (1959) yellow label titled Early Miles; *reissued* Prestige 7168 (1964) blue label with logo on right side.

QUINTET/SEXTET — Prestige 7034 (1956) yellow label **$80**; *reissued* Prestige 7034 (1964) blue label with logo on right side **$30**.

COLLECTOR'S ITEMS — Prestige 7044 (1956) yellow label **$80**; *reissued* Prestige 7044 (1964) blue label with logo on right side **$30**.

BLUE HAZE — Prestige 7054 (1956) yellow label **$80**; *reissued* Prestige 7054 (1964) blue label with logo on right side **$30**.

WALKIN' — Prestige 7076 (1957) yellow label **$75**; *reissued* Prestige 7076 (1964) blue label with logo on right side **$30**.

COOKIN' — Prestige 7094 (1957) yellow label **$75**; *reissued* Prestige 7094 (1964) blue label with logo on right side **$30**.

BAG'S GROOVE — Prestige 7109 (1957) yellow label **$70**; *reissued* Prestige 7109 (1964) blue label with logo on right side **$30**.

RELAXIN' — Prestige 7129 (1957) yellow label **$70**; *reissued* Prestige 7129 (1964) blue label with logo on right side **$30**.

AND THE MODERN JAZZ GIANTS — Prestige 7150 (1958) yellow label **$70**; *reissued* Prestige 7150 (1964) blue label with logo on right side **$30**.

WORKIN' — Prestige 7166 (1958) yellow label **$75**; *reissued* Prestige 7166 (1964) blue label with logo on right side **$35**.

EARLY MILES — Prestige 7168 (1960) yellow label **$70**; *reissued* Prestige 7168 (1964) blue label with logo on right side **$30**.

STEAMIN' — Prestige 7200 (1961) yellow label **$75**; *reissued* Prestige 7200 (1964) blue label with logo on right side **$35**.

BEGINNING — Prestige 7221 (1962) yellow label **$45**; *reissued* Prestige 7221 (1965) blue label with logo on right side **$30**.

ORIGINAL QUINTET — Prestige 7254 (1963) yellow label **$45**; *reissued* Prestige 7254 (1965) blue label with logo on right side **$30**.

DIGGIN' — Prestige 7281 (1964) yellow label **$40**; *reissued* Prestige 7281 (1965) blue label with logo on right side **$30**.

PLAYS RICHARD RODGERS — Prestige 7332 (1964) blue label with logo on right side **$35**.

PLAYS FOR LOVERS — Prestige 7352 (1965) blue label with logo on right side **$35**.

PLAYS JAZZ CLASSICS — Prestige 7373 (1965) blue label with logo on right side **$35**.

MILES DAVIS — Blue Note 5013 (1952) 10" **$150**; EP 204 (1952) **$50**; *reissued* in part Blue Note 1501 (1956).

TEMPUS FUGIT — Blue Note 5022 (1953) 10" **$150**; *reissued* in part Blue Note 1502 (1956).

MILES DAVIS QUARTET — Blue Note 5044 (1954) 10" **$150**; *reissued* Blue Note 1502 (1956).

MILES DAVIS — Vol 1 — Blue Note 1501 (1956) with NY address **$80**; with A Division of Liberty **$20**.

MILES DAVIS — Vol 2 — Blue Note 1502 (1956) with NY address **$80**; with A Division of Liberty **$20**.

BLUE MOODS — Debut 120 (1955) **$80**; *reissued* Fantasy 6001/86001 (1962) red vinyl **$40**.

'ROUND ABOUT MIDNIGHT — Columbia 949 (1957) with 3 black logos on each side **$45**; *reissued* Columbia 949/8649 with one white logo on each side **$25**.

MILES AHEAD & 19 — Columbia 1041 (1957) with 3 black logos on each side **$45**; *reissued* Columbia 1041 (1963) with one white logo on each side **$25**.

MILESTONE — Columbia 1193 (1958) with 3 black logos on each side **$45**; *reissued* Columbia 1193 (1963) with one white logo on each side **$25**.

JAZZ TRACK — Columbia 1268 (1958) with 3 black logos on each side **$45**; *reissued* Columbia 1268 (1963) with one white logo on each side **$25**.

PORGY & BESS — Columbia 1274/8085 (1958) with 3 black logos on each side **$40**; *reissued* Columbia 1274/8085 (1963) with one white logo on each side **$20**.

KIND OF BLUE — Columbia 1355/8163 (1959) with 3 black logos on each side **$45**; *reissued* Columbia 1355/8163 (1963) with one white logo on each side **$25**.

SKETCHES OF SPAIN — Columbia 1480/8271 (1960) with 3 black logos on each side **$40**; *reissued* Columbia 1480/8271 (1963) with one white logo on each side **$20**.

SOMEDAY MY PRINCE WILL COME — Columbia 1656/8456 (1961) with 3 black logos on each side **$35**; *reissued* Columbia 1656/8456 (1964) with one white logo on each side **$15**.

FRIDAY AND SATURDAY NIGHTS IN PERSON — Columbia C2L-20/C2S-820 (1961) 2 LP's with 3 black logos on each side **$60**.

FRIDAY NIGHT IN PERSON — Columbia 1669/8469 (1961) with 3 black logos on each side **$30**.

SATURDAY NIGHT IN PERSON — Columbia 1670/8470 (1961) with 3 black logos on each side **$30**.

AT CARNEGIE HALL — Columbia 1812/8612 (1961) with 3 black logos on each side **$30**.

QUIET NIGHTS — Columbia 2106/8906 (1963) with one white logo on each side **$20**.

SEVEN STEPS TO HEAVEN — Columbia 2051/8851 (1963) with one white logo on each side **$20**.

IN EUROPE — Columbia 2183/8983 (1964) with one white logo on each side **$15**.

MY FUNNY VALENTINE — Columbia 2306/9106 (1965) with one white logo on each side **$15**.

MILES AHEAD — Savoy 12153 (1961) maroon label **$25**.

PLAYS RICHARD RODGERS — Moodsville 32 (1963) **$35**.

JAZZ ON THE SCREEN — Fontana 27532/67532 (1965) **$15**.

WALTER DAVIS JR.
piano, composer - born 1932 East Orange, NJ

DAVIS CUP/with Jackie McLean — Blue Note 4018 (1960) with NY address on label **$60**; with A Division of Liberty on label **$20**.

WILD BILL DAVIS
cornet, leader - born 1906 Defiance, OH

WILD BILL DAVIS — Epic 1004 (1954) 10" **$45**.

AT BIRDLAND — Epic 3118 (1955) **$30**.

EVENING CONCERTO — Epic 3308 (1956) **$30**.

IN HOLLYWOOD — Imperial 9015 (1956) **$25**.

ON BROADWAY — Imperial 9010 (1956) **$25**.

PRETTY WILD — Columbia 871 (1956) with 3 black logos on each side **$30**.

FLYING HIGH — Everest 5052/1052 (1959) **$35**.

DANCE THE MADISON — Everest 5094/1094 (1960) **$30**.

DIS HEAH — Everest 5125 (1961) **$30**.

THE MUSIC FROM MILK AND HONEY — Everest 5133 (1961) **$35**.

MESS OF BLUES/with Johnny Hodges — Verve 8570/68570 (1963) with MGM on bottom of label **$35**.

BLUE RABBIT/with Johnny Hodges — Verve 8599/68599 (1964) with MGM on bottom of label **$35**.

JOE'S BLUES/with Johnny Hodges — Verve 8617/68617 (1965) with MGM on bottom of label **$30**.

BLUE PYRAMID/with Johnny Hodges — Verve 8635/68635 (1965) with MGM on bottom of label **$30**.

CARA LEE DAY
vocals

MY CRYING HOUR — Roulette 52048 (1960) light & dark orange label with checked roulette wheel **$25**.

BILL DE ARANGO
guitar - born 1921 Cleveland, OH

BILL DE ARANGO — EmArcy 26020 (1954) 10" **$60**.

BUDDY DE FRANCO
clarinet, bass clarinet, leader - born 1923 Camden, NJ

Well known as a soloist in big bands during the 40's, De Franco led his own big band and various other groups throughout the 50's and into the 60's. In the late 60's, De Franco began playing bass clarinet and subsequently became leader of the Glenn Miller Band. Although highly regarded as a soloist, De Franco has suffered to some extent from the decline in popularity of the clarinet as a jazz instrument but his ability is such that his popularity continues.

QUARTET — Norgran 3 (1953) 10" **$80**.

PRETTY MOODS — Norgran 16 (1954) 10" **$80**.

THE PROGRESSIVE MR. DE FRANCO — Norgran 1006 (1954) **$50**; *reissued* Norgran 1094 (1957) titled Odalisque **$45**; *reissued* Verve 1094 (1958) **$35**.

THE ARTISTRY OF — Norgran 1012 (1954) **$60**; *reissued* Norgran 1096 (1957) *reissued* Verve 8183 (1958).

PLAYS GEORGE GERSHWIN/with Oscar Peterson — Norgran 1016 (1954) **$65**; *reissued* Verve 2022 (1957).

QUARTET — Norgran 1026 (1955) **$60**.

JAZZ TONES — Norgran 1068 (1956) **$55**; *reissued* Verve 8158 (1957).

MR. CLARINET — Norgran 1069 (1956) **$55**; *reissued* Verve 1026 (1957).

IN A MELLOW MOOD — Norgran 1079 (1956) **$55**; *reissued* Verve 8169 (1957).

WAILERS — Norgran 1085 (1957) **$50**; *reissued* 8175 (1957).

ODALISQUE — Norgran 1094 (1957) **$45**; *reissued* Verve 8182 (1957) **$35**; *reissue* of Norgran 1006.

AUTUMN LEAVES — Norgran 1096 (1957) **$45**; *reissued* Verve 8183 (1957) **$35**; *reissue* of Norgran 1012.

QUARTET — Clef 149 (1953) 10" **$80**.

KING OF THE CLARINET — MGM 177 (1952) 10" **$90**.

WITH STRINGS — MGM 253 (1953) 10" **$80**.

BUDDY DE FRANCO — MGM 3396 (1956) **$50**; *reissue* of MGM 177.

TAKES YOU TO THE STARS — Gene Norman Presents 2 (1954) 10" **$75**; *reissued* Gene Norman Presents 2 (1956) 12" **$45**.

PRESENTING THE BUDDY DE FRANCO/TOMMY GUMINA QUINTET — Mercury 20685/60685 (1962) black label **$25**.

KALEIDOSCOPE/with Tommy Gumina — Mercury 20743/60743 (1962) black label **$25**.

POLYTONES/with Tommy Gumina — Mercury 20833/60833 (1963) black label **$25**.

THE GIRL FROM IPANEMA — Mercury 20900/60900 (1963) black label **$25**.

CROSS-COUNTRY SUITE — Dot 9006 (1958) **$30**; *reissued* Hamilton 133/12133 (1964) **$15**.

BLUES BAG — Vee Jay 2506 (1965) **$20**.

PACIFIC STANDARD SWINGIN' TIME/with Tommy Gumina — Decca 74031 (1961) black with rainbow strip **$25**.

UNIVERSITY OF NEW MEXICO STAGE BAND — Advance Guard 1001 (1961) **$35**.

BROADWAY SHOWCASE — Verve 2033 (1956) with Verve Records, Inc. on bottom of label **$35**.

PLAYS BENNY GOODMAN — Verve 2089 (1958) with Verve Records, Inc. on bottom of label **$35**.

PLAYS ARTIE SHAW — Verve 2090 (1958) with Verve Records, Inc. on bottom of label **$35**.

HEAR BENNY GOODMAN & ARTIE SHAW — Verve 2108/6032 (1959) with Verve Records, Inc. on bottom of label **$35**.

BUDDY DE FRANCO AND THE OSCAR PETERSON QUARTET — Verve 8210 (1958) with Verve Records, Inc. on bottom of label **$45**.

COOKING THE BLUES — Verve 8221 (1958) with Verve Records, Inc. on bottom of label **$55**.

SWEET AND LONELY — Verve 8224 (1958) with Verve Records, Inc. on bottom of label **$45**.

BRAVURA — Verve 8315/6051 (1960) with Verve Records, Inc. on bottom of label **$35**.

GENERALISSIMO — Verve 8363/6132 (1960) with Verve Records, Inc. on bottom of label **$45**.

WHOLLY CATS — Verve 8375/6150 (1960) with Verve Records, Inc. on bottom of label **$35**.

CLOSED SESSION — Verve 8382/68382 (1961) with Verve Records, Inc. on bottom of label **$30**.

LIVE DATE — Verve 8383/68383 (1961) with Verve Records, Inc. on bottom of label **$30**.

WANDA DE SAH
vocals - born Ipanema, Brazil

HERE; BRAZIL '65 INTRODUCING WANDA DE SAH — Capitol 2294 (1965) black label with logo on top **$25**.

SOFTLY — Capitol 2325 (1965) black label with logo on top **$20**.

BLOSSOM DEARIE
vocals, piano - born 1926 East Durham, NY

Possessor of a unique voice with good intonation, Dearie worked in the 40's with Woody Herman. Through most of the 50's she lived and worked in Europe, most commonly Paris, and returned to the U.S. in the late 50's. Since she has worked extensively in clubs and unhappy with possibilities offered by recording companies, started her own with which she distributes her work by mail.

BLOSSOM DEARIE — Verve 2037 (1956) with Verve Records, Inc. on bottom of label **$50**.

GIVE HIM THE OOH LA LA — Verve 2081 (1958) with Verve Records, Inc. on bottom of label **$40**.

SINGS COMDEN AND GREEN — Verve 2109/6050 (1959) with Verve Records, Inc. on bottom of label **$35**.

ONCE UPON A SUMMERTIME — Verve 2111/6020 (1959) with Verve Records, Inc. on bottom of label **$35**.

MY GENTLEMAN FRIEND — Verve 2125/6112 (1959) with Verve Records, Inc. on bottom of label **$35**.

SINGS BROADWAY HIT SONGS — Verve 2133/62133 (1959) with Verve Records, Inc. on bottom of label **$30**.

RUSTY DEDRICK
trumpet, composer - born 1918 Delevan, NY

RUSTY—RHYTHM AND WINDS — Esoteric 9 (1955) 10" **$60**.

SALUTE TO BUNNY — Counterpoint 552 (1957) **$35**.

THE BIG BAND SOUND — Four Corners 4207 (1964) **$20**.

A JAZZ JOURNEY — Monument 6502 (1965) **$20**.

COUNTERPOINT FOR SIX VALVES — Riverside 12-218 (1956) white label with Bill Grauer Pro. **$60**; *reissued* (1958) blue label **$45**.

DELEGATES
Portland, OR
organ - Billy Larkin/guitar - Hank Swarn
drums - Mel Brown

THE DELEGATES; PIGMY — Aura 3002 (1964) **$25**.

BLUE LIGHTS/with Clifford Scott — Aura 83003/23003 (1965) **$25**.

*MARTIN DENNY
vibes

A TASTE OF HONEY — Liberty 3237/7237 (1962) **$15**.

*The only LP's within the scope of this book.

35

PAUL DESMOND
alto sax - born 1924 San Francisco, CA
died 1977

Desmond's initial popularity came through his work with Dave Brubeck beginning in 1951 and continuing until 1967. When it disbanded, the Dave Brubeck Quartet was one of the most popular and successful jazz groups producing many recordings, the most popular being Take Five, a Desmond composition in 5/4 time that was a tremendous hit. Beginning in 1954, and occasionally every year or two since (until his death), Desmond recorded as leader on various labels with a variety of personnel. In the 70's he recorded with Brubeck and others and participated in a 25th Anniversary Reunion of the Brubeck Group for a short tour and recording session. Desmond died in 1977 but will long be remembered for his quick wit, lyrical, melodic playing and clean, dry sound.

PAUL DESMOND —Fantasy 3-21 (1954) 10" **$125**; *reissued* Fantasy 3-220 (1956).

GERRY MULLIGAN QUARTET/PAUL DESMOND QUINTET — Fantasy 3-220 (1956) one side of LP each **$50**.

PAUL DESMOND QUARTET — Fantasy 3-235 (1956) **$40**.

AND FRIENDS — Warner Brothers 1356 (1960) **$40**.

THE GERRY MULLIGAN/PAUL DESMOND QUARTET — Verve 8246 (1958) **$50**; *reissued* Verve 8478 (1962).

BLUES IN TIME — Verve 8478/68478 (1962) **$35**; *reissue* of Verve 8246.

DESMOND BLUE — RCA Victor 2438 (1962) dog on top **$35**.

TAKE TEN — RCA Victor 2569 (1962) dog on top **$45**.

TWO OF A MIND/with Gerry Mulligan — RCA Victor 2624 (1962) **$45**.

GLAD TO BE UNHAPPY — RCA Victor 3407 (1965) dog on top **$25**.

EASY LIVING — RCA Victor 3480 (1965) dog on top **$25**.

WALT DICKERSON
vibes, composer - born 1931 Philadelphia, PA

THIS IS — New Jazz 8254 (1961) **$35**.

A SENSE OF DIRECTION — New Jazz 8268 (1962) **$35**.

RELATIVITY — New Jazz 8275 (1962) **$35**.

TO MY QUEEN — New Jazz 8283 (1963) **$25**.

JAZZ IMPRESSIONS OF LAWRENCE OF ARABIA — Dauntless 4313 (1962) **$25**.

BILL DIXON
composer, trumpet - born 1925 Nantucket, MA

THE BILL DIXON 7-TETTE/ARCHIE SHEPP AND THE NEW YORK CONTEMPORARY 5 — Savoy 12184 (1964) maroon label **$25**.

MARGE DODSON
vocals - born Philadelphia, PA

IN THE STILL OF THE NIGHT — Columbia 1309 (1959) with 3 black logos on each side **$35**.

NEW VOICE IN TOWN — Columbia 1458 (1960) with 3 black logos on each side **$35**.

KLAUS DOLDINGER
tenor and soprano saxes - born 1936 Berlin, Germany

DIG DOLDINGER/with Ingfried Hoffman — Philips 200-125/600-125 (1964) **$35**.

ERIC DOLPHY
alto sax, bass clarinet, clarinet, flute, composer
born 1928 Los Angeles, CA died 1964

After growing up and studying in Los Angeles, Dolphy's early career was with many groups from that area; Gerald Wilson and fellow-

flutist Buddy Collette as the first. Later he worked and recorded with drummer Chico Hamilton in the late 50's. In the 60's, after moving to New York City, he worked with another West Coast expatriat, Charles Mingus, where he quickly gained wide recognition for his great ability on all his instruments. He co-led a group with Booker Little in 1961 and worked with John Coltrane extensively during that time and until 1964. At this time he worked as leader of several groups and as a sideman in others for several recording labels. In 1964 he toured to Europe with Mingus, recorded and suddenly died while in Berlin.

OUTWARD BOUND/with Freddie Hubbard — New Jazz 8236 (1960) with artistic cover **$45**; *reissued* New Jazz 8252 with picture cover **$25**.

OUT THERE — New Jazz 8252 (1960) with artistic cover **$45**; *reissued* New Jazz 8252 with picture cover **$25**.

FAR CRY — New Jazz 8270 (1962) **$35**.

CARIBE/with Latin Jazz Quintet — New Jazz 8251 (1960) **$35**.

AT THE FIVE SPOT/with Booker Little — New Jazz 8260 (1961) **$45**.

LAST DATE — Limelight 2013/86013 (1964) with double cover **$30**.

IN EUROPE — Prestige 7304 (1964) yellow label **$35**; *reissued* Prestige 7304 (1965) blue label with logo on right side **$25**.

IN EUROPE - Vol 2 — Prestige 7350 (1965) blue label logo on right side **$25**.

AT THE FIVE SPOT - Vol 2 — Prestige 7294 (1964) yellow label **$35**; *reissued* Prestige 7294 (1965) blue label with logo on right side **$25**.

MEMORIAL ALBUM — Prestige 7334 (1965) blue label with logo on right side **$25**.

CONVERSATIONS — FM 308 (1963) **$60**.

THE MEMORIAL ALBUM — Vee Jay 2503 (1964) **$35**.

ARNE DOMNERUS
alto sax, clarinet - born 1924 Stockholm, Sweden

CLARINET — NEW SOUNDS FROM SWEDEN — Prestige 134 (1952) 10" **$80.**

DOMNERUS/GULLIN GROUPS — NEW SOUNDS FROM SWEDEN — Prestige 133 (1952) 10" **$250.**

SWEDISH MODERN JAZZ — RCA Camden 417 (1958) **$50.**

LOU DONALDSON
alto sax - born 1926 Baden, NC

QUINTET — Blue Note 5021 (1952) 10" **$150**; *reissued* Blue Note 1537 (1957).

WITH CLIFFORD BROWN — Blue Note 5030 (1953) 10" **$150.**

SEXTET/with Kenny Dorham — Blue Note 5055 (1954) 10" **$100**; *reissued* Blue Note 1537 (1957).

QUARTET/QUINTET — Blue Note 1537 (1957) with NY address on label **$65**; with A Division of Liberty on label **$20.**

WAILING WITH/with Donald Byrd — Blue Note 1545 (1957) with NY address on label **$65**; with A Division of Liberty on label **$20.**

SWING AND SOUL — Blue Note 1566 (1957) with NY address on label **$60**; with A Division of Liberty on label **$20.**

LOU TAKES OFF/with Donald Byrd — Blue Note 1591 (1958) with NY address on label **$50**; with A Division of Liberty on label **$20.**

BLUES WALK — Blue Note 1593 (1958) with NY address on label **$50**; with A Division of Liberty on label **$20.**

LIGHT FOOT — Blue Note 4053 (1958) with NY address on label **$45**; with A Division of Liberty on label **$20.**

AND THE THREE SOUNDS — Blue Note 4012 (1959) with NY address on label **$50**; with A Division of Liberty on label **$20.**

THE TIME IS RIGHT/with Blue Mitchell — Blue Note 4025 (1960) with NY address on label **$45**; with A Division of Liberty on label **$20.**

SUNNY SIDE UP/with Bill Hardman — Blue Note 4036 (1960) with NY address on label **$45**; with A Division of Liberty on label **$20.**

HERE 'TIS — Blue Note 4066 (1961) with NY address on label **$35**; with A Division of Liberty on label **$20.**

GRAVY TRAIN — Blue Note 4079 (1961) with NY address on label **$35**; with A Division of Liberty on label **$20.**

NATURAL SOUL/with Tommy Turrentine — Blue Note 4108 (1962) with NY on label **$35**; with A Division of Liberty on label **$20.**

GOOD GRACIOUS — Blue Note 4125 (1963) with NY on label **$30**; with A Division of Liberty on label **$20.**

SIGNIFYIN'/with Tommy Turrentine — Argo 724 (1963) **$35.**

POSSUM HEAD — Argo 734 (1964) **$35.**

COLE SLAW — Argo 747 (1964) **$35.**

MUSTY RUSTY/with Bill Hardman — Argo 759 (1965) **$35.**

DOROTHY DONEGAN
piano - born 1924 Chicago, IL

DOROTHY DONEGAN PIANO — MGM 278 (1953) 10" **$45.**

DOROTHY DONEGAN TRIO — Jubilee 11 (1954) 10" **$45.**

SEPTEMBER SONG — Jubilee 1013 (1956) **$35.**

AT THE EMBERS — Roulette 25010 (1957) white label with multicolored pinwheel **$35.**

LIVE! — Capitol 1155 (1959) black label with logo at left side **$35.**

KENNY DORHAM
trumpet, tenor sax - born 1924 Fairfield, TX died 1972

Quickly recognized as a musician with his own personal style, Dorham worked with many major bands in the 40's. In the 50's he was one of the original members of the Art Blakey's Jazz Messengers and, thereafter, replaced Clifford Brown in the Max Roach Quintet. In the 60's and 70's, he composed for films, continued to work, record and tour intermittently until his death of kidney failure in 1972.

QUINTET/with Jimmy Heath — Debut 9 (1954) 10" **$100.**

'ROUND ABOUT MIDNIGHT/with J.R. Monterose — Blue Note 1524 (1956) with NY address on label **$60**; with A Division of Liberty on label **$20.**

WHISTLE STOP/with Hank Mobley — Blue Note 4063/84063 (1961) with NY address on label **$45**; with A Division of Liberty on label **$20.**

AFRO CUBAN/with Hank Mobley — Blue Note 1535 (1956) with NY address on label **$60**; with A Division of Liberty on label **$20.**

UNA MAS/with Joe Henderson — Blue Note 4127/84127 (1963) with NY on label **$35**; with A Division of Liberty on label **$20.**

TROMPETA TOCCATA/with Joe Henderson — Blue Note 4181/84181 (1965) with NY on label **$35**; with A Division of Liberty on label **$20.**

JAZZ CONTRASTS/with Sonny Rollins — Riverside 12-239/1105 (1957) **$45**; *reissued* in part Jazzland 82 (1960).

TWO HORNS, TWO RHYTHMS/with Ernie Henry — Riverside 12-255 (1957) **$45**; *reissued* in part Jazzland 14 (1960).

THIS IS THE MOMENT, KENNY DORHAM SINGS — Riverside 12-275 (1958) **$50.**

BLUE SPRING/with Cannonball Adderley — Riverside 12-297/1139 (1959) **$45**; *reissued* in part Jazzland 82 (1960).

JAZZ CONTEMPORARY/with Charles Davis — Time 52004/2004 (1960) **$45.**

SHOWBOAT/with Jimmy Heath — Time 52024/2024 (1960) **$50.**

MATADOR — United Artists 14007/15007 (1963) with silhouette of sax player **$35.**

THE ARRIVAL OF/with Charles Davis — Jaro 5007/8007 (1959) $60.
QUIET KENNY — New Jazz 8225 (1959) $35.
INTA SOMETHING/with Jackie McLean — Pacific Jazz 41 (1962) $35.
AND FRIENDS — Jazzland 82/982 (1962) $35.
KENNY DORHAM — Jazzland 14/914 (1961) $35.

BOB DOROUGH
piano, vocals, composer - born 1923 Cherry Hill, AR
DEVIL MAY CARE — Bethlehem 11 (1955) maroon label $55.
OLIVER — Music Minus One 225 (1963) maroon label $30.
JUST ABOUT EVERYTHING — Focus 336 (1965) maroon label $20.

DIANA DORS
vocals - born England died 1984
SWINGING DORS/with Wally Stott — Columbia 1436 (1960) red label with 3 black logos on each side $40.

DOUBLE SIX OF PARIS
DOUBLE SIX OF PARIS — Capitol 10259 (1961) black label $20.
SWINGIN' SINGIN' — Philips 600-026/200-026 (1962) $20.
DIZZY GILLESPIE AND DOUBLE SIX OF PARIS — Philips 600-106/200-106 (1963) $35.
SINGS RAY CHARLES — Philips 600-141/200-141 (1964) $20.

RAY DRAPER
tuba, composer - born 1940 New York City, NY died 1982
TUBA SOUNDS/with Jackie McLean — Prestige 7096 (1957) yellow label $60.
QUINTET/with John Coltrane — New Jazz 8228 (1959) $60.
TUBA JAZZ — Jubilee 1090 (1959) $45; *reissued* Josie 3504 (1963) $25.

KENNY DREW
piano - born 1928 New York City, NY
TRIO — Blue Note 5053 (1953) 10" $60.
UNDERCURRENT/with Hank Mobley — Blue Note 4059 (1961) with NY address on label $50; with A Division of Liberty on label $20.
IDEATION OF — Norgran 29 (1953) 10" $60; EP 60, EP 61, EP 62 (1953) $30 ea.; *reissued* Norgran 1066 (1956); *reissued* Verve 8156 (1957).
THE MODERNITY — Norgran 1002 (1954) $50; EP 21, EP 22 (1953) $30 ea.; *reissued* Norgran 1066 (1956); *reissued* Verve 8156 (1957).
HIS PROGRESSIVE PIANO — Norgran 1066 (1956) $40; *reissued* Verve 8156 (1957) $35.
TALKIN' AND WALKIN'/with Joe Maini — Jazz West 4 (1955) $60.
TRIO — Riverside 12-224 (1956) white label $50; blue label $40; *reissued* Jazzland 9 (1960).
THIS IS NEW/with Hank Mobley — Riverside 12-236 (1956) white label $75; blue label $60; *reissued* Jazzland 6 (1960).
I LOVE JEROME KERN — Riverside 12-811 (1958) blue label with Bill Grauer Pro. $30.
JAZZ IMPRESSION OF PAL JOEY — Riverside 12-249/1112 (1958) blue label with Bill Grauer Pro. $35.
HARD BOP — Jazzland 6 (1960) $45; *reissue* of Riverside 12-236.
TOUGH PIANO TRIO — Jazzland 9 (1960) $30; *reissue* of Riverside 12-224.

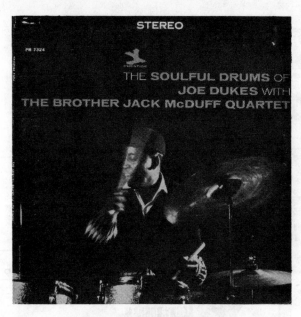

JEAN DU SHON
vocals - born 1936 Detroit, MI
MAKE WAY FOR — Argo 4039 (1964) $25.
YOU BETTER BELIEVE IT/with Ramsey Lewis — Argo 750 (1965) $35.

JOE DUKES
drums
SOULFUL DRUMS/with The Brother Jack McDuff Quartet — Prestige 7324 (1964) black label with logo at top $30.

ALLAN EAGER
tenor, alto saxes - born 1927 New York City, NY
Most active from the mid-40's to late 50's as a member of many groups closely associated with the less intense approach to jazz often referred to as "cool." Eager recorded with many of the best musicians on various labels and was said to be capable of making a meaningful statement in a short period. In the 60's he could be found on the set with people like Miles Davis, Kai Winding and Charlie Parker but, of late, Eager is not indulging in his music.
NEW TRENDS OF JAZZ — Savoy 9015 (1953) 10" $100.
TENOR SAX — Savoy 15044 (1954) 10" $100.

JON EARDLEY
trumpet - born 1928 Altoona, PA
HEY THERE — Prestige 207 (1955) 10" $75.
IN HOLLYWOOD — New Jazz 1105 (1954) 10" $75; *reissued* Prestige 205 (1955) 10" $60.
JON EARDLEY SEVEN — Prestige 7033 (1956) yellow label $50.

JOHNNY EATON
piano, composer - born 1935 Philadelphia, PA
FAR OUT, NEAR IN/with Herbie Mann — Columbia 996 (1957) $45.

*BILLY ECKSTINE
vocals - born 1914 Pittsburgh, PA
Note: Recordings made on Rendition Records were issued in 1949 as EP's only, and with his best band; Miles Davis, Gene Ammons, Sonny Stitt, Fats Navarro, Dizzy Gillespie, Leo Parker, Art Blakey, etc. In the 1940's these were 78's for National Records.
BILLY ECKSTINE — Rendition EP 101, EP 102, EP 108, EP 109, EP 110, EP 114 (1949) $45 ea.

SINGS — National 2001 (1950) 10" **$100**.

BLUES FOR SALE — EmArcy 26025 (1954) 10" *reissue* of Rendition EP's **$100**; EmArcy EP 6040, EP 6041 (1954) **$35** ea.; *reissued* EmArcy 36029 (1955) **$60**; *reissued* in part Regent 6058 (1957).

LOVE SONGS OF MR. B — EmArcy 26027 (1954) 10" *reissue* of Rendition EP's **$100**; EmArcy EP 6045 **$35**; *reissued* EmArcy 36030 (1955) **$60**; *reissued* in part Regent 6058 (1957).

I SURRENDER DEAR — EmArcy 36010 (1955) **$60**; *reissue* of Rendition EP's and National LP 2001; *reissued* Regent 6053 (1957).

IMAGINATION/including Bud Shank — EmArcy 36129 (1956) **$50**.

THE DUKE, THE BLUES AND ME — Regent 6053 (1957) green label **$45**; *reissue* of EmArcy 36010.

YOU CALL IT MADNESS — Regent 6058 (1957) green label **$45**; *reissue* in part of EmArcy 26025 and 26037.

MY DEEP BLUE DREAM — Regent 6054 (1957) green label **$45**; *reissue* of Rendition EP's.

PRISONER OF LOVE — Regent 6052 (1957) green label **$45**; *reissue* of Rendition EP's.

GREAT MR. B — King 265-12 (1954) 10" **$85**; EP 258 titled Blowing the Blues Away **$35**.

NO COVER, NO MINIMUM — Roulette 52052 (1960) **$35**.

I LET A SONG GO OUT OF MY HEART (sings Duke Ellington songs) — MGM 257 (1952) 10" **$40**; EP 1110, EP 1111 (1952) **$15** ea.

MR. B — Audio Lab 1549 (1960) **$30**; *reissue* of King 265-12.

*The only LP's within the scope of this book.

HARRY "SWEETS" EDISON
trumpet - born 1915 Columbus, OH

Famous for his individual trumpet sound and swinging style, Edison began the first important phase of his career with Count Basie during the late 40's which continued off and on for twelve years or more. He then experienced considerable nightclub engagements as well as orchestra work in film soundtracks. As the demand for his "sweet" sound increased, Edison formed his own group and signed with the Roulette label which began the second phase of his very successful career. He can be found on recordings with artists such as Eddie "Lockjaw" Davis, Joe Williams, Billie Holiday and Buddy Rich just to name a very few.

HARRY EDISON/with Willie Smith — Aladdin EP 515 (1953) **$45**.

HARRY EDISON QUARTET — Pacific Jazz 4 (1953) 10" **$90**; EP 4-6, EP 4-5 (1953) **$35** ea.; *reissued* Pacific Jazz 11 (1960).

THE INVENTIVE — Pacific Jazz 11 (1960) **$40**; *reissue* of Pacific Jazz 4.

SWEETS/with Ben Webster — American Recording Society 430 (1956) **$60**; *reissued* Clef 717 (1956) **$50**; *reissued* Verve 8097 (1957) **$45**.

GEE, BABY AIN'T I GOOD TO YOU/with Ben Webster — Verve 8211 (1957) with Verve Records, Inc. on bottom of label **$45**.

HARRY "SWEETS" EDISON SWINGS BUCK CLAYTON — Verve 8293/6016 (1958) with Verve Records, Inc. on bottom of label **$45**.

THE SWINGER — Verve 8295/6037 (1959) with Verve Records, Inc. on bottom of label **$45**.

MR. SWING — Verve 8353/6118 (1959) with Verve Records, Inc. on bottom of label **$45**.

SWEETENINGS — Roulette 52023 (1959) white label with multicolored pinwheel **$45**; stereo Roulette 52023 (1959) light and dark orange roulette wheel **$45**.

PATENTED BY EDISON — Roulette 52041 (1960) light and dark roulette wheel **$30**.

JAWBREAKERS/with Eddie Lockjaw Davis — Riverside 430/9430 (1962) **$35**.

BEN WEBSTER/SWEETS EDISON — Columbia 1891/8691 (1962) with 3 black logos on each side **$35**.

SWEETS FOR THE SWEET TASTE OF LOVE — Vee Jay 1104 (1964) **$20**.

SWEET FOR THE SWEET — Sue 1030 (1965) **$20**.

TEDDY EDWARDS
tenor sax, composer - born 1924 Jackson, MS

Edwards is a well known and respected tenorman who began playing in the late 40's on the West Coast; here he played with Gerald Wilson and Benny Carter after which he was with the Howard Rumsey's Lighthouse All Stars. Edwards has been termed "a musician's musician" and has backed big names like Miles Davis, Charlie Parker and Sonny Stitt, but is credited with having a very identifiable sound of his own.

IT'S ABOUT TIME/with Les McCann — Pacific Jazz 6 (1960) **$35**.

SUNSET EYES — Pacific Jazz 14 (1960) **$40**.

TEDDY'S READY — Contemporary 3583/7583 (1960) yellow label **$35**.

TOGETHER AGAIN — Contemporary 3588/7588 (1961) yellow label **$35**.

GOOD GRAVY — Contemporary 3592/7592 (1961) yellow label **$30**.

HEART AND SOUL — Contemporary 3606/7606 (1962) yellow label **$30**.

ROY ELDRIDGE
trumpet, fluegelhorn, vocals, leader - born 1911 Pittsburgh, PA

After Louis Armstrong's powerful influence on jazz in general, and jazz trumpet in particular, it is not surprising that it took sometime for another jazz trumpet player to merge with his own unique and personal style. Beginning in the 30's and continuing into the 40's, Roy Eldridge was in many ways the most important trumpet player in jazz. Early in his career he worked mostly in someone else's name band with which he toured finally forming his own group. Eldridge has continued to work and record, most often as a single or in tours with other name stars.

ROY ELDRIDGE IN SWEDEN — Prestige 114 (1952) 10" **$150.**

COLLATES — Clef 113 (1953) 10" **$90**; EP 181, EP 158 (1953) **$35** ea.; *reissued in part* Clef 704 (1956); *reissued* Verve 8088 (1957).

QUINTET — Clef 150 (1953) 10" **$90**; EP 199 **$35**; *reissued in part* Clef 705 (1956); *reissued* Verve 8089 (1957).

STROLLING MR. ELDRIDGE — Clef 162 (1953) 10" **$90.**

ROY AND DIZ/with Dizzy Gillespie — Clef 641 (1955) **$75.**

ROY AND DIZ - Vol 2/with Dizzy Gillespie — Clef 671 (1955) **$75.**

ROCKIN' CHAIR — Clef 704 (1956) **$60**; EP 240, EP 227 (1956) **$20**; *reissued* Verve 8088 (1957) **$45.**

DALE'S WAIL — Clef 705 (1956) **$60**; *reissued* Verve 8089 **$45.**

LITTLE JAZZ — Clef 683 (1956) **$60**; *reissued* Verve 8068 (1957) **$45.**

TRUMPET BATTLE/with Dizzy Gillespie — Clef 730 (1956) **$70**; *reissued* Verve 8190 (1957) **$50.**

THE TRUMPET KINGS/with Dizzy Gillespie — Clef 731 (1956) **$70**; *reissued* Verve 8110 (1957) **$50.**

SWING GOES DIXIE — American Recording Society 420 (1956) **$50**; *reissued* Verve 1010 **$40.**

THE URBANE JAZZ OF/with Benny Carter — American Recording Society 413 (1956) **$50**; *reissued* Verve 8202 (1957) **$40.**

QUARTET — London 375 (1954) 10" **$75.**

LITTLE JAZZ FOUR: TRUMPET FANTASY — Dial 304 (1953) 10" **$90.**

ROY'S GOT RHYTHM — EmArcy 36084 **$45.**

WITH ZOOT SIMS — Discovery 2009 (1954) 10" **$100.**

THE WARM FEELING — Verve 2088 (1957) with Verve Records, Inc. on bottom of label **$40.**

SWINGIN' ON THE TOWN — Verve 8389/68389 (1960) with Verve Records, Inc. on bottom of label **$45.**

ROY ELDRIDGE — Metro 513 (1965) **$20.**

DUKE ELLINGTON
piano, lyricist, composer leader - born 1899 Washington, DC died 1974

Through Ellington's long career, his talents were put to their best possible use with his orchestra of some of the finest musicians available. The scope of his career is so great that a listing of all the musicians who worked with him would be too long for our purposes, but a short list of a few of his accomplishments and contributions might give some idea of his place in any jazz study.

Ellington and his orchestra became famous in the 20's for their unique sound, inspired ensemble and improvised playing. They performed in and broadcasted from nightclubs such as the Kentucky Club and the Cotton Club and introduced innovations like wordless vocals in 1927. In the 30's Ellington increased in popularity through continued recordings, movies and tours of America and Europe. Innovations continued as well, with miniature concertos written for specific soloists, and works that exceeded the usual three minute recording length. Throughout the 40's, in addition to continued recordings and concert appearances, there were annual Carnegie Hall concerts which each featured a specially written extended composition.

In the 50's new heights of popularity were attained with recordings, concert and festival appearances and another tour of Europe. Later in the decade, Ellington and the orchestra recorded a film score, Anatomy Of A Murder, which won three grammy awards. In the 60's and into the 70's, Ellington and his orchestra continued touring, recording and gathering awards of every kind until his death in 1974 of lung cancer.

LIBERIAN SUITE — Columbia 6073 (1950) 10" **$50**; *reissued* Columbia 848 (1956) with 3 black logos on each side **$30.**

MOOD ELLINGTON — Columbia 6024 (1950) 10" **$50**; Columbia 164 (1950) 7" 4 record box set **$20.**

ELLINGTON UPTOWN — Columbia 4639 (1955) **$60**; EP 1629 (1955) **$25**; *reissued* Columbia 830 (1956) with 3 black logos on each side **$30**; *reissued* EP 8302 (1956) **$10.**

MASTERPIECES — Columbia 4418 (1955) **$60**; *reissued* Columbia 825 (1957) with 3 black logos on each side **$30.**

MUSIC OF ELLINGTON — Columbia 558 (1954) with Columbia in gold on top **$40**; *reissued* Columbia 558 (1956) with 3 black logos on each side **$30.**

BLUE LIGHT — Columbia 663 (1956) with 3 black logos on each side **$40.**

WITH BUCK CLAYTON AT NEWPORT — Columbia 933 (1956) with 3 black logos on each side **$40.**

DRUM IS A WOMAN — Columbia 951 (1957) with 3 black logos on each side **$40.**

SUCH SWEET THUNDER — Columbia 1033 (1957) with 3 black logos on each side **$50.**

ELLINGTON INDIGOS — Columbia 1085/8053 (1958) with 3 black logos on each side **$35.**

BROWN, BLACK AND BEIGE — Columbia 1162 (1958) with 3 black logos on each side **$40.**

ELLINGTON JAZZ PARTY — Columbia 1323/8129 (1959) with 3 black logos on each side **$35.**

THE COSMIC SCENE — Columbia 1198 (1958) with 3 black logos on each side **$75.**

NEWPORT 1958 — Columbia 1245/8072 (1958) with 3 black logos on each side **$40.**

T THE BAL MASQUE — Columbia 1282/8098 (1958) with 3 black logos on each side **$35**.

NATOMY OF A MURDER (Soundtrack) — Columbia 1360/8166 (1959) with 3 black logos on each side **$50**.

LUES IN ORBIT — Columbia 1445/8241 (1960) with 3 black logos on each side **$35**.

IANO IN THE BACKGROUND — Columbia 1546/8346 (1961) with three black logos on each side **$45**.

PEER GYNT" SUITE/SUITE THURSDAY — Columbia 1597/8397 (1961) with 3 black logos on each side **$30**.

LL AMERICAN — Columbia 1790/8590 (1962) with 3 black logos on each side **$25**.

MIDNIGHT IN PARIS — Columbia 1907/8707 (1962) with 3 black logos on each side **$25**.

IANO IN THE FOREGROUND — Columbia 2029/8829 (1963) with 3 black logos on each side **$45**.

HE ELLINGTON ERA - Vol 1 — Columbia C3L-27 (1963) 3 record box set with 24 page booklet **$60**.

HE ELLINGTON ERA - Vol 2 — Columbia C3L-39 (1963) 3 record box set with 24 page booklet **$60**.

IRST TIME/with Count Basie — Columbia 1715/8515 (1962) with 3 black logos on each side **$30**.

ERDIDO AND TAKE THE A TRAIN — Columbia EP 1566 (1949) **$10**.

OPHISTICATED LADY/SOLITUDE — Columbia EP 391 (1950) 2 records **$25**.

ND HIS ORCHESTRA — Columbia EP 2553 (1954) **$10**.

LAYS ELLINGTON — Capitol H477 (1953) 10" **$50**; *reissued* Capitol T477 (1957) green label **$35**.

REMIERED BY ELLINGTON — Capitol 440 (1953) 10" **$50**.

LLINGTON '55 — Capitol 521 (1955) **$45**; EP 1-521, EP 2-521, EP 3-521, EP 4-521 (1955) **$10** ea.

BEST — Capitol 1602 (1961) black label with logo on left side **$20**. (A)

DANCE TO THE DUKE — Capitol 637 (1956) green label **$35**.

LLINGTON SHOWCASE — Capitol 679 (1956) green label **$45**.

HISTORICALLY SPEAKING — Bethlehem 60 (1957) maroon label **$45**.

RESENTS — Bethlehem 6005 (1956) maroon label **$45**.

LLINGTONIA — Brunswick 58002 (1954) 10" **$55**; Vol 1 - Brunswick 9-7005 (1954) 7" 4 record box set **$25**; *reissued* in part Brunswick 54007.

LLINGTONIA - Vol 2 — Brunswick 58012 (1954) 10" **$55**; Vol 2 - Brunswick 9-7025 (1954) 7" 4 record box set **$25**; *reissued* in part Brunswick 54007.

EARLY ELLINGTON — Brunswick 54007 (1956) black label **$30**; *reissue* in part of Brunswick 58002 & 58012.

PLAYS THE BLUES — RCA Victor 3067 (1953) 10" **$60**; EP 3067 (1952) 2 records **$20**.

SEATTLE CONCERT — RCA Victor 1002 (1954) silver label dog on top **$50**.

GREATEST — RCA Victor 1004 (1954) silver label dog on top **$45**; EP 1004 (1953) 2 records **$15**.

DUKE AND HIS MEN — RCA Victor 1092 (1955) silver label dog on top **$45**.

IN A MELLOTONE — RCA Victor 1364 (1957) dog on top **$45**.

AT HIS VERY BEST — RCA Victor 1715 (1959) dog on top **$30**.

DAY BREAK EXPRESS — RCA Victor 506 (1965) **$20**.

THE INDISPENSABLE — RCA Victor 6009 (1961) dog on top 2 LP's **$60**.

JUMPIN' PUNKINS' — RCA Victor 517 (1965) **$20**.

AT THE COTTON CLUB — RCA Camden 459 (1958) **$35**.

DUO/with Jimmy Blanton — RCA Victor EP 619 (1955) **$35**.

MODERN JAZZ PIANO — RCA Victor EP 3031 (1952) 2 records **$20**.

THIS IS DUKE — RCA Victor EP 3071 (1952) 2 records **$20**.

CARAVAN — RCA Victor EP 5054 (1958) **$10**.

DUKE ELLINGTON — RCA Victor EP 5002 (1958) **$10**.

PLAYS — Allegro 4014 (1954) 10" **$45**.

PLAYS — Allegro 4038 (1954) 10" **$45**.

DUKE ELLINGTON AND ORCHESTRA — Ron-Lette 7 (1958) **$35**.

EARLY RECORDING — X Label 3037 (1954) 10" **$50**.

BIRTH OF BIG BAND JAZZ/with Fletcher Henderson — Riverside 129 (1956) blue label with Bill Grauer Pro. **$45**.

DUETS/with Billy Strayhorn — Riverside 475/9475 (1962) blue label with Bill Grauer Pro. **$30**.

AFRO BOSSA — Reprise 6069 (1964) **$15**.

HITS OF THE 60'S — Reprise 6122 (1964) **$20**.

ELLINGTON '66 — Reprise 6154 (1965) **$20**.

MARY POPPINS — Reprise 6141 (1964) **$15**.

THE SYMPHONIC — Reprise 6097 (1964) **$15**.

MONEY JUNGLE/with Max Roach and Charlie Mingus — United Artists 14017/15017 (1962) **$45**.

BACK TO BACK/with Johnny Hodges — Verve 8317/6055 (1959) with Verve Records, Inc. on bottom of label **$45**.

SIDE BY SIDE/with Johnny Hodges — Verve 8345/6109 (1960) with Verve Records, Inc.on bottom of label **$45**.

AND JOHN COLTRANE — Impulse 30 (1962) orange label **$35**.

MEETS COLEMAN HAWKINS — Impulse 26 (1962) orange label **$35**.

DON ELLIOTT

trumpet, vibes, mellophone, composer - born 1926
Somerville, NJ

THE VERSATILE — Savoy 9033 (1953) 10" **$60**.

VIB-RATIONS — Savoy 12054 (1956) maroon label **$40**.

QUINTET — RCA Victor 1007 (1954) silver label dog on top **$40**.

DOUBLES IN BRASS — Vanguard 8016 (1954) 10" **$50**.

MELLOPHONE — Bethlehem 12 (1955) maroon label **$45**.

SINGS — Bethlehem 15 (1955) maroon label **$45**.

MELLO SOUND — Decca 9208 (1958) **$30**.

MUSICAL OFFERING — ABC Paramount 106 (1956) **$25**.

AT THE MODERN JAZZ ROOM — ABC Paramount 142 (1956) **$25**.

JAMAICA JAZZ/with Candido — ABC Paramount 228 (1958) **$25.**

THE VOICES OF — ABC Paramount 190 (1957) **$25.**

THE VOICE OF MARTY BELL, QUARTET OF DON ELLIOTT — Riverside 12-206 (1956) white label with Bill Grauer Pro. **$65;** *reissued* blue label with Bill Grauer Pro. (1958) **$35.**

COUNTERPOINT FOR SIX VALVES/with Rusty Dedrick — Riverside 12-218 (1956) white label with Bill Grauer Pro. **$65;** *reissued* blue label with Bill Grauer Pro. (1958) **$45.**

ANITA ELLIS
vocals - born Montreal, Canada

I WONDER WHAT BECAME OF ME — Epic 3280 (1956) **$65.**

HIM — Epic 3419 (1958) **$45.**

THE WORLD IN MY ARMS — Elektra 179/7179 (1960) **$45.**

HERB ELLIS
guitar, composer - born 1921 Farmersville, TX

Ellis has been known throughout his career for his ever-swinging style. He began in the 40's with big bands and in the 50's he replaced Barney Kessell in the Oscar Peterson Trio. Through much of the 60's he worked in a succession of groups on television talk shows and continued to appear and record with other fine jazz musicians.

ELLIS IN WONDERLAND/with Jimmy Giuffre — Norgran 1081 (1956) **$50;** *reissued* Verve 8171 (1957) **$45.**

NOTHING BUT THE BLUES/with Stan Getz — Verve 8252 (1958) with Verve Records, Inc. on bottom of label **$50.**

MEETS JIMMY GIUFFRE/with Art Pepper — Verve 8311/6045 (1959) with Verve Records, Inc. on bottom of label **$45.**

THANK YOU CHARLIE CHRISTIAN — Verve 8381/68381 (1960) with Verve Records, Inc. on bottom of label **$30.**

SOFTLY/with Vic Feldman — Verve 8448/68448 (1962) with MGM on bottom of label **$30.**

THE MIDNIGHT ROLL/with Buddy Tate — Epic 16034/17034 (1962) **$30.**

THREE GUITARS IN BOSSA NOVA TIME/with Laurindo Almeida and Johnny Gray — Epic 16036/17036 (1963) **$25.**

TOGETHER/with Stuff Smith — Epic 16039/17039 (1963) **$30.**

GUITAR/with Charlie Byrd — Columbia 2330/9130 (1965) with one white logo on each side **$25.**

MAN WITH THE GUITAR/with Teddy Edwards — Dot 3678/25678 (1965) black label with tricolored Dot **$25.**

BUDDIE EMMONS
steel guitar

STEEL GUITAR JAZZ/with Jerome Richardson — Mercury 20843/60843 **$20.**

BOBBY ENEVOLDSEN
bass, valve trombone, tenor sax, composer, arranger born 1920 Billings, MT

Beginning in the early 50's on the West Coast, Enevoldsen demonstrated his ability on many instruments and perhaps this is the reason he has never been particularly related to one with a significant recognition. Enevoldsen also exercised his composing and arranging skills with jazz and commercial groups and has worked in the studio for both television and radio.

SMORGASBORD — Liberty 6008 (1956) green label **$45.**

BOB ENEVOLDSEN — Nocturne 6 (1954) 10" **$60.**

REFLECTIONS IN JAZZ — Tampa 14 (1957) **$45.**

*ETHEL ENNIS
vocals - born 1934 Baltimore, MD

Initially recognized as a vocalist with Benny Goodman in the late 50's, Ms. Ennis worked extensively and improved significantly throughout the 60's in nightclubs, jazz clubs and on recordings.

LULLABIES FOR LOSERS — Jubilee 1021 (1956) **$50.**

SINGS — Jubilee 5024 (1963) **$20.**

EYES FOR YOU — RCA Victor 2984 (1964) dog on top **$20.**

---

*The only LP's within the scope of this book.

ROLF ERICSON
trumpet - born 1927 Stockholm, Sweden

Ericson came to the U.S. in the late 40's and was very quickly involved with top-notch musicians and groups such as Benny Goodman, Benny Carter, Charlie Barnet and Woody Herman. He toured and recorded with his own combo and did extensive work on the West Coast where he teamed up with Les Brown and Howard Rumsey.

SWEDISH PASTRY/with Lars Gullin and Arne Domnerus — Discovery 2008 (1954) 10" **$90.**

AND HIS ALL AMERICAN STARS/with Cecil Payne — EmArcy 36106 (1957) **$45.**

BOOKER ERVIN
tenor sax - born 1930 Denison, TX died 1970

QUINTET — Savoy 12154 (1960) maroon label **$45**.

THE BOOK-THE BOOK COOKS/with Zoot Sims — Bethlehem 6048 (1960) **$50**.

THAT'S IT — Candida 8014/9014 (1962) **$45**.

EXULTATIONS — Prestige 7293 (1963) yellow label **$35**; *reissued* Prestige 7293 (1964) blue label with logo on right side **$30**.

THE FREEDOM BOOK — Prestige 7295 (1963) yellow label **$35**; *reissued* Prestige 7295 (1964) blue label with logo on right side **$30**.

THE SONG BOOK — Prestige 7318 (1964) yellow label **$30**; *reissued* Prestige 7318 (1965) blue label with logo on right side **$25**.

THE SPACE BOOK — Prestige 7386 (1965) blue label with logo on right side **$20**.

THE BLUE BOOK — Prestige 7340 (1964) blue label with logo on right side **$20**.

EUROPEAN JAZZ QUARTET
*Wolfgang Lauth, Fritz Hartschuh
Joe Hacbarth, Wolfgang Wagner*

NEW JAZZ FROM THE OLD WORLD — Pulse 3001 (1957) **$35**.

BILL EVANS
piano, composer - born 1929 Plainfield, NJ died 1983

Originally gained recognition with Tony Scott which led to work with Miles Davis in '58 and '59. Although he was with Davis for a relatively short period, the recordings he was involved on are some of that groups most popular. Following this time he recorded mostly with his own trio on several labels and these recordings showcase his lyricism, sensitive touch and introspective approach to standards, ballads and his own compositions. Evans continued to tour and record until his death in 1983.

NEW JAZZ CONCEPTIONS — Riverside 12-223 (1956) white label with Bill Grauer Pro. with picture cover **$60**; *reissued* with artistic cover **$40**.

EVERYBODY DIGS — Riverside 12-291/1129 (1958) blue label with Bill Grauer Pro. **$45**.

PORTRAIT IN JAZZ — Riverside 12-315/1162 (1959) blue label with Bill Grauer Pro. **$45**.

EXPLORATIONS — Riverside 351/9351 (1961) blue label with Bill Grauer Pro. **$35**.

SUNDAY AT THE VILLAGE VANGUARD — Riverside 376/9376 (1961) blue label with Bill Grauer Pro. **$35**.

WALTZ FOR DEBBY — Riverside 399/9399 (1961) blue label with Bill Grauer Pro. **$35**.

MOONBEAMS — Riverside 428/9428 (1962) blue label with Bill Grauer Pro. **$40**.

INTERPLAY — Riverside 445/9445 (1962) blue label with Bill Grauer Pro. **$40**.

HOW MY HEART SINGS — Riverside 473/9473 (1963) blue label with Bill Grauer Pro. **$30**.

AT SHELLY'S MANNE HOLE — Riverside 487/9487 (1963) blue label with Bill Grauer Pro. **$25**.

THE IVORY HUNTERS/with Bob Brookmeyer — United Artists 3044/6044 (1959) **$60**.

UNDERCURRENT — United Artists 14003/15003 (1962) with silhouette of sax player **$35**.

EMPATHY — Verve 8497/68497 (1962) **$35**.

CONVERSATIONS WITH MYSELF (SOLO) — Verve 8526/68526 (1963) with MGM on bottom of label **$25**.

TRIO '64 — Verve 8578/68578 (1964) with MGM on bottom of label **$20**.

TRIO '65 — Verve 8613/68613 (1965) with MGM on bottom of label **$20**. Ⓐ

THE V.I.P. THEME PLUS OTHERS — MGM 4184 (1963) **$20**.

GIL EVANS
piano, composer - born 1912 Toronto, Canada

The most important endeavor for Evans early in his career was as an arranger for the Claude Thornhill Band in the 40's. This opportunity in itself did not make him famous but as a result he was part of the group of musicians that made the recordings Birth Of The Cool on Capitol in the early 50's and associated him with fellow Thornhill arrangers Gerry Mulligan, John Lewis, who is a leader of the M.J.Q., and Miles Davis.

The subsequent collaborations between Davis and Evans produced a series of recordings that were huge critical successes in addition to being extremely popular with the audiences. Over twenty years later these recordings; Miles Ahead, Porgy and Bess, Sketches of Spain and Miles Davis at Carnegie Hall, all on the Columbia label, are considered to be true classics. In the ensuing years, Gil Evans has continued to explore orchestral possibilities, usually on recordings, with a few appearances in New York City with bands of continually evolving personnel.

GIL EVANS AND TEN — Prestige 7120 (1957) yellow label **$50**; *reissued* New Jazz 8215 (1959).

BIG STUFF — New Jazz 8215 (1959) **$25**.

NEW BOTTLE, OLD WINE — World Pacific 1246/1011 (1958) **$45**.

ORCHESTRA — GREAT JAZZ STANDARDS — World Pacific 1270/1027 (1959) **$40**; *reissued* Pacific Jazz 28 (1961).

AMERICA'S #1 ARRANGER — Pacific Jazz 28 (1961) **$25**.

OUT OF THE COOL — Impulse 4 (1960) orange label **$25**.

IN THE HOT — Impulse 9 (1961) orange label **$25**.

THE INDIVIDUALISM OF — Verve 8555/68555 (1964) **$20**.

RICHARD EVANS
bass - born 1932 Birmingham, AL

RICHARD'S ALMANAC — Argo 658 (1959) **$35**.

TAL FARLOW
guitar - born 1921 Greensboro, NC

A self-taught guitarist, Farlow's inspiration came from the great Charlie Christian. His two-part career began in the early 50's when he worked with Red Norvo on and off, and with Artie Shaw. These works earned him recognition as one of the best guitarists of that period. He then went into a period of retirement until his gradual reemergence period with occasional appearances and a return to recording which once again confirmed him as a superb guitarist.

QUARTET — Blue Note 5042 (1954) 10" **$125**.

QUARTET — Norgran 19 (1954) 10" **$90**; EP 35, EP 36 (1954) **$30** ea.; *reissued* Norgran 1047 (1955) **$75**; *reissued* Verve 8138 (1957) **$60**.

ARTISTRY OF — Norgran 1014 (1954) **$75**; EP 84, EP 85, EP 86 (1954) **$30** ea.; *reissued* Norgran 1097 (1956); *reissued* Verve 8184 (1957).

THE INTERPRETATIONS OF — Norgran 1027 (1955) **$70**; EP 125, EP 126, EP 127 (1955) **$25** ea.; *reissued* Verve 8011 (1957).

AUTUMN IN NEW YORK — Norgran 1097 (1956) **$65**; *reissued* Verve 8184 (1957) **$55**; *reissue* of Norgran 1014.

A RECITAL BY/with Bill Perkins and Bob Gordon — Norgran 1030 (1955) **$125**; EP 134 (1955) **$50**; *reissued* Verve 8123 (1957) **$80**.

TAL — Norgran 1102 (1956) **$60**; *reissued* Verve 8021 (1957) **$50**.

FASCINATIN' RHYTHM — Verve 8011 (1957) **$55**; *reissue* of Norgran 1027.

THE SWINGING — American Recording Society 418 (1956) **$60**; *reissued* Verve 8201 (1957) **$50**.

THIS IS — Verve 8289 (1958) **$45**.

THE GUITAR ARTISTRY OF/with Bobby Jaspar — Verve 8370/6143 (1959) **$60**.

PLAYS THE MUSIC OF HAROLD ARLEN — Verve 8371 (1959) **$45**.

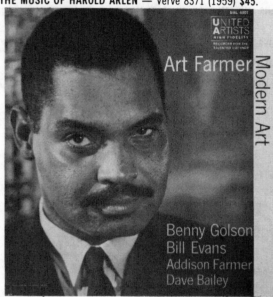

ART FARMER
trumpet, fluegelhorn - born 1928 Council Bluffs, IA

Farmer is a versatile trumpet player with good range and tone. His early work was predominantly on the West Coast with name bands and then, in New York City, he formed his first group with Gigi Gryce in the mid-50's. Later in the 50's, he co-led the Jazztet with Benny Golson producing some very popular recordings. Farmer spent most of the 60's in European studios and occasional jazz settings performing most usually on the fluegelhorn.

SEPTET — Prestige 162 (1953) 10" **$125**; EP 1354 (1953) **$40**; *reissued* Prestige 7031 (1956) **$75**; *reissued* New Jazz 8278 (1962).

QUINTET/with Sonny Rollins — Prestige 177 (1954) 10" **$125**; *reissued* in part New Jazz 8258 (1961).

QUINTET/with Gigi Gryce — Prestige 181 (1954) 10" **$125**; *reissued* Prestige 7085 (1956).

QUARTET/with Wynton Kelly — Prestige 193 (1954) 10" **$100**; *reissued* New Jazz 8258 (1961).

QUINTET/with Gigi Gryce — Prestige 209 (1955) 10" **$100**; *reissued* Prestige 7085 (1957).

WHEN FARMER MET GRYCE — Prestige 7085 (1956) yellow label **$75**; *reissue* of Prestige 181 & 209.

QUINTET/with Gigi Gryce — Prestige 7017 (1956) yellow label **$75**; *reissued* New Jazz 8289 (1962).

TWO TRUMPETS/with Donald Byrd — Prestige 7062 (1956) yellow label **$75**.

THREE TRUMPETS/with Donald Byrd and Ira Sulieman — Prestige 7092 (1957) yellow label **$75**.

FARMER'S MARKET/with Hank Mobley — New Jazz 8203 (1958) **$60**.

EARLY ART — New Jazz 8258 (1961) **$35**; *reissue* of Prestige 177 & 193.

WORK OF ART — New Jazz 8278 (1961) **$35**; *reissue* of Prestige 162.

EVENING IN CASABLANCA — New Jazz 8289 (1962) **$30**; *reissue* of Prestige 7017.

LAST NIGHT WHEN WE WERE YOUNG — ABC Paramount 200 (1958) **$40**.

PORTRAIT — Contemporary 3554/7027 (1958) yellow label **$45**.

MODERN ART/with Benny Golson — United Artists 4007/5007 (1958) red label **$50**.

BRASS SHOUT/with Lee Morgan — United Artists 4047/5047 (1959) red label **$50**.

AZTEC SUITE/with Zoot Sims — United Artists 4062/5062 (1959) red label **$40**.

ART — Argo 678 (1961) **$35**.

PERCEPTION — Argo 738 (1964) **$30**.

LISTEN TO ART FARMER AND THE ORCHESTRA — Mercury 20766/60766 (1963) **$30**.

INTERACTION — Atlantic 1412 (1963) with logo on right side **$30**.

LIVE AT THE HALF NOTE — Atlantic 1421 (1964) with logo on right side **$40**.

TO SWEDEN WITH LOVE — Atlantic 1430 (1964) with logo on right side **$25**.

SING ME SOFTLY OF THE BLUES — Atlantic 1442 (1965) with logo on right side **$25**.

THE MANY FACES OF — Scepter 521 (1964) **$30**.

FRANCES FAYE
vocals, piano - born Brooklyn, NY

NO RESERVATIONS — Capitol H512 (1954) 10" **$60**; *reissued* Capitol T512 (1955) green label **$50**.

I AM WILD AGAIN — Bethlehem 23 (1955) maroon label **$45**.

RELAXIN' WITH — Bethlehem 62 (1956) maroon label **$45**.

SINGS FOLK SONGS — Bethlehem 6017 (1957) maroon label **$45**.

CAUGHT IN THE ACT — Gene Norman Presents 41 (1958) gray label **$35**.

SWINGS FATS DOMINO — Imperial 9059/12007 (1959) **$30**.

IN FRENZY — Verve 2147/62147 (1961) **$25**.

SWINGING ALL THE WAY — Verve 8434/68434 (1962) **$25**.

YOU GOTTA GO! GO! GO! — Regina 315 (1964) **$20**.

LEONARD FEATHER
piano, vibories, arranger, composer, producer and jazz author

IN SWEDEN - NEW SOUNDS OF SWEDEN/with Arne Domnerus and Lars Gullin — Prestige 119 (1951) 10" **$150**.

LEONARD FEATHER — Prestige 180 (1954) 10" **$100**.

BEST FROM THE WEST/with Charles Mariano — Blue Note 5059 (1954) 10" **$100**.

WINTER SEQUENCE — MGM 270 (1954) 10" **$80**.

WEST COAST VS. EAST COAST/with Buddy Collette and Frank Wess — MGM 3390 (1955) **$75**; EP 631 (1955) **$40**.

HI FI SUITE/with Dick Hyman — MGM 3494 (1957) **$50**.

OH CAPTAIN!/with Dick Hyman — MGM 3650 (1958) **$50**.

SWINGIN' ON THE VIBORIES/with Bob Enevoldsen — ABC Paramount 110 (1956) **$45**.

THE SEVEN AGES OF JAZZ/with Coleman Hawkins and Georgie Auld — Metrojazz 2-E 1009 (1959) 2 LP's **$70**.

PRESENTS BOP/with Phil Woods — Mode 127 (1957) **$50**; *reissued* Interlude 511/1011 (1959).

PRESENTS 52ND STREET — Interlude 511/1011 (1959) **$40**.

THE ENCYCLOPEDIA OF JAZZ ON RECORD — Decca DXF 140 (1956) 4 LP deluxe set, black label with silver lettering **$125.**

JAZZ OF THE TWENTIES - Vol 1 — Decca 8398 (1956) black label with silver lettering **$30.**

JAZZ OF THE THIRTIES - Vol 2 — Decca 8399 (1956) black label with silver lettering **$30.**

JAZZ OF THE FORTIES - Vol 3 — Decca 8400 (1956) black label with silver lettering **$30.**

JAZZ OF THE FIFTIES - Vol 4 — Decca 8401 (1956) black label with silver lettering **$30.**

JAZZ OF THE SIXTIES - GIANTS OF THE SAXOPHONE — Vee Jay 2501 (1964) **$25.**

VICTOR FELDMAN
vibes, drums, piano, composer - born 1934
London, England

Beginning as a child prodigy in England, Feldman became his country's most popular vibraphonist before coming to the U.S. in 1955. After arriving in the U.S., he worked with Woody Herman in the late 50's, "Cannonball" Adderley in 1961 and Miles Davis for much of the 60's, the later unfolded a recording featuring his composition Seven Steps To Heaven. For much of the 60's and 70's most of his work was in movie and television studios and with non-jazz artists except for occasional recordings under his own name or with younger jazz oriented musicians.

SUITE SIXTEEN — Contemporary 3541 (1958) yellow label **$35.**

THE ARRIVAL OF — Contemporary 3549 (1958) yellow label **$35.**

LATINSVILLE — Contemporary 5005/9005 (1960) yellow label **$30.**

ON VIBES — Mode 120 (1958) **$50;** *reissued* Interlude 510/1010 (1959).

WITH MALLETS A FORE THOUGHT — Interlude 510/1010 (1959) **$40;** *reissue of* Mode 120 (1958).

LOVE ME WITH ALL YOUR HEART — Vee Jay 1006 (1959) **$40.**

IT'S A WONDERFUL WORLD/with Bill Perkins — Vee Jay 2507 (1965) **$25.**

MERRY OLE SOUL — Riverside 366/9366 (1960) **$35.**

STOP THE WORLD I WANT TO GET OFF — World Pacific 1807 (1962) yellow vinyl **$35.**

SOVIET JAZZ THEMES — Ava 19 (1963) **$35.**

*MAYNARD FERGUSON
trumpet, leader, baritone horn, valve trombone
born 1928 Montreal, Canada

HOLLYWOOD PARTY/with Bob Cooper and Bob Gordon — EmArcy 26017 (1954) 10" **$90;** EP 1-6027 (1954) **$30;** *reissued* EmArcy 36046 (1956) **$75.**

DIMENSIONS — EmArcy 26024 (1954) 10" **$80;** *reissued* EmArcy 36044 (1956) **$60.**

JAM SESSION/with Bob Gordon — EmArcy 36009 (1955) **$75;** EP 1-6109, EP 1-6110 (1955) **$30** ea.

OCTET — EmArcy 36021 (1956) **$50.**

AROUND THE HORN — EmArcy 36076 (1956) **$45.**

BOYS WITH LOTS OF BRASS — EmArcy 36114 (1957) **$45;** *reissued* Mercury 20556/60124 (1960) **$30.**

AND SEXTET — Mainstream 56060 (1965) **$25.**

TWO'S COMPANY/with Chris Connor — Roulette 52068 (1958) white label with multicolored pinwheel **$45.**

DOUBLE EXPOSURE/with Chris Connor — Atlantic 8049 (1961) with logo on right side **$35.**

---

*The only LP's within the scope of this book.

JANE FIELDING
vocals

JAZZ TRIO FOR VOICE, PIANO AND BASS — Jazz West 3 (1956) **$60.**

EMBERS GLOW/with Kenny Drew — Jazz West 5 (1956) **$60.**

*JERRY FIELDING

composer, leader, arranger - born 1922
Pittsburgh, PA

GREAT NEW ORCHESTRA/with William Collette — Trend 1000 (1953) 10" **$50.**

ORCHESTRA — Trend 1004 (1954) 10" **$50.**

---

*The only LP's within the scope of this book.

HERBIE FIELDS

saxes, clarinet - born 1919 Elizabeth, NJ died 1958

BLOW HOT, BLOW COOL/with Bob Gordon — Decca 8130 (1956) **$40.**

A NIGHT AT KITTY'S — RKO Unique 124 (1957) **$35.**

THE FIRST JAZZ PIANO QUARTET

Morris Nanton, Moe Wechsler,
Bernie Leighton, Irv Joseph

THE FIRST JAZZ PIANO QUARTET — Warner Brothers 1274 (1958) gray label **$55.**

CLARE FISCHER

composer, piano, organ - born 1928 Durand, MI

FIRST TIME OUT — Pacific Jazz 52 (1962) **$35.**

SURGING AHEAD — Pacific Jazz 67 (1962) **$35.**

EXTENSION — Pacific Jazz 77 (1963) **$25.**

SO DANCO SAMBA — World Pacific 1830 (1964) **$20.**

ELLA FITZGERALD

vocals - born 1918 Newport News, VA

Ella Fitzgerald became famous in 1939 with the recording A Tisket, A Tasket which she made with the Chick Webb Band. She was in Webb's band from 1935 to 1939 and when Webb died she assumed leadership of the band herself for a year. During her years with this band, her great voice and swinging style made her one of the most respected and most popular female jazz vocalists. Her resulting successes have continued throughout a career that has included tours of every continent and repeated movie and television appearances with many of her finest contemporaries and has won her enumerable critical and popular awards of every kind.

ELLA, LENA, BILLIE/with Lena Horne and Billie Holiday — Columbia 2531 (1956) 10" **$75.**

SOUVENIR ALBUM — Decca 5084 (1950) 10" **$125.**

GERSHWIN SONGS — Decca 5300 (1951) 10" **$150;** *reissued* Decca 8378 (1957) black label with silver lettering **$75.**

SONGS IN A MELLOW MOOD — Decca 8068 (1955) black label with silver lettering **$70;** EP 2148, EP 2149, EP 2150 (1954) **$35** ea.

SWEET AND HOT — Decca 8155 (1955) black label with silver lettering **$75.**

LULLABIES OF BIRDLAND — Decca 8149 (1955) black label with silver lettering **$75;** EP 2028, EP 2312 (1955) **$35** ea.

PETE KELLY'S BLUES/with Peggy Lee — Decca 8166 (1955) black label with silver lettering **$80;** EP 2269 (1955) **$40.**

ELLA AND HER FELLAS — Decca 8477 (1956) black label with silver lettering **$60;** EP 2014 (1956) **$25.**

FIRST LADY OF SONG — Decca 8695 (1958) black label with silver lettering **$50.**

INVITE YOU TO LISTEN AND RELAX — Decca 8696 (1958) black label with silver lettering **$40.**

FOR SENTIMENTAL REASONS — Decca 8832 (1959) black label with silver lettering **$35.**

BEST OF ELLA — Decca DX156 (1958) 2 LP's black label with silver lettering **$50.**

STAIRWAY TO THE STARS — Decca 4446/74446 (1964) black label with rainbow strip **$20.**

GOLDEN FAVORITES — Decca 4129 (1961) black label with rainbow strip **$20.**

EARLY ELLA — Decca 4447/74447 (1964) black label with rainbow strip **$20.**

SINGS THE COLE PORTER SONGBOOK — Verve 4001-2 (1956) 2 LP's with Verve Records, Inc. on label **$80;** EP 5004, EP 5005, EP 5006, EP 5007, EP 5008, EP 5009, EP 5010, EP 5011 (1956) **$25** ea.

SINGS THE RODGERS AND HART SONGBOOK — Verve 4002-2 (1956) 2 LP's with Verve Records, Inc. on label **$80;** EP 5027, EP 5028, EP 5029, EP 5030, EP 5031 (1956) **$25** ea.

SINGS THE DUKE ELLINGTON SONGBOOK - Vol 1 — Verve 4008-2 (1956) 2 LP's with Verve Records, Inc. on label **$70.**

SINGS THE DUKE ELLINGTON SONGBOOK - Vol 2 — Verve 4009-2 (1956) 2 LP's with Verve Records, Inc. on label **$70.**

SINGS THE DUKE ELLINGTON SONGBOOK — Verve 4010-4 (1956) 4 LP box set with booklet and Verve Records, Inc. on label **$150.**

SINGS THE IRVING BERLIN SONGBOOK — Verve 4019-2/6005-2 (1958) 2 LP's with Verve Records, Inc. on label **$65.**

SINGS THE GEORGE AND IRA GERSHWIN SONGBOOK "LIMITED EDITION" — Verve Records, Inc. in solid walnut box with leather pockets, 5 LP's **$300.**

SINGS THE GEORGE AND IRA GERSHWIN SONGBOOK — Verve 4029-5 (1959) 5 LP box set with artistic cover and Verve Records, Inc. on label **$100.**

SINGS THE HAROLD ARLEN SONGBOOK — Verve 4057/8; 64057/8 (1962) 2 LP's **$50.**

SINGS THE JEROME KERN SONGBOOK — Verve 4060/64060 (1965) **$25.**

LIKE SOMEONE IN LOVE — Verve 4004/6000 (1957) with Verve Records, Inc. on label **$50;** EP 5058, EP 5059, EP 5060, EP 5061 (1957) **$15** ea.

PORGY AND BESS/with Louis Armstrong — Verve 4011-2/6040-2 (1957) 2 LP's with Verve Records, Inc. on label **$75.**

ELLA AND BILLIE AT NEWPORT — Verve 8234/6022 (1958) one side each with Verve Records, Inc. on label **$60.**

AT THE OPERA HOUSE — Verve 8264/6026 (1958) with Verve Records, Inc. on label **$45.**

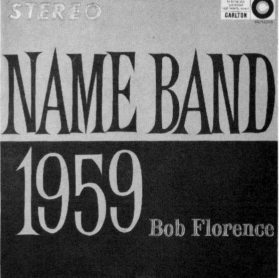

LLA SWINGS LIGHTLY — Verve 4021/6019 (1959) with Verve Records, Inc. on label **$40**.

LLA AND LOUIS/with Louis Armstrong — Verve 4003 (1956) with Verve Records, Inc. on label **$50**.

LLA AND LOUIS AGAIN/with Louis Armstrong — Verve 4006-2 (1956) 2 LP's with Verve Records, Inc. on label **$75**.

INGS SWEET SONGS FOR SWINGERS — Verve 4032/6072 (1959) with Verve Records, Inc. on label **$35**.

MACK THE KNIFE IN BERLIN — Verve 4041 (1960) with Verve Records, Inc. on label **$35**.

ET NO MAN WRITE MY EPITAPH — Verve 4043 (1960) with Verve Records, Inc. on label **$30**.

HELLO LOVE — Verve 4034/6100 (1959) with Verve Records, Inc. on label **$40**.

GET HAPPY — Verve 4036 (1959) with Verve Records, Inc. on label **$40**.

N HOLLYWOOD — Verve 4052 (1961) **$25**.

WINGS BRIGHTLY — Verve 4054 (1962) **$25**.

WINGS GENTLY — Verve 4055 (1962) **$30**.

RHYTHM IS MY BUSINESS/with Bill Doggett — (1962) **$30**.

CLAP HANDS HERE COMES CHARLIE — Verve 4053 (1962) **$30**.

HESE ARE THE BLUES — Verve 4062 (1963) **$25**.

HELLO DOLLY — Verve 4064 (1965) **$20**.

LLA WORLD — Metro 567 (1965) **$15**.

LLA FITZGERALD — Metro 500 (1965) **$15**.

THE FIVE
Bill Perkins, Conte Candoli, Pete Jolly,
Buddy Clark, Mel Lewis
THE FIVE — RCA Victor 1121 (1955) dog on top **$75**.

THE FIVE BROTHERS
Enevoldsen, Harper, Overburg, Capp, Mitchell
FIVE BROTHERS — Tampa 25 (1957) **$40**.

TOMMY FLANAGAN
piano - born 1930 Detroit, MI
JAZZ. . . IT'S MAGIC/with Curtis Fuller — Regent 6055 (1958) green label **$45**.

OVERSEAS — Prestige 7134 (1958) yellow label **$60**.

TRIO — Moodsville 9 (1960) **$35**.

KING FLEMMING
piano
MISTY NIGHT — Argo 4004 (1960) **$30**.

STAND BY — Argo 4019 (1962) **$25**.

BOB FLORENCE
composer, piano - born 1932 Los Angeles, CA
NAME BAND 1959/with Herbie Harper and Herb Geller — Carlton 12/115 (1959) **$45**.

TRIO — Era 20003 (1957) **$30**.

JIMMY FORREST
tenor sax - born 1920 St. Louis, MO died 1980
Forrest's hard swinging style first gained him recognition through his work with Jay McShann in the early 40's. He went on to gigging with Andy Kirk and later replaced Ben Webster in the Duke Ellington Band for a short time. Forrest then formed the first of his many groups in the 50's and continued into the 60's, joining Count Basie in 1973. Forrest has many recordings under his own name with various sidemen and has performed as sideman on many other recordings.

FORREST FIRE — New Jazz 8250 (1960) **$45**.

SOUL STREET — New Jazz 8293 (1962) **$40**.

OUT OF THE FORREST — Prestige 7202 (1961) yellow label **$45**; *reissued* Prestige 7202 (1964) blue label with logo on right side **$25**.

MOST MUCH — Prestige 7218 (1961) yellow label **$45**; *reissued* Prestige 7218 (1964) blue label with logo on right side **$25**.

SIT DOWN AND RELAX — Prestige 7235 (1962) yellow label **$45**; *reissued* Prestige 7235 (1964) blue label with logo on right side **$25**.

SOUL BATTLE/with Oliver Nelson — Prestige 7223 (1962) yellow label **$50**; *reissued* Prestige 7223 (1965) blue label with logo on right side **$25**.

FRANK FOSTER
tenor sax, composer - born 1928 Cincinnati, OH
Foster established his reputation primarily on the tenor sax and as a composer. In 1949 he played with Wardell Gray in Detroit and by 1953 he was with the Count Basie Band as player and arranger. Foster is a highly regarded musician although underrated.

HERE COMES FRANK FOSTER — Blue Note 5043 (1954) 10" **$150**.

NO COUNT/with Frank Wess — Savoy 12078 (1956) **$45**.

HOPE MEETS FOSTER — Prestige 7021 (1956) yellow label **$100**; *reissued* Prestige 7021 (1957).

WAIL FRANK, WAIL/with Elmo Hope — Prestige 7021 (1957) yellow label **$75**; *reissued* Prestige 7021 (1964) blue label with logo on right side **$20**; *reissue* of Prestige 7021 titled Hope Meets Foster.

THE SWINGERS/with Kenny Dorham — Jazzland 3 (1960) **$45**.

BASIE IS OUR BOSS — Argo 717 (1963) **$35**.

HERMAN FOSTER

piano - born 1928 Philadelphia, PA

THE EXPLOSIVE PIANO OF — Epic 16016/17016 (1961) yellow label **$35.**

HAVE YOU HEARD — Epic 16010/17010 (1960) yellow label **$35.**

READY AND WILLING — Argo 727 (1963) **$25.**

THE FOUR MOST

*Al Cohn, Gene Quill, Mundell Lowe, Mat Mathews,
Joe Puma, Oscar Pettiford, Hank Jones*

THE FOUR MOST — Dawn 1112 (1956) **$75.**

PANAMA FRANCIS

congas, bongos, drums - born 1918 Miami, FL

EXPLODING DRUMS/with Joe Newman and King Curtis — Epic 3839/629
(1959) **$45.**

ERMA FRANKLIN

vocals

HER NAME IS ERMA — Epic 3824 (1962) **$25.**

*BUD FREEMAN

tenor sax - born 1906 Chicago, IL

One of the most influential tenors of jazz beginning in the 20's,
Freeman was a musician who kept his own sound while working and
absorbing many of the developments in jazz through over half a
century. He has contributed many fine compositions and recordings
and toured many parts of the world through the course of his work.

PANORAMA — ABC Paramount 105 (1950) 10" **$80.**

CLASSICS IN JAZZ — Capitol H625 (1953) 10" **$80.**

AND HIS TRIO — Grand Award 33-313 (1955) **$50.**

BUD FREEMAN — Bethlehem 29 (1955) **$45.**

AND HIS SUMMA CUM LUADE TRIO — Dot 3166 (1958) with tricolored Dot **$45.**

MIDNIGHT SESSION/with Mary Mulligan — Dot 3254 (1959) with tricolored Dot
$40.

ALL STARS — Swingville 2012 (1960) **$35.**

SOMETHING TENDER AND TWO GUITARS/with George Barnes and Carl Krass —
United Artists 14033/15033 (1963) **$35.**

*The only LP's within the scope of this book.

RUSS FREEMAN

piano - born 1926 Chicago, IL

Freeman worked extensively in the Los Angeles area in the late 40's
and early 50's with several top musicians such as Wardell Gray,
Dexter Gordon and is widely known for his work with Chet Baker
and, later, his grouping with Shelly Manne in 1955. Freeman was a
most popular and sought after artist on the West Coast and his
recordings were in great demand. Through the 60's Freeman
ventured more strongly into movie scores where he had a hand in the
soundtracks for the great screenplays Porgy and Bess and I Want To
Live, afterwhich he devoted his time to writing and publishing
various forms of music.

RUSS FREEMAN TRIO — Pacific Jazz 8 (1953) 10" **$90**; EP 4-19, EP 4-12, (1953)
$35 ea.

RUSS FREEMAN/with Richard Twardzik Trio — Pacific Jazz 1212 (1956) one side
each **$45**; *reissue* of Pacific Jazz 8.

DON FRIEDMAN

piano - born 1935 San Francisco, CA

A DAY IN THE CITY — Riverside 384/9384 (1962) **$35.**

FLASHBACK — Riverside 463/9463 (1963) **$20.**

CIRCLE WALTZ — Riverside 431/9431 (1962) **$25.**

DON FRONTIERE

SEXTET — Liberty 6002 (1956) **$40.**

TONY FRUSCELLA

trumpet - born 1927 Orangeburg, NJ died 1969

TONY FRUSCELLA — Atlantic 1220 (1956) black label **$75.**

CURTIS FULLER

trombone, composer - born 1934 Detroit, MI

Curtis first played in an Army band and returned to his hometown of
Detroit to join with many fine musicians before moving to New York
City in 1957. Subsequently he worked with many major groups of the
time including the Jazztet and The Jazz Messengers on and off until
1965. His flexibility on the trombone permitted him to continue to
work with a variety of groups and produce recordings under his own
name, many to be found on the Savoy and Blue Note labels. Fuller
teamed up with Count Basie for a few years and continues to perform
to date and is still regarded as a highly respected musician.

NEW TROMBONE/with Sonny Red — Prestige 7107 (1957) yellow label **$60**;
reissued Prestige 7107 (1964) blue label with logo on right side **$25.**

THE OPENER/with Hank Mobley — Blue Note 1567 (1957) with NY address on
label **$60**; with A Division of Liberty on label **$20.**

BONES AND BARI/with Sonny Clark — Blue Note 1572 (1957) with NY address on
label **$45**; with A Division of Liberty on label **$20.**

CURTIS FULLER — Vol 3/with Art Farmer — Blue Note 1583 (1958) with NY
address on label **$60**; with A Division of Liberty on label **$20.**

BLUES-ETTE/with Benny Golson — Savoy 12141 (1958) maroon label **$45.**

JAZZTET/with Lee Morgan — Savoy 12143 (1958) maroon label **$45.**

48

MAGINATION/with Benny Golson — Savoy 12144 (1959) maroon label **$40**.

URTIS FULLER — Savoy 12151 (1959) maroon label **$35**.

MAGES — Savoy 12164 (1960) maroon label **$35**.

LIDING EASY/with Hank Mobley — United Artists 4041/5041 (1959) red label **$60**.

OSS OF THE SOUL STREAM TROMBONE/with Yusef Lateef — Warwick 2038 (1961) **$50**.

HE MAGNIFICENT TROMBONE/with Les Spann — Epic 16013/17013 (1961) **$45**.

OUTH AMERICAN COOKIN'/with Zoot Sims — Epic 16020/17020 (1961) **$45**.

AZZ CONFERENCE ABROAD/with Phil Woods — Smash 27034/67034 (1961) **$35**.

WITH RED GARLAND — New Jazz 8277 (1961) **$35**.

ND HAMP HAWES WITH FRENCH HORNS — Status 8305 (1965) **$25**.

AZZ... IT'S MAGIC — Regent 6055 (1958) green label **$45**.

GIL FULLER
composer - born 1920 Los Angeles, CA

ND THE MONTEREY JAZZ FESTIVAL ORCHESTRA/with Dizzy Gillespie — Pacific Jazz 93 (1965) **$30**.

DICK GARCIA
guitar - born 1931 New York City, NY

MESSAGE FROM GARCIA/with Gene Quill — Dawn 1106 (1956) **$65**; *reissued* Seeco 428 (1960) **$30**.

RED GARLAND
piano - born 1923 Dallas, TX

A very popular and influential piano player who began with the Miles Davis Group in the late 50's. He recorded extensively with Davis as well as under his own group name during the same period. The Red Garland Quintet consisted of notable musicians such as the great John Coltrane, Donald Byrd and Paul Chambers. In the mid-60's Garland returned to his hometown of Dallas where, except for local club work and only a couple of recordings, he remained. He began appearing and recording to great enthusiastic response from his audiences. Pay particular attention to LPs All Morning Long and Soul Junction which both represent Garland at his best.

A GARLAND OF RED — Prestige 7064 (1956) yellow label **$60**; *reissued* Prestige 7064 (1964) blue label with logo on right side **$30**.

RED GARLAND'S PIANO — Prestige 7086 (1957) yellow label **$60**; *reissued* Prestige 7086 (1964) blue label with logo on right side **$30**.

GROOVY — Prestige 7113 (1957) yellow label **$50**; *reissued* Prestige 7113 (1964) blue label with logo on right side **$30**.

ALL MORNING LONG/with John Coltrane and Donald Byrd — Prestige 7130 (1958) yellow label **$80**; *reissued* Prestige 7130 (1964) blue label with logo on right side **$40**.

SOUL JUNCTION/with John Coltrane and Donald Byrd — Prestige 7181 (1960) yellow label **$80**; *reissued* Prestige 7181 (1965) blue label with logo on right side **$40**.

HIGH PRESSURE/with John Coltrane and Donald Byrd — Prestige 7209 (1962) yellow label **$70**; *reissued* Prestige 7209 (1965) blue label with logo on right side **$30**.

DIG IT/with John Coltrane and Donald Byrd — Prestige 7229 (1962) yellow label **$70**; *reissued* Prestige 7229 (1965) blue label with logo on right side **$30**.

MANTECA — Prestige 7139 (1958) yellow label **$45**; *reissued* Prestige 7139 (1964) blue label with logo on right side **$25**.

ALL KINDS OF WEATHER — Prestige 7148 (1959) yellow label **$40**; *reissued* Prestige 7148 (1964) blue label with logo on right side **$25**.

RED IN BLUESVILLE — Prestige 7157 (1959) yellow label **$40**; *reissued* Prestige 7157 (1964) blue label with logo on right side **$25**.

AT THE PRELUDE — Prestige 7170 (1959) yellow label **$35**; *reissued* Prestige 7170 (1964) blue label with logo on right side **$25**.

ROJO — Prestige 7193 (1961) yellow label **$35**; *reissued* Prestige 7193 (1965) blue label with logo on right side **$25**.

WHEN THERE WERE GRAY SKIES — Prestige 7258 (1963) yellow label **$35**; *reissued* Prestige 7258 (1965) blue label with logo on right side **$20**.

CAN'T SEE FOR LOOKING — Prestige 7276 (1963) yellow label **$35**.

HALLELOO' Y'ALL — Prestige 7288 (1964) yellow label **$30**; *reissued* Prestige 7288 (1965) blue label with logo on right side **$25**.

SOUL BURNIN' — Prestige 7307 (1964) blue label with logo on right side **$30**.

THE NEARNESS OF YOU — Jazzland 62/962 (1962) **$25**.

BRIGHT AND BREEZY — Jazzland 48/948 (1961) **$25**.

SOLAR — Jazzland 73/973 (1962) **$25**.

RED'S GOOD GROOVE/with Pepper Adams — Jazzland 87/987 (1962) **$40**.

PLUS EDDIE LOCKJAW DAVIS — Moodsville 1 (1960) **$45**.

RED ALONE — Moodsville 3 (1960) **$30**.

ALONE WITH THE BLUES — Moodsville 10 (1960) **$30**.

SUGAN — Status 8304 (1965) **$30**.

LITTLE DARLIN' — Status 8314 (1965) **$25**.

ERROLL GARNER
piano, composer - born 1923 Pittsburgh, PA died 1977

It could be because he was self-taught and never learned to read music that Erroll Garner's style was very personal and quite recognizable. Throughout his career he made many recordings, composed several pieces and made radio and television appearances resulting in him being one of the most popular and sought-after jazz artists in the world. Garner's best known composition is Misty which was used as the theme song for a motion picture.

AT THE PIANO — Savoy 15000 (1950) 10" **$75.**

AT THE PIANO — Savoy 15001 (1950) 10" **$75.**

AT THE PIANO — Savoy 15002 (1950) 10" **$75.**

AT THE PIANO — Savoy 15004 (1950) 10" **$75.**

AT THE PIANO — Savoy 15026 (1951) 10" **$70.**

ERROLL GARNER - Vol 1 — Savoy 12002 (1955) maroon label **$35.**

ERROLL GARNER - Vol 2 — Savoy 12003 (1955) maroon label **$35.**

ERROLL GARNER/with Billy Taylor — Savoy 12008 (1955) maroon label **$40.**

OVERTURE TO DAWN — Blue Note 5007 (1952) 10" **$65.**

OVERTURE TO DAWN - Vol 2 — Blue Note 5008 (1952) 10" **$65.**

OVERTURE TO DAWN - Vol 3 — Blue Note 5014 (1953) 10" **$65.**

OVERTURE TO DAWN - Vol 4 — Blue Note 5015 (1953) 10" **$65.**

OVERTURE TO DAWN - Vol 5 — Blue Note 5016 (1953) 10" **$65.**

RHAPSODY — Atlantic 109 (1950) 10" **$60.**

PIANO SOLOS — Atlantic 112 (1951) 10" **$60.**

PASSPORT TO FAME — Atlantic 128 (1952) 10" **$50.**

PIANO SOLOS — Atlantic 138 (1952) 10"; EP 506, EP 507, EP 508, EP 509 (1952) titled At The Piano **$10 ea.**

GREATEST GARNER — Atlantic 1227 (1956) **$40;** EP 574 (1956) **$10.**

GARNERING — EmArcy 26016 (1954) 10" **$50;** *reissued* EmArcy 36026 (1955) **$35.**

GONE WITH GARNER — EmArcy 26042 (1954) 10" **$50.**

CONTRASTS — EmArcy 36001 (1955) **$35.**

ERROLL — EmArcy 36069 (1956) **$35.**

PIANO STYLIST — King 265-17 (1954) 10" **$50;** *reissued* King 540 (1958).

PIANO VARIATIONS — King 540 (1958) **$35;** *reissue* of King 265-17 (1954).

ERROLL GARNER - Vol 1 — Dial 205 (1950) 10" **$80.**

GASLIGHT — Dial 902 (1950) **$50.**

PIANO MAGIC — Roost 10 (1952) 10" **$55.**

GIANTS OF THE PIANO/with Art Tatum — Roost 2213 (1956) one side each **$45.**

JAZZ PIANO — Grand Award 33-321 (1956) **$40.**

EARLY ERROLL — Jazztone 1269 (1957) **$40.**

SINGIN' KAY STARR/SWINGIN' ERROLL GARNER — Modern 1203 (1956) **$45;** *reissued* Crown 5003 (1957) one side each with liner notes on cover **$40.**

INFORMAL PIANO IMPROVISATIONS — Baronet 109 (1961) **$25.**

ERROLL GARNER — Ron-Lette 15 (1958) **$30.**

DREAMSTREE — ABC Paramount 365 (1961) **$25.**

CLOSEUP — ABC Paramount 395 (1961) **$25.**

AT THE PIANO — Mercury 25117 (1951) 10" **$50.**

GONE WITH GARNER — Mercury 25157 (1951) 10" **$50.**

AT THE PIANO — Mercury 20009 (1950) **$50.**

MAMBO MOVES GARNER — Mercury 20055 (1954) **$35.**

SOLITAIRE — Mercury 20063 (1954) **$35.**

AFTERNOON OF AN ELF — Mercury 20090 (1955) **$35.**

PLAYS MISTY — Mercury 20662/60662 (1962) black label **$30.** (A)

NEW KIND OF LOVE — Mercury 20859/60859 (1963) **$30.**

PIANO MOODS — Columbia 6139 (1950) 10" **$60;** *reissued* Columbia 535 (1954)

GEMS — Columbia 6173 (1951) 10" **$60;** *reissued* Columbia 583 (1954) red label with Columbia in gold on top **$40;** *reissued* Columbia 583 (1956) with 3 black logos on each side **$35.**

FOR DANCING — Columbia 6259 (1951) 10" **$50;** *reissued* Columbia 667 (1955) with 3 black logos on each side **$35.**

GONE GARNER GONEST — Columbia 617 (1954) red label with Columbia in gold on top **$35;** *reissued* Columbia 617 (1955) with 3 black logos on each side **$35.**

ERROLL GARNER AT THE PIANO — Columbia 535 (1954) red label with Columbia in gold on top **$40;** *reissued* Columbia 535 (1956) with 3 black logos on each side **$35.**

GARNERLAND — Columbia 2540 (1956) 10" **$40.**

CONCERT BY THE SEA — Columbia 883 (1956) with 3 black logos on each side **$40.**

MOST HAPPY PIANO — Columbia 939 (1957) with 3 black logos on each side **$35**

SOLILOQUY — Columbia 1060 (1958) with 3 black logos on each side **$30.**

ENCORES IN HI FI — Columbia 1141 (1958) with 3 black logos on each side **$30**

ONE AND ONLY — Columbia 1452 (1960) with 3 black logos on each side **$20**

SWINGING SOLOS — Columbia 1512 (1961) with 3 black logos on each side **$20**

THE PROVOCATIVE — Columbia 1587 (1961) with 3 black logos on each side **$20**

KEVIN GAVIN
vocals

HEY! THIS IS/with Mundell Lowe — Charlie Parker 810 (1962) **$35.**

MATTHEW GEE
trombone - born 1925 Houston, TX

A fine bop-styled, driving trombonist who began playing at the age of 11. Gee teamed up with Coleman Hawkins in the early 40's. Through the 50's he performed with Dizzy Gillespie, Gene Ammons, Sonny Stitt and then Duke Ellington in 1959. Well received for his forthright trombone sound, Gee appears on many recordings on various labels but, unfortunately, has only two LPs under his own name.

JAZZ BY GEE/with Frank Foster — Riverside 12-221 (1956) white label **$85**

SOUL GROOVE/with Johnny Griffin — Atlantic 1431 (1965) logo on right side **$2**

HERB GELLER
alto sax, flute, composer - born 1928 Los Angeles, CA

Geller has been noted as a gifted musician since his early West Coast works. In the late 50's he ventured to the East Coast to perform with many bands; two being Louis Bellson and Benny Goodman. In the early 60's Geller made another big move to Europe where he has remained devoting considerable time and effort to radio orchestras with occasional recordings.

HERB GELLER QUARTET — Imperial EP 121 (1954) **$50**.

GELLER PLAYS/with Lorraine Geller — EmArcy 26045 (1954) 10" **$150**; EP 1-6078, EP 1-6079 (1954) **$50 ea.**; *reissued* EmArcy 36040 (1956).

THE GELLERS/with Lorraine Geller — EmArcy 36024 (1955) with drummer logo **$80**.

SEXTETTE — EmArcy 36040 (1956) with drummer logo **$65**; *reissue* of EmArcy 26045 (1954).

PLAYS/with Lorraine Geller — EmArcy 36045 (1956) with drummer logo **$65**; EP 1-6142 (1956) **$35**.

FIRE IN THE WEST/with Kenny Dorham — Jubilee 1044 (1957) **$60**; *reissued* Josie 3502 (1964).

STAX OF SAX/with Vic Feldman — Jubilee 1094 (1958) **$45**.

PLAYS GYPSY/with Thad Jones — Atco 33-109 (1959) **$35**.

ALTO SAXOPHONE — Josie 3502 (1964) **$25**; *reissue* of Jubilee 1044 (1957).

LORRAINE GELLER
piano - born 1928 Portland, OR

LORRAINE GELLER/with Leroy Vinnegar — Dot 3174/25174 (1958) **$45**.

EDDIE GETZ
alto sax

QUINTETTE/with Don Momblow — MGM 3462 (1957) **$45**.

STAN GETZ
tenor sax - born 1927 Philadelphia, PA

Getz' professional endeavors began when he was only 16 years old and quickly led him into working with bands like those of Jack Teagarden, Stan Kenton, Benny Goodman and, in the late 40's, Woody Herman as one of the original Four Brothers. The latter gained Getz vast recognition and credited him as a forerunner of 'cool' jazz. In result, he was known then and is now for his warm sound and lyrical style and enjoyed several popular recordings in the 50's with his own group. He spent the late 50's and early 60's in Europe, entering into a new era of popularity with his close association with Bossa Nova and other Latin American styles.

IN RETROSPECT — Dale 21 (1951) 10" **$200**, EP 200, EP 201 (1949) **$50 ea**.

BILLIE AND STAN/with Billie Holiday — Dale 25 (1951) 10" **$200**.

HIGHLIGHTS IN MODERN JAZZ/with Wardell Gray — Seeco 7 (1954) 10" one side each **$150**.

ALL STAR SERIES/with Zoot Sims and Al Cohn — Savoy 9004 (1953) 10" **200**.

STAN GETZ/with Al Cohn, Zoot Sims, Eager Allen and Brew Moore — Prestige 102 (1952) 10" **$200**; EP 1309 (1949) **$50**; *reissued* Prestige 7022 (1956).

STAN GETZ — Prestige 104 (1952) 10" **$150**; EP 1311 (1950) **$50**; *reissued* Prestige 7002 (1955).

GETZ-KONITZ/with Lee Konitz — Prestige 108 (1952) **$150**; EP 1310 (1949) **$50**.

QUARTETS — Prestige 7002 (1955) yellow label **$85**; *reissued* Prestige 7002 (1964) blue label **$35**; *reissue* in part of Prestige 104.

THE BROTHERS/with Al Cohn, Zoot Sims, Eager Allen and Brew Moore — Prestige 7022 (1956) yellow label **$85**; *reissued* Prestige 7252 (1963) yellow label **$45**; *reissued* Prestige 7252 (1965) blue label **$30**.

EARLY STAN — Prestige 7255 (1963) yellow label **$45**.

GREATEST HITS — Prestige 7256 (1963) yellow label **$45**; *reissued* Prestige 7256 (1965) blue label **$25**.

STAN GETZ - Vol 1 — Roost 402 (1951) 10" **$150**; EP 301; EP 306 (1951) **$50 ea.**; *reissued* Roost 2207 (1958).

SWEDISH ALL STARS — Roost 404 (1951) 10" **$200**; EP 302, EP 304 (1951) **$60 ea.**

JAZZ AT STORYVILLE — Roost 407 (1951) 10" **$125**; EP 312 (1951) **$40**; *reissued* Roost 2209 (1958) **$45**.

JAZZ AT STORYVILLE - Vol 2 — Roost 411 (1951) 10" **$125**; *reissued* in part Roost 2209 and 2225 (1958).

JAZZ AT STORYVILLE - Vol 3 — Roost 420 (1952) 10" **$125**; *reissued* Roost 2225 (1958) **$45**.

CHAMBER MUSIC — Roost 417 (1952) 10" **$125**.

SPLIT KICK — Roost 423 (1952) 10" **$100**.

THE SOUNDS — Roost 2207 (1958) **$45**; *reissue* of Roost 402.

GETZ AGE — Roost 2258 (1963) **$30**.

THE GREATEST OF — Roost 2249 (1963) **$35**.

THE STAN GETZ YEARS — Roost SRK103 (1964) 2 LP box set **$45**.

MODERN WORLD — Roost 2255 (1963) **$30**.

MOONLIGHT IN VERMONT — Roost 2251 (1963) **$30**.

THE ARTISTRY OF — Clef 143 (1953) 10" **$125**; EP 189, EP 188 (1953) **$45 ea.**; *reissued* in part Norgran 1042.

PLAYS — Clef 137 (1953) 10" **$125**; EP 149, EP 155 (1953) **$45 ea.**; *reissued* Norgran 1042 (1955) **$80**; *reissued* Verve 8133 (1957) **$60**.

STAN GETZ — Norgran 4 (1953) 10" **$200.**

INTERPRETATIONS/QUINTET — Norgran 1000 (1954) **$100**; EP 11, EP 12 (1953) **$40 ea.**

INTERPRETATIONS/QUINTET - Vol 2 — Norgran 1008 (1954) **$100**; EP 54 (1953) **$40.**

INTERPRETATIONS/QUINTET - Vol 3 — Norgran 1029 (1954) **$100**; EP 132; EP 133 (1953) **$40 ea.**

WEST COAST JAZZ — Norgran 1032 (1955) **$80**; EP 136, EP 137, EP 138 (1955) **$25 ea.**; *reissued* Verve 8028 (1957) with Verve Records, Inc. at bottom of label **$60**; with MGM at bottom of label **$35.**

STAN GETZ '57 — Norgran 1087 (1956) **$75**; EP 108 (1953) **$55**; *reissued* Verve 8029 (1957) with Verve Records, Inc. at bottom of label **$60**; with MGM at bottom of label **$35.**

MORE WEST COAST JAZZ — Norgran 1088 (1956) **$80**; *reissued* Verve 8177 (1957) with Verve Records, Inc. at botton of label **$60**; with MGM at bottom of label **$35.**

AT THE SHRINE — Norgran 2000-2 (1954) 2 LP box set with booklet **$200**; EP 2000-6 (1954) 6 record box set **$100**; *reissued* Verve 8188-2 (1957) 2 LP box set with booklet and Verve Records, Inc. at bottom of label **$125.**

CAL TJADER/STAN GETZ SEXTET — Fantasy 3266/8005 (1958) mono is on red vinyl, stereo is on blue vinyl **$45.**

STAN GETZ/with Max Roach — American Recording Society 407 (1956) **$70.**

INTIMATE PORTRAIT — American Recording Society 428 (1957) **$70**; *reissued* Verve 8213 (1958).

STAN GETZ — American Recording Society 443 (1957) **$65.**

GROOVIN' HIGH/with Wardell Gray — Modern 1202 (1956) **$60**; *reissued* Crown 5002 with liner notes on cover (1957) **$45.**

LONG ISLAND SOUND — New Jazz 8214 (1959) **$35**; *reissue* of Prestige 7002.

THE SAXES OF/with Charlie Parker — Jazztone 1240 (1957) **$45.**

PAIR OF KINGS/with Horace Silver — Baronet 102 (1962) **$25**; *reissue* of Roost days.

THE MELODIC — Metro 501 (1965) **$20.**

RHYTHMS/with Horace Silver — Blue Ribbon 8012 (1961) **$20**; *reissue* of Roost days.

MICKEY ONE (Soundtrack) — MGM 4312 (1965) 2 page picture insert and MGM in rainbow colors on black label **$20.**

COOL SOUND — Verve 8200 (1957) with Verve Records, Inc. at bottom of label **$60**; with MGM at bottom of label **$35**; *reissue* of American Recording Society 407.

IN STOCKHOLM — Verve 8213 (1958) with Verve Records, Inc. at bottom of label **$60**; with MGM at bottom of label **$35**; *reissue* of American Recording Society 428.

GETZ MEETS MULLIGAN IN HI FI — Verve 8249/6003 (1958) with Verve Records, Inc. at bottom of label **$60**; *reissued* Verve 8535 with MGM at bottom of label **$35.**

STAN MEETS CHET/with Chet Baker — Verve 8263 (1958) with Verve Records, Inc. at bottom of label **$65**; with MGM at bottom of label **$35.**

AND THE OSCAR PETERSON TRIO — Verve 8251 (1958) with Verve Records, Inc. at bottom of label **$50**; with MGM at bottom of label **$30.**

THE STEAMER — Verve 8294 (1959) with Verve Records, Inc. at bottom of label **$60**; with MGM at bottom of label **$35.**

AWARD WINNER — Verve 8296 (1959) with Verve Records, Inc. at bottom of label **$45**; with MGM at bottom of label **$30.**

IMPORTED FROM EUROPE — Verve 8331 (1959) with Verve Records, Inc. at bottom of label **$50**; with MGM at bottom of label **$30.**

WITH GERRY MULLIGAN AND OSCAR PETERSON — Verve 8348 (1960) with Verve Records, Inc. at bottom of label **$40**; with MGM at bottom of label **$30.**

AT LARGE — Verve 8393-2/68393-2 (1960) 2 LPs with Verve Records, Inc. at bottom of label **$60**; with MGM at bottom of label **$40.**

COOL VELVET — Verve 8379/68379 (1960) with Verve Records, Inc. at bottom of label **$40**; with MGM at bottom of label **$30.**

SOFT SWING — Verve 8321 (1959) with Verve Records, Inc. at bottom of label **$40**; with MGM at bottom of label **$30.**

RECORDED FALL 1961/with Bob Brookmeyer — Verve 8418/68418 (1961) with MGM at bottom of label **$35.**

FOCUS — Verve 8412/68412 (1962) with MGM at bottom of label **$35.**

AT THE OPERA HOUSE/with J.J. Johnson — Verve 8265 (1958) with Verve Records, Inc. on bottom of label **$65**; *reissued* Verve 8490/68490 (1962) with MGM at bottom of label **$35.** (A)

JAZZ SAMBA/with Charlie Byrd — Verve 8432/68432 (1962) with MGM at bottom of label **$25.**

BIG BAND BOSSA NOVA — Verve 8494/68494 (1962) with MGM at bottom of label **$25.**

GETZ/GILBERTO/with Joao Gilberto — Verve 8545/68545 (1963) with MGM at bottom of label **$20.**

WITH GUEST ARTIST LAURINDO ALMEIDA — Verve 8665/68665 (1963) with MGM at bottom of label **$20.**

REFLECTIONS — Verve 8554/68554 (1963) with MGM at bottom of label **$20.**

AU GO GO — Verve 8600/68600 (1964) with MGM at bottom of label **$20.**

JAZZ SAMBA ENCORE — Verve 8523/68523 (1963) with MGM at bottom of labe **$25.**

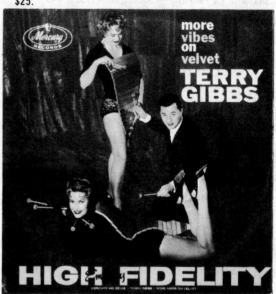

TERRY GIBBS
vibes, percussion, composer, leader - born 1924
Brooklyn, NY

QUARTET — Brunswick 58055 (1954) 10" **$75**; EP 71026, EP 71027 (1954) **$25 ea.**

TERRY — Brunswick 54009 (1954) black label with silver lettering **$75.**

TERRY GIBBS — EmArcy 36047 (1955) **$45**; EP 1-6137 (1955) with drummer logo **$20.**

VIBES ON VELVET — EmArcy 36064 (1955) with drummer logo **$40.**

MALLETS A PLENTY — EmArcy 36075 (1956) with drummer logo **$45.**

SWINGIN' — EmArcy 36103 (1956) with drummer logo **$40.**

TERRY DIGS THE DUKE — EmArcy 36128 (1957) with drummer logo **$40.**

MORE VIBES ON VELVET — EmArcy 36148 (1958) with Mercury logo **$35.**

LAUNCHING A NEW BAND — Mercury 20440/60112 (1959) **$30.**

EXPLOSION — Mercury 20704/60704 (1962) **$30.**

A JAZZ BAND BALL — Mode 123 (1957) **$45**; *reissued* Interlude 506/1006 (1959).

VIBRATIONS — Interlude 506/1006 (1959) **$35**; *reissue* of Mode 123.

JEWISH MELODIES IN JAZZTIME — Mercury 20812/60812 (1963) **$20.**

SWING IS HERE — Verve 2134/6140 (1960) with Verve Records, Inc. on bottom o label **$35**; with MGM on bottom of label **$20.**

CAN CAN — Verve 2136/6145 (1960) with Verve Records, Inc. on bottom of label **$35**; with MGM on bottom of label **$20**.

LIVE AT THE SUMMIT — Verve 2151/62151 (1961) with MGM on bottom of label **$25**.

STRAIGHT AHEAD — Verve 8496/68496 (1962) with MGM on bottom of label **$25**.

HOOTENANNY MY WAY — Time 52105/2105 (1963) **$45**; *reissued* Mainstream 56048/6048 (1965).

EL NUTTO — Limelight 82005/86005 (1964) **$20**.

TAKE IT FROM ME — Impulse 58 (1964) orange label **$20**. (A)

LATINO — Roost 2260 (1965) **$20**.

IT'S TIME WE MET — Mainstream 56048/6048 (1965) **$20**.

ASTRUD GILBERTO
vocals - born 1940 Bahia, Brazil

THE ASTRUD GILBERTO ALBUM — Verve 8608/68608 (1965) with MGM on bottom of label **$10**.

THE SHADOW OF YOUR SMILE — Verve 8629/68629 (1965) with MGM on bottom of label **$10**.

DIZZY GILLESPIE
trumpet, vocals, composer, leader - born 1917 Cheraw, SC

Dizzy Gillespie is one of the greatest of innovators and communicators of jazz who gained reputation and experience with many name bands in the 30's. New York City and the next decade displayed him and several other musicians playing in ways that demonstrated increasing sophistication and ability. This style of playing continued to evolve and became known as "be-bop" and Gillespie's importance through the emergence and continued evolution of be-bop is well documented.

In the decades following these very important contributions, "Diz" has continued to break new ground in many aspects, international tours for the State Department and the use of Latin instruments and rhythms to name a couple. He has also continued to record and tour with groups of the finest musical artists and his importance to jazz is profound.

DIZZY GILLESPIE MODERN TRUMPETS — Dial 212 (1952) 10" **$100**.

ORCHESTRA — Allegro 4023 (1953) 10" **$45**.

PLAYS — Allegro 3017 (1952) 10" **$45**.

DIZZY GILLESPIE — Allegro 3083 (1953) 10" **$45**; *reissued* Allegro 1593 (1957) **$25**.

HORN OF PLENTY/with Don Byas — Blue Note 5017 (1952) 10" **$175**.

DIZZY GILLESPIE-STAN GETZ SEXTET — Norgran 2 (1953) 10" **$200**; EP 3, EP 4 (1953) **$45 ea.**; *reissued* Norgran 1050 (1956) **$75**; *reissued* Verve 8141 (1957) **$50**.

DIZZY GILLESPIE-STAN GETZ SEXTET — Norgran 18 (1953) 10" **$200**; EP 32 (1953) **$45**; *reissued* Norgran 1050 (1956) **$75**; *reissued* Verve 8141 (1957) **$50**.

AFRO DIZZY — Norgran 1003 (1954) **$65**; *reissued* Verve 8191 (1957) **$50**.

DIZ BIG BAND — Norgran 1023 (1955) **$75**; EP 114, EP 115 (1954) **$35 ea.**; *reissued* Norgran 1090 (1956) **$60**; *reissued* Verve 8178 (1957) **$45**.

JAZZ RECITAL — Norgran 1083 (1956) **$80**; *reissued* Verve 8173 (1957) **$50**.

WORLD STATESMAN — Norgran 1084 (1956) **$75**; *reissued* Verve 8174 (1957) **$45**.

WITH STRINGS — Clef 136 (1953) 10" **$120**; EP 153 (1952) **$25**; *reissued* Verve 8015 (1957).

ROY AND DIZ/with Roy Eldridge — Clef 641 (1955) **$75**; EP 291, EP 292, EP 293, EP 294 (1954) **$25 ea.**

ROY AND DIZ - Vol 2/with Roy Eldridge — Clef 671 (1955) **$75**.

THE TRUMPET KINGS/with Roy Eldridge — Clef 730 (1956) **$70**; *reissued* Verve 8109 (1957) with Verve Records, Inc. at bottom of label **$60**; with MGM at bottom of label **$30**.

TRUMPET BATTLE/with Roy Eldridge — Clef 731 (1956) **$70**; *reissued* Verve 8110 (1957) with Verve Records, Inc. at bottom of label **$60**; with MGM at bottom of label **$30**.

DIZZY GILLESPIE/with Joe Carroll — Dee Gee 1000 (1951) 10" **$150**; EP 4000, EP 4004, EP 4003 (1951) **$45 ea.**

PLAYS/with Johnny Richards — Discovery 3013 (1950) 10" **$125**; EP 13 (1950) **$35**.

DIZZY GILLESPIE - Vol 1/with Don Byas — Atlantic 138 (1952) 10" **$200**; *reissued* Atlantic 1257 (1957).

DIZZY GILLESPIE - Vol 2/with Don Byas — Atlantic 142 (1952) 10" **$200**; EP 521, EP 514 (1952) **$50**; *reissued* Atlantic 1257 (1957).

DIZZY AT HOME AND ABROAD — Atlantic 1257 (1957) black label **$80**; *reissued* Atlantic 1257 (1959) with logo on right side **$35**; *reissue* of Atlantic 138 and 142.

GAILLARD AND GILLESPIE — Ultraphonic 50273 (1958) **$30**.

BIG BAND JAZZ — American Recording Society 423 (1955) **$70**.

DIZZY GILLESPIE — American Recording Society 405 (1955) **$70**.

DIZZY IN PARIS — Contemporary 2504 (1953) 10" **$125**.

DIZZY GILLESPIE — Ron-Lette 11 (1958) **$30**; *reissue* of Allegro 3083.

DIZZY OVER PARIS — Roost 414 (1953) 10" **$175**; *reissued* Roost 2214 (1957).

THE BEGINNING DIZ 'N BIRD — Roost SK106 (1959) 2 LP box set **$75**.

DIZ 'N BIRD IN CONCERT — Roost 2234 (1959) **$45**.

CONCERT IN PARIS — Roost 2214 (1957) **$60**; *reissue* of Roost 414.

GROOVIN' HIGH/with Charlie Parker and Sonny Stitt — Savoy 12020 (1955) maroon label **$45**.

THE CHAMP — Savoy 12047 (1956) maroon label **$40**.

DIZZY GILLESPIE STORY — Savoy 12110 (1957) maroon label **$40.**

SCHOOL DAYS — Regent 6043 (1957) green label **$45;** *reissue* of Dee Gee 1000.

DIZZIER AND DIZZIER — RCA Victor 1009 (1954) silver label dog on top **$50;** EP 432 (1954) **$25.**

THE GREATEST — RCA Victor 2398 (1961) dog on top **$40.**

AND HIS ORCHESTRA — Gene Norman Presents 4 (1949) 10" **$100;** EP 1, EP 2, EP 3, EP 4 (1949) **$25 ea.;** *reissued* Gene Norman Presents 23 (1957) **$45.**

A HANDFUL OF MODERN JAZZ — Baronet 105 (1961) **$25.**

JAZZ ON THE FRENCH RIVIERA/with Leo Wright — Philips 200-048/600-048 (1962) **$25.**

NEW WAVE!/with Charlie Ventura — Philips 200-070/600-070 (1963) **$25.**

SOMETHING OLD, SOMETHING NEW/with James Moody — Philips 200-091/600-091 (1963) **$25.**

AND THE DOUBLE SIX OF PARIS/with Bud Powell — Philips 200-106/600-106 (1964) **$35.**

GOES HOLLYWOOD/with James Moody — Philips 200-123/600-123 (1964) **$25.**

COOL WORLD/with James Moody — Philips 200-138/600-138 (1964) **$35.**

JAMBO CARIBE/with James Moody — Limelight 86007/82007 (1964) fold out cover **$25.**

THE NEW CONTINENT — Limelight 86022/82022 (1965) fold out cover **$25.**

DIZZY IN GREECE — Verve 8017 (1957) with Verve Records, Inc. at bottom of label **$60;** with MGM at bottom of label **$30.**

AND STUFF SMITH — Verve 8214 (1958) with Verve Records, Inc. at bottom of label **$50;** with MGM at bottom of label **$25.**

BIRK'S WORK/with Lee Morgan — Verve 8222 (1958) with Verve Records, Inc. at bottom of label **$50;** with MGM at bottom of label **$25.**

DUETS/with Sonny Rollins and Sonny Stitt — Verve 8260 (1958) with Verve Records, Inc. at bottom of label **$70;** with MGM at bottom of label **$45.**

SUNNY SIDE UP/with Sonny Rollins and Sonny Stitt — Verve 8262 (1958) with Verve Records, Inc. at bottom of label **$75;** with MGM at bottom of label **$45.**

JAZZ FROM PARIS/with Django Reinhardt — Verve 8015 (1957) with Verve Records, Inc. at bottom of label **$60;** with MGM at bottom of label **$30** - this LP is a *reissue* of Clef 136 only on Dizzy's side of LP.

FOR MUSICIANS ONLY/with Stan Getz and Sonny Stitt — Verve 8198 (1958) with Verve Records, Inc. at bottom of label **$75;** with MGM at bottom of label **$45.**

MANTECIA — Verve 8208 (1958) with Verve Records, Inc. at bottom of label **$40;** with MGM at bottom of label **$25;** *reissue* of Norgran 1003 and Verve 8191.

EBULLIENT — Verve 8328/6068 (1959) with Verve Records, Inc. at bottom of label **$40;** with MGM at bottom of label **$25.**

HAVE TRUMPET WITH EXCITE — Verve 8313/6047 (1959) with Verve Records, Inc. at bottom of label **$45;** with MGM at bottom of label **$25.**

GREATEST TRUMPET OF THEM ALL — Verve 8352/6117 (1960) with Verve Records, Inc. at bottom of label **$40;** with MGM at bottom of label **$25.**

PORTRAIT OF DUKE ELLINGTON — Verve 8386/68386 (1960) with Verve Records, Inc. at bottom of label **$40;** with MGM at bottom of label **$20.**

GILLESPIANA — Verve 8394/68394 (1961) with Verve Records, Inc. at bottom of label **$40;** with MGM at bottom of label **$25.**

PERCEPTIONS/with J.J. Johnson — Verve 8411/68411 (1961) with MGM at bottom of label **$25.**

ELECTRIFYING EVENING — Verve 8401/68401 (1962) with MGM at bottom of label **$25.**

CARNEGIE HALL CONCERT — Verve 8423/68423 (1962) with MGM at bottom of label **$25.**

ESSENTIAL — Verve 8566/68566 (1964) with MGM at bottom of label **$20.**

JOHN GILMORE
tenor sax - born 1931 Summit, MS

Beginning in the late 50's Gilmore was best known as a player of wide range and style with the group Sun Ra. He has remained an important member of that group with occasional periods of outside work, including Art Blakey in 1964 and several other recordings of interest in addition to the many with Sun Ra.

BLOWING IN FROM CHICAGO/with Clifford Jordan — Blue Note 1549 (1957) with NY address on label **$80.**

JIMMY GIUFFRE
tenor, baritone saxes, clarinet, woodwinds, composer born 1921 Dallas, TX

Giuffre first performed with various name bands through the 40's including Woody Herman in 1949, for whom he wrote Four Brothers. A highly respected clarinetist through the 50's, Giuffre has continued to study composing, arranging, various instruments and to teach at many levels throughout his career. In the 60's he acquired an interest in a more abstract approach to jazz and through the 60's had several phases of avant-garde to mainstream groups.

JIMMY GIUFFRE — Capitol H549 (1954) 10" **$100;** EP 1-549 (1955) **$25;** *reissued* Capitol T549 (1955) green label **$75.**

TANGENTS IN JAZZ — Capitol T634 (1955) green label **$85.**

CLARINET — Atlantic 1238 (1956) black label **$50;** *reissued* Atlantic 1238 with logo on right side **$30.**

JIMMY GIUFFRE 3 — Atlantic 1254 (1957) black label **$50;** EP 604 (1957) **$25;** *reissued* Atlantic 1254 with logo on right side **$30.**

MUSIC MAN — Atlantic 1276 (1958) black label **$45;** EP 610 (1958) **$20;** *reissued* Atlantic 1276 with logo on right side **$25.**

TRAV'LIN' LIGHT/with Bob Brookmeyer — Atlantic 1282 (1958) black label **$65;** *reissued* Atlantic 1282 with logo on right side **$30.**

FOUR BROTHERS SOUND/with Bob Brookmeyer — Atlantic 1295 (1959) black label **$60;** *reissued* Atlantic 1295 with logo on right side **$30.**

WESTERN SUITE — Atlantic 1330 (1959) with logo on right side **$35.**

SEVEN PIECES/with Jim Hall — Verve 8307/6039 (1959) with Verve Records, Inc. at bottom of label **$75;** with MGM at bottom of label **$30.**

HERB ELLIS MEETS JIMMY GIUFFRE — Verve 8311/6045 (1959) with Verve Records, Inc. at bottom of label **$75;** with MGM at bottom of lebel **$35.**

LEE KONITZ MEETS JIMMY GIUFFRE — Verve 8335/6073 (1959) with Verve Records, Inc. at bottom of label **$75;** with MGM at bottom of label **$35.**

THE EASY WAY — Verve 8337/6095 (1959) with Verve Records, Inc. at bottom of label **$60;** with MGM at bottom of label **$25.**

AD LIB — Verve 8361/6130 (1959) with Verve Records, Inc. at bottom of label **$60;** with MGM at bottom of label **$25.**

IN PERSON — Verve 8387/68387 (1961) with Verve Records, Inc. at bottom of label **$35.**

THESIS — Verve 8402/68402 (1962) with MGM at bottom of label **$35.**

PIECE FOR CLARINET AND ORCHESTRA — Verve 8395/68395 (1961) with Verve Records, Inc. at bottom of label **$35.**

FUSION — Verve 8397/68397 (1961) with Verve Records, Inc. at bottom of label **$35.**

FREE FALL — Columbia 1964/8764 (1963) with one white logo on each side **$25.**

JOHN GLASEL
trumpet - born 1930 New York City, NY

JAZZ SESSION/with Dick Garcia — ABC Paramount 165 (1957) **$45.**

BRASSTET/with Louis Mucci — Jazz Unlimited 1002 (1960) **$30.**

take a number from 1 to 10

DON GOLDIE
trumpet - born 1930 Newark, NJ

BRILLANT/with Eddie Higgins — Argo 4010 (1960) $45.

TRUMPET CALIENTE/with Leo Wright — Argo 708 (1962) $35.

TRUMPET EXODUS — Verve 8475/68475 (1962) with MGM at bottom of label $35.

BENNY GOLSON
tenor sax, composer, arranger - born 1929 Philadelphia, PA

Golson began playing in well known bands in the early 50's where he soon demonstrated his writing and arranging skills. He went on to work with Dizzy Gillespie in the late 50's and further to co-lead the Jazztet with Art Farmer in the early 60's. Golson's work then took him to Europe during the mid-60's and on his return to the U.S. he became involved in recording studios doing considerable commercial television and radio work in the Los Angeles area. Golson is still a widely known and well respected musician to date.

NEW YORK SCENE/with Art Farmer — Contemporary 3552 (1957) yellow label $60.

THE MODERN TOUCH/with Kenny Dorham — Riverside 12-256 (1957) with Bill Grauer Pro. on label $55; *reissued* Jazzland 85/985 (1962).

THE OTHER SIDE OF/with Curtis Fuller — Riverside 12-290 (1958) with Bill Grauer Pro. on label $45.

REUNION — Jazzland 85/985 (1962) $35.

GONE WITH GOLSON/with Curtis Fuller — New Jazz 8235 (1959) $45.

GROOVIN' WITH/with Curtis Fuller — New Jazz 8220 (1959) $45.

GETTIN' WITH IT/with Curtis Fuller — New Jazz 8248 (1960) $40.

TAKE A NUMBER FROM 1 TO 10 — Argo 681 (1961) $35.

FREE — Argo 716 (1962) $35.

AND THE PHILADELPHIANS/with Lee Morgan — United Artists 4020/5020 (1959) red label $50.

POP + JAZZ = SWING/with Wayne Shorter — Audio Fidelity 1978/5978 (1962) $30.

TURNING POINT/with Wynton Kelly — Mercury 20801/60801 (1963) black label $35.

STOCKHOLM SOJOURN — Prestige 7361 (1965) blue label with logo on right side $25.

PAUL GONSALVES
tenor sax - born 1920 Boston, MA died 1974

The recognition Gonsalves gained in the early 40's was enhanced when he teamed up with Count Basie a few years later. He then moved on to begin a long association with Duke Ellington in the early 50's which continued, with many recordings and tours, until a few years before his death in 1974.

COOKIN'/with Clark Terry — Argo 626 (1957) $45.

GETTIN' TOGETHER/with Nat Adderley — Jazzland 36/936 (1960) $35.

CLEOPATRA FEELIN' JAZZY — Impulse 41 (1963) orange label $30.

SALT & PEPPER/with Sonny Stitt — Impulse 52 (1963) orange label $35.

TELL IT THE WAY IT IS/with Johnny Hodges — Impulse 55 (1963) orange label $35.

VIRGIL GONSALVES
baritone sax, clarinet - born 1931 Monterey, CA

Gonsalves was a well known West Coast musician through the 50's who worked on a local basis with many groups and recorded with his own sextet.

VIRGIL GONSALVES — Nocturn 8 (1954) 10" $75; EP 14, EP 18 (1954) $25 ea.

JAZZ SAN FRANCISCO STYLE/with Dan Pateris — Liberty 6010 (1955) blue label $45.

BIG BAND PLUS SIX "JAZZ AT MONTEREY" — Omega 1047 (1959) $25.

BABS GONZALES
vocals - born 1919 Newark, NJ died 1980

VOILA!/with Johnny Griffin — Hope 001 (1958) $75.

TALES OF MANHATTEN/with Les Spann — Jaro 5000 (1959) $70.

SUNDAYS AT SMALL'S PARADISE — Dauntless 4311/6311 (1963) $45.

BOB GORDON
baritone sax - born 1928 St. Louis, MO died 1955

One of the main baritone saxophonists of the 50's, Gordon worked extensively on the West Coast with many notable musicians. He was seemingly on the verge of a great career when killed in an auto accident enroute to a gig in San Diego in 1955.

MEET MR. GORDON — Pacific Jazz 12 (1954) 10" $150; EP 4-18 (1954) $50.

DEXTER GORDON
tenor, soprano saxes, composer - born 1923 Los Angeles, CA

Gordon's early work of the 40's reflected his admiration for the style of Lester Young. As he progressed and worked with Charlie Parker and other musicians, his style became his own and he made recordings that epitomized be-bop tenor and were very influential through the 50's. Beginning in the early 60's Gordon lived and worked in Europe, returning only occasionally to America for personal appearances.

QUINTET/with Teddy Edwards — Dial 204 (1950) 10" **$200.**

ALL STAR SERIES/with Fats Navarro — Savoy 9003 (1949) 10" **$150.**

NEW TRENDS IN MODERN JAZZ/with Bud Powell — Savoy 9016 (1949) **$150.**

THE CHASE/STEEPLECHASE/with Wardell Gray — Decca 7025 (1952) 10" **$200.**

DADDY PLAYS THE HORN — Bethlehem 36 (1955) maroon label **$65.**

QUINTET/with Carl Perkins — Dootone 207 (1956) **$65.**

THE RESURGENCE OF — Jazzland 29/929 (1960) **$45.**

DOIN' ALRIGHT/with Freddie Hubbard — Blue Note 4077/84077 (1961) with NY address on label **$45**; with a Division of Liberty on label **$20.**

DEXTER CALLING/with Paul Chambers — Blue Note 4083/84083 (1961) with NY address on label **$45**; with A Division of Liberty on label **$20.**

GO/with Sonny Clark — Blue Note 4112/84112 (1962) with NY on label **$40**; with A Division of Liberty on label **$20.**

A SWINGIN' AFFAIR/with Sonny Clark — Blue Note 4133/84133 (1962) with NY on label **$40**; with A Division of Liberty on label **$20.**

OUR MAN IN PARIS/with Bud Powell — Blue Note 4146/84146 (1963) with NY on label **$35**; with A Division of Liberty on label **$20.**

ONE FLIGHT UP/with Donald Byrd — Blue Note 4176/84176 (1964) with NY on label **$35**; with A Division of Liberty on label **$20.**

GETTING AROUND/with Bobby Hutcherson — Blue Note 4204/84204 (1965) with NY on label **$35**; with A Division of Liberty on label **$20.**

HONI GORDON
vocals

SINGS/with Ken McIntyre — Prestige 7230 (1962) yellow label **$45.**

JOE GORDON
trumpet - born 1928 Boston, MA died 1963

For nearly two decades, beginning with his own combo in 1947, Gordon worked with one great band after another including Dizzy Gillespie in 1956. He then started another group for a short time before moving to Los Angeles where he continued working with quality groups including Shelly Manne into the 60's. Gordon died in a fire in 1963.

INTRODUCING/with Charlie Rouse — EmArcy 26046 (1954) 10" **$75**; EP 1-6089, EP 1-6090 (1954) **$25 ea.**; *reissued* EmArcy 36025 (1956) with drummer logo **$45.**

LOOKING GOOD/with Jimmy Woods — Contemporary 3597/7597 (1961) yellow label **$35.**

JOHN GRAAS
french horn, composer - born 1924 Dubuque, IA died 1962

Most likely a result of his extensive classical background and his love of jazz, Graas was one of the early composer/performers who attempted to combine different idioms while exploring both. Only a few of his recordings remain to demonstrate his, then, very unique approach to jazz music.

FRENCH HORN JAZZ — Trend 1005 (1954) **$60**; EP 507 (1954) **$25**; *reissued* Kapp 1046 (1958).

JAZZ STUDIO TWO — Decca 8079 (1955) **$45.**

JAZZ STUDIO THREE — Decca 8104 (1955) **$45**; EP 2190, EP 2191 (1955) **$20 ea.**

JAZZ LAB ONE — Decca 8343 (1956) **$45.**

JAZZ LAB TWO — Decca 8478 (1956) **$45.**

JAZZMANTICS — Decca 8677 (1958) **$40.**

COUP DE GRAAS — EmArcy 36117 (1958) Mercury logo **$40.**

PREMIERE IN JAZZ — Andex 3003 (1959) **$30.**

FRENCH HORN JAZZ — Kapp 1046 (1958) **$40**; *reissue* of Trend 1005 (1954).

THELMA GRACEN
vocals - born Chicago, IL

THELMA GRACEN/with George Auld and Barney Kessel — Wing 60005 (1956) $75.

JOE GRAVES
trumpet

THE GREAT NEW SWINGERS/with Plas Johnson — Capitol 1977 (1963) black label with logo on top $35.

WARDELL GRAY
tenor sax - born 1921 Oklahoma City, Ok died 1955

Gray worked with name bands on both coasts beginning in the early 40's including Earl Hines, Benny Carter, Benny Goodman and Count Basie. A good, Young and Parker influenced tenorman who has several recordings with other artists and a few under his own name which are all definitely collectors items. Gray is well known for his contributions on the LP on the Decca label with Dexter Gordon titled Chase/Steeplechase.

TENOR SAX — Prestige 115 (1952) 10" $200; *reissued* Prestige 7008 (1956).

LOS ANGELES ALL STARS/with Dexter Gordon — Prestige 128 (1952) 10" $175; *reissued* Prestige 7009 (1956).

WARDELL GRAY QUINTET — Prestige 147 (1953) 10" $175; EP 1345 (1952) $50; *reissued* Prestige 7009 (1956).

CHASE/STEEPLECHASE/with Dexter Gordon — Decca 7025 (1954) 10" $200.

MEMORIAL ALBUM — Prestige 7008 (1956) yellow label $80; *reissue* of Prestige 115.

MEMORIAL ALBUM — Prestige 7009 (1956) yellow label $80; *reissue* of Prestige 128 and 147.

WAY OUT WARDELL — Modern 1204 (1956) $45; *reissued* Crown 5004 (1957) with liner notes on cover $35.

BENNIE GREEN
trombone, baritone horn - born 1923 Chicago, IL died 1977

A fine modern trombonist whose original popularity was with Earl Hines Band in the mid-40's and later with Charlie Ventura, Sonny Stitt, Paul Quinichette and Gene Ammons.

BENNY GREEN — Jubilee EP 5008 (1954) $40.

MODERN JAZZ TROMBONES/with J.J. Johnson — Prestige 123 (1952) $150; EP 1343 (1952) $50.

BENNIE GREEN — Prestige EP 1304 (1952) $50.

BENNIE GREEN AND ART FARMER — Prestige 7041 (1956) yellow label $70.

WALKIN' DOWN — Prestige 7049 (1956) yellow label $70.

BLOWS HIS HORN — Prestige 7052 (1956) yellow label $60; *reissued* Prestige 7160 (1958) yellow label $40.

BLOW YOUR HORN/with Paul Quinichette — Decca 8176 (1956) $60; EP 2291, EP 2292, EP 2293 (1953) $45 ea.

BACK ON THE SCENE/with Charlie Rouse — Blue Note 1597 (1958) with NY address on label $60.

SOUL STIRRIN'/with Gene Ammons — Blue Note 1599 (1958) with NY address on label $50.

WALKIN' & TALKIN'/with Eddy Williams — Blue Note 4010 (1959) with NY address on label $40.

THE SWINGIN'EST/with Gene Ammons — Vee Jay 1005 (1960) maroon label $50.

SWINGS THE BLUES/with Jimmy Forrest — Enrica 2002 (1960) $35.

HORNFULL OF SOUL — Bethlehem 6054 (1960) $35.

GLIDIN' ALONG — Jazzland 43/943 (1961) $30.

BENNIE GREEN — Time 5021/2021 (1960) $45.

MY MAIN MAN/with Sonny Stitt — Argo 744 (1964) $30.

BUNKY GREEN
alto, tenor saxes - born 1935 Milwaukee, WI

TESTIFYIN' TIME/with Walter Strickland — Argo 753 (1965) $35.

FREDDIE GREEN
guitar - born 1911 Charleston, SC

Since 1937 Freddie Green has been playing unamplified rhythm guitar in the rhythm section of the Count Basie Band. Highly regarded for his work, which is widely considered the epitome of taste in rhythm guitar, Green has been recorded extensively but, due to his approach, has only one LP under his own name.

MR. RHYTHM/with Al Cohn — RCA Victor 1210 (1956) dog on top $75.

GRANT GREEN
guitar - born 1931 St. Louis, MO died 1979

GRANT'S FIRST STAND/with Baby Face Willette — Blue Note 4068/84068 (1961) with NY address on label $30; with A Division of Liberty on label $20.

GREEN STREET — Blue Note 4071/84071 (1961) with NY address on label $30; with A Division of Liberty on label $20.

GRANTSTAND/with Yusef Lateef — Blue Note 4086/84086 (1961) with NY address on label $40; with A Division of Liberty on label $20.

SUNDAY MORNIN'/with Kenny Drew — Blue Note 4099/84099 (1961) with NY address on label $35; with A Division of Liberty on label $20.

THE LATIN BIT/with Willie Bobo — Blue Note 4111/84111 (1962) with NY on label $30; with A Division of Liberty on label $20.

FEELIN' THE SPIRIT/with Herbie Hancock — Blue Note 4132/84132 (1963) with NY on label $30; with A Division of Liberty on label $20.

AM I BLUE/with Joe Henderson — Blue Note 4139/84139 (1963) with NY on label $35; with A Division of Liberty on label $20.

IDLE MOMENTS/with Joe Henderson — Blue Note 4154/84154 (1964) with NY on label $35; with A Division of Liberty on label $20.

TALKIN' ABOUT/with Larry Young — Blue Note 4183/84183 (1965) with NY on label $30; with A Division of Liberty on label $20.

HIS MAJESTY KING FUNK/with Harold Vick — Verve 8627/68627 (1965) with MGM on bottom of label $20.

URBIE GREEN
trombone - born 1926 Mobile, AL

SEXTET — Blue Note 5036 (1954) 10" **$60**.

AND HIS BAND/with Ruby Braff — Vanguard 8010 (1954) 10" **$50**.

A COOL YULETIDE — Label X 3026 (1954) 10" **$65**.

OCTET/VIC DICKENSON SEXTET "SLIDIN' SWING" — Jazztone 1259 (1956) **$35**.

SEPTET — Bethlehem 14 (1955) maroon label **$45**.

BLUES AND OTHER SHADES OF GREEN — ABC Paramount 101 (1956) **$50**.

ALL ABOUT URBIE GREEN — ABC Paramount 137 (1956) **$45**.

LET'S FACE THE MUSIC AND DANCE — RCA Victor 1667 (1958) dog on top **$35**.

JIMMY McHUGH IN HI FI — RCA Victor 1741 (1958) dog on top **$35**.

BEST OF NEW BROADWAY SHOW HITS — RCA Victor 1969 (1959) dog on top **$30**.

THE PERSUASIVE TROMBONE OF — Command 33-815/815 (1963) fold out cover **$20**.

VOL 2 — Command 838 (1963) fold out cover **$20**.

6-TET — Command 857 (1964) fold out cover **$20**.

WILLIAM GREEN
alto, tenor saxes, flute born 1925 Kansas City, KS

SHADES OF GREEN — Everest 5213 (1963) **$20**.

DODO GREENE
vocals - born Buffalo, NY

MY HOUR OF NEED/with Ike Quebec — Blue Note 9001/89001 (1962) with NY on label **$40**; with A Division of Liberty on label **$20**.

AL GREY
trombone - born 1925 Aldie, VA

After establishing himself with some great jazz names in the 40's and 50's, Grey began working with Count Basie in 1957 and continued in that association. He has many recordings with Basie and several under his own name or with other well known musicians such as JATP, Quincy Jones, Oscar Peterson and Ella Fitzgerald.

THE LAST OF THE BIG PLUNGERS/with Joe Newman — Argo 653 (1959) **$35**.

THE THINKING MAN'S TROMBONE/with Joe Newman — Argo 677 (1960) **$35**.

THE AL GREY/BILLY MITCHELL SEXTET — Argo 689 (1961) **$40**.

SNAP YOUR FINGERS/with Billy Mitchell — Argo 700 (1962) **$40**.

NIGHT SONG/with Billy Mitchell — Argo 711 (1962) **$40**.

HAVING A BALL/with Dave Burns — Argo 718 (1963) **$30**.

BOSS BONES/with Leo Blevins — Argo 731 (1964) **$30**.

SHADES OF GREY/with Eddie Lockjaw Davis — Tangerine 1504 (1965) **$25**.

JOHNNY GRIFFIN
tenor sax - born 1928 Chicago, IL

True to his reputation, Griffin has been a hard driving be-bop tenor player since the mid-40's and was widely recorded in the 50's with many groups including Art Blakey and Thelonious Monk. He led a group with "Lockjaw" Davis in the early 60's and has since lived and worked in Europe with many appearances and occasional recording sessions.

INTRODUCING NEW SAX STAR — Blue Note 1533 (1956) with NY address on label **$95**; with A Division of Liberty on label **$30**.

A BLOWING SESSION/with John Coltrane and Hank Mobley — Blue Note 1559 (1957) with NY address on label **$90**; with A Division of Liberty on label **$30**.

CONGREGATION/with Sonny Clark — Blue Note 1580 (1958) with NY address on label **$65**; with A Division of Liberty on label **$30**.

SEXTET/with Pepper Adams — Riverside 12-264 (1958) Bill Grauer Pro. **$65**.

WAY OUT — Riverside 12-274 (1958) Bill Grauer Pro. **$50**.

THE LITTLE GIANT/with Blue Mitchell — Riverside 12-304 (1959) **$50**; *reissued* Riverside 1179 (1960) Bill Gauer Pro. **$45**; *reissued* Jazzland 93/99 (1961) **$35**.

THE BIG SOUL-BAND/with Clark Terry — Riverside 12-331/1179 (1960) **$45** EP 3203 (1960) Bill Grauer Pro. **$25**.

STUDIO JAZZ PARTY/with Dave Burns — Riverside 338/9339 (1960) Bill Grauer Pro. **$40**.

CHANGE OF PACE/with Julius Watkins — Riverside 368/9368 (1961) Bill Grauer Pro. **$45**.

WHITE GARDENIA/with Clark Terry — Riverside 387/9387 (1961) Bill Grauer Pro. **$45**.

KERRY DANCE/with Barry Harris — Riverside 420/9420 (1961) Bill Grauer Pro **$40**.

GRAB THIS/with Paul Bryant — Riverside 437/9437 (1962) Bill Grauer Pro. **$40**.

DO NOTHING TILL YOU HEAR FROM ME/with Buddy Montgomery — Riverside 462/9462 (1963) **$35**.

SOUL GROOVE/with Matthew Gee — Atlantic 1431 (1965) with logo on right side **$25**.

JOHNNY GRIFFIN — Argo 624 (1958) **$45**.

TINY GRIMES
guitar - born 1917 Newport News, VA

Most popular in the 40's when gigging with Art Tatum and later his own group into the 50's. Grimes worked in New York City in the 60's with tours and many club appearances and occasional recordings.

BLUES GROOVE/with Coleman Hawkins — Prestige 7138 (1958) yellow label **$60**.

CALLIN' THE BLUES/with Eddie Lockjaw Davis — Prestige 7144 (1958) yellow label **$60**; *reissued* Swingsville 2004 (1960) **$35**.

TINY IN SWINGSVILLE/with Jerome Richardson — Swingsville 2002 (1960) **$35**.

BIG TIME GUITAR — United Artists 3232/6232 (1962) **$25**.

THE JAZZ LAB QUINTET/with Donald Byrd — Riverside 12-229 (1957) **$50**; *reissued* Jazzland 1 (1960) **$35**.

JAZZ LAB/with Donald Byrd — Columbia 998 (1957) with 3 black logos on each side **$50**.

MODERN JAZZ PERSPECTIVE/JAZZ LAB - Vol 2 — Columbia 1059 (1957) with 3 black logos on each side **$50**.

JAZZ LABORATORY/with Donald Byrd — Verve 8238 (1958) with Verve Records, Inc. on bottom of label **$40**; with MGM on bottom of label **$30** one side only.

QUARTET — Signal 1201 (1956) **$75**; *reissued* Savoy 12137 (1960).

NICA'S TEMPO — Savoy 12137 (1960) maroon label **$35**.

GIGI GRYCE — Metrojazz 1006 (1958) **$45**.

REMINISCIN' — Mercury 20628/60628 (1961) **$35**.

WHEN FARMER MET GRYCE — Prestige 7085 (1957) yellow label **$75**.

SAYIN' SOMETHING — New Jazz 8230 (1959) **$45**.

THE HAP'NIN'S — New Jazz 8246 (1960) **$45**.

THE RAT RACE BLUES — New Jazz 8262 (1961) **$40**.

VINCE GUARALDI
piano, composer - born 1928 San Francisco, CA died 1976

MODERN MUSIC FROM SAN FRANCISCO — Fantasy 3-213 (1956) **$45**.

VINCE GUARALDI TRIO — Fantasy 3-225 (1956) **$40**.

A FLOWER IS A LOVESOME THING — Fantasy 3257 (1958) **$40**.

JAZZ IMPRESSIONS OF BLACK ORPHEUS — Fantasy 3337/8089 (1962) **$35**; *reissued* Fantasy 3337/8089 (1965) with date at bottom right of back cover **$20**.

IN PERSON — Fantasy 3352/8352 (1963) **$25**.

BOLA SETE AND FRIENDS — Fantasy 3358/8358 (1963) **$20**.

JAZZ IMPRESSIONS OF CHARLIE BROWN — Fantasy 5017/85017 (1964) **$25**.

THE LATIN SIDE OF — Fantasy 3360/8360 (1964) **$15**.

JAZZ IMPRESSIONS — Fantasy 3359/8359 (1964) **$15**.

FROM ALL SIDES — Fantasy 3362/8362 (1965) **$15**.

JIMMY GRISSOM
vocals - born Leland, MS

WORLD OF TROUBLE/with Jay Peters — Argo 729 (1963) **$40**.

THE GROUP
Larry Benson/Anne Gable/Tom Kampman vocals

THE GROUP — RCA Victor 2663 (1963) dog on top **$45**.

DAVE GRUSIN
piano, composer - born 1934 Denver, CO

SUBWAYS ARE FOR SLEEPING — Epic 3829 (1962) **$35**.

KALEIDOSCOPE — Columbia 2344/1944 (1965) red label with one white logo on each side **$20**.

GIGI GRYCE
alto sax, flute, composer - born 1927 Pensacola, FL died 1983

A serious and well-trained musician with good arranging abilities, Gryce was first known around the New York City area in the early 50's. Very soon he worked with Max Roach, Lionel Hampton, Howard McGhee and, in 1957, with the experimental group Jazz Lab which he co-led with Donald Byrd. He recorded extensively during this time and into the early 60's but little has been heard from him since.

GIGI GRYCE/with Clifford Brown Sextet — Blue Note 5048 (1954) 10" **$150**.

AND HIS BIG BAND/with Clifford Brown — Blue Note 5049 (1954) 10" **$125**.

AND HIS BAND/with Clifford Brown — Blue Note 5050 (1954) 10" **$125**.

QUINTET/SEXTET/with Clifford Brown — Blue Note 5051 (1954) 10" **$125**.

JAZZ LAB/with Donald Byrd — Jubilee 1059 (1956) **$50**; *reissued* Josie 3500 (1963).

GIGI GRYCE/DONALD BYRD — Josie 3500 (1963) **$30**; *reissue* of Jubilee 1059 (1956).

LARS GULLIN
baritone sax, composer, arranger born 1928 Gotland, Sweden died 1976

Inspired to play the baritone sax after hearing Gerry Mulligan, within a few years Gullin was playing and recording with top U.S. jazz musicians and was considered amongst the very best of artists. To emphasize his overwhelming popularity in the States, Gullin was one of the first European jazz musicians to win an American poll award in the early 50's. He continued to play, record and compose his very original and sometimes unusual compositions until his death in 1976. Although the quantity of his original recordings is few, the quality of Gullin's work is adequate compensation.

NEW SOUNDS FROM SWEDEN - Vol 2/with Bengt Hallberg Trio — Prestige 121 (1952) 10" **$250**.

NEW SOUNDS FROM SWEDEN - Vol 3/with Arne Domnerus — Prestige 133 (1952) 10" **$250**.

NEW SOUNDS FROM SWEDEN - Vol 5/with Arne Domnerus — Prestige 144 (1953) 10" **$250**.

NEW SOUNDS FROM SWEDEN - Vol 7/with Ake Persson — Prestige 151 (1953) 10" **$250**.

ALL STARS/with Zoot Sims and Lee Konitz — Prestige EP 1341 (1953) **$50**.

MODERN SOUND/with Weine Renlider — Contemporary 2505 (1953) 10" **$200**.

QUARTET/with Rolf Berg — EmArcy 26041 (1954) 10" **$200**; EP 1-6071, EP 1-6072 (1954) **$50** ea.

GULLIN'S GARDEN/with Ake Persson — EmArcy 26044 (1954) 10" $200; EP 1-6079 $50.

QUARTET + QUINTET/with Carl Henrik Norin — EmArcy 36012 (1955) blue label with drummer logo $100; EP 1-6121, EP 1-6122, EP 1-6123, EP 1-6125 (1953) $35 ea.

WITH MORETONE SINGERS — EmArcy 36059 (1955) blue label with drummer logo $80.

BARITONE SAX — Atlantic 1246 (1956) black label $90.

SWINGS — East-West 4003 (1958) $100.

*BOBBY HACKETT

trumpet, cornet, guitar - born 1915 Providence, R.I. died 1976

TRUMPET SOLOS — Brunswick 58014 (1950) 10" $50; Brunswick 9-7007 (1950) 7" 4 record box set $35.

HORN A PLENTY — Commodore 20-016 (1951) 10" $75.

JAZZ SESSION — Columbia 6156 (1950) 10" $75.

THE BOBBY HACKETT HORN — Columbia 2566 (1956) 10" $50.

SOFT LIGHTS — Capitol H458 (1954) 10" $50; *reissued* Capitol T458 (1955) green label $40.

IN A MELLOW MOOD — Capitol T575 (1955) green label $40.

COAST CONCERT — Capitol T692 (1956) green label $50; EP 1-692, EP 2-692, EP 3-692 (1956) $15 ea.

RENDEZVOUS — Capitol T719 (1956) green label $40.

GOTHAM JAZZ SCENE — Capitol T857 (1957) green label $40.

JAZZ ULTIMATE/with Jack Teagarden — Capitol T933 (1958) green label $45.

AT THE EMBERS — Capitol 1077 (1958) green label $45.

BLUES WITH A KICK — Capitol 1172 (1959) black label with logo on left side $35.

QUARTET — Capitol 1235 (1959) black label with logo on left side $45.

EASY BEAT — Capitol 1413 (1960) black label with logo on left side $35.

---

*The only LP's within the scope of this book.

AL HAIG

piano - born 1923 Newark, NJ died 1982

A respected member of many prominent groups of the 40's, namely Charlie Parker and Dizzy Gillespie. Haig worked with Stan Getz, among others, during the 50's and got through the 60's by playing pop music in cocktail lounges. The 70's showed a more prosperous period and Haig was once again in demand, playing jazz clubs, concerts and tours.

TRIO — Prestige EP 1318 (1950) $40.

TRIO — Esoteric 7 (1950) 10" $90; *reissued* Counterpoint 551 (1958).

QUARTET/with Benny Weeks — Period 1104 (1954) 10" $80.

TRIO — Pacific Jazz 18 (1954) 10" $80; EP 4-26 (1954) $40.

JAZZ-WILL-O-THE-WISP — Counterpoint 551 (1958) $60.

JIM HALL

guitar - born 1930 Buffalo, NY

JAZZ GUITAR/with Carl Perkins — World Pacific 1227 (1958) $60; *reissued* Pacific Jazz 79 (1963) $35.

BENGT HALLBERG

piano - born 1932 Gothenburg, Sweden

NEW SOUNDS FROM SWEDEN/with Arne Domnerus — Prestige 145 (1953) 10" $100.

NEW SOUNDS FROM SWEDEN — Prestige 176 (1954) 10" $95.

MODERN PIANOS/with Reinhold Svensson — Prestige 174 (1954) 10" $80.

BENGT HALLBERG — Pacific Jazz EP 4-17 (1954) $50.

BENGT HALLBERG — Epic 3375 (1957) $60.

LENNY HAMBRO

alto sax - born 1923 New York City, NY

MAMBO HAMBRO/with Eddie Bert — Savoy 15031 (1954) 10" $80.

QUINTET/with Dick Garcia — Columbia 757 (1955) with 3 black logos on each side $60.

THE NATURE OF THINGS/with Sal Salvador — Epic 3361 (1956) $50.

CHICO HAMILTON

drums - born 1921 Los Angeles, CA

Well known on the West Coast since the early 40's, with a great degree of experience in name bands throughout the late 40's, Hamilton became a member of the original Mulligan Quartet in 1952. Beginning in 1956, he fronted a group of unusual instrumentation with musicians like Buddy Collette, Jim Hall and Fred Katz and, in 1960, reformed the group with Charles Lloyd and Gabor Szabo. In the mid-60's Hamilton moved into television and radio studio work.

CHICO HAMILTON TRIO — Pacific Jazz 17 (1955) 10" $90; EP 4-20 (1955) $45; *reissued* Pacific Jazz 1220 (1956) $60.

QUINTET/with Buddy Collette — Pacific Jazz 1209 (1955) $75; EP 4-39, EP 4-40 (1955) $35 ea.; *reissued* World Pacific 1209 (1958) $45; *reissued* Pacific Jazz 39 (1962).

QUINTET IN HI FI/with Buddy Collette — Pacific Jazz 1216 (1956) $60; EP 4-45 (1956) $30.

QUINTET/with Paul Horn — Pacific Jazz 1225 (1957) $50; *reissued* World Pacific 1005 (1958) stereo $45.

TRIO — Pacific Jazz 1220 (1957) **$40.**

SPECTACULAR — Pacific Jazz 39 (1962) **$15**; *reissue* of Pacific Jazz 1209.

THE MUSIC OF FRED KATZ/with Paul Horn — World Pacific 1231 (1958) **$45.**

SOUTH PACIFIC IN HI FI — World Pacific 1238 (1958) **$40.**

TRIO/with Freddie Gambrell — World Pacific 1242/1008 (1958) **$45.**

ELLINGTON SUITE/with Buddy Collette — World Pacific 1258/1016 (1959) **$45.**

JAZZ FROM SWEET SMELL OF SUCCESS — Decca 8614 (1957) **$60**; *EP 2541* (1957) **$25.**

WITH STRINGS ATTACHED/with Eric Dolphy — Warner Brothers 1245 (1958) **$65.**

GONGS EAST/with Eric Dolphy — Warner Brothers 1271 (1958) **$65.**

THE THREE FACES OF CHICO/with Eric Dolphy — Warner Brothers 1344 (1959) **$60.**

SPECIAL/with Charles Lloyd — Columbia 1619/8419 (1960) with 3 black logos on each side **$30.**

SELECTIONS FROM BYE BYE BIRDIE/with Charles Lloyd —Columbia 1590/8390 (1960) with 3 black logos on each side **$25.**

DRUMFUSION/with Charles Lloyd — Columbia 1807/8607 (1962) with 3 black logos on each side **$25.**

A DIFFERENT JOURNEY — Reprise 6078/96078 (1963) **$30.**

THAT HAMILTON MAN/with Eric Dolphy — Sesac 2901/2902 (1959) **$75.**

PASSIN' THRU/with Charles Lloyd — Impulse 29 (1962) orange label **$30.**

MAN FROM TWO WORLDS/with Charles Lloyd — Impulse 59 (1963) orange label **$25.**

CHIC CHIC CHICO/with Harold Land — Impulse 82 (1965) orange label **$20.**

EL CHICO/with Jimmy Cheatham — Impulse 9102 (1965) orange label **$20.**

CHICO HAMILTON WITH PAUL HORN — Crown Records 5310/310 (1963) **$15.**

THE GREAT/with Paul Horn — Crown Records 5341/341 (1963) **$15.**

DAVE HAMILTON
vibes

BLUE VIBRATIONS — Workshop Jazz 206 (1963) **$45.**

JIMMY HAMILTON
clarinet, tenor sax - born 1917 Dillion, SC

CLARINET IN HIGH-FI/with Lucky Thompson — Urania 1003 (1954) 10" **$90**; *reissued* Urania 1208 (1955) **$60.**

ACCENT ON CLARINET/with Clark Terry — Urania 1204 (1955) **$60.**

SWING LOW SWEET CLARINET/with Paul Gonsalves — Everest 5100 (1960) **$45.**

IT'S ABOUT TIME/with Clark Terry — Swingsville 2022 (1961) **$45.**

CAN'T HELP SWINGING/with Tommy Flanagan — Swingsville 2028 (1961) **$45.**

BOB HAMMER
piano, composer - born 1930 Indianapolis, IN

BEATLE JAZZ/with Phil Woods — ABC Paramount 497 (1964) **$25.**

LIONEL HAMPTON
vibes, drums, piano - born 1913 Louisville, KY

Already a drummer for many name bands, Hampton began playing vibes around 1930 and soon started his own group. He moved on then with Benny Goodman for several years and many memorable recordings and popularity gained during this time allowed him to again start a band under his own name. The group proved very popular until changes in styles forced him, in the mid-60's, to adopt the smaller framework of a sextet which he has continued to use except for occasional festival appearances or reunions with his many famous former collegues. His position in jazz as the first vibraphonist is forever documented.

BOOGIE WOOGIE — Decca 5230 (1950) 10" **$60.**

JUST JAZZ — Decca 7013 (1953) 10" **$55**; *reissued* Decca 9055 (1958) **$35**; Decca 9-154 (1953) 4 record box set **$20.**

MOONGLOW — Decca 5297 (1951) 10" **$55**; *reissued* Decca 8230 (1956) **$35**; Decca 9-140 (1951) 7" 4 record box set **$20.**

ALL AMERICAN AWARD CONCERT/with Dinah Washington — Decca 8088 (1954) **$45.**

ORIGINAL STAR DUST — Decca 4194/74194 (1962) **$35.**

GOLDEN FAVORITES — Decca 4296/74296 (1963) **$35.**

OH ROCK — MGM E285 (1951) 10" **$50**; *reissued* MGM 3386 (1956) **$30.**

CRAZY HAMP — EmArcy 26038 (1953) 10" **$60**; *reissued* EmArcy 36032 (1956) **$45.**

HAMP IN PARIS — EmArcy 26037 (1953) 10" **$60**; *reissued* EmArcy 36032 (1956) **$45.**

CRAZY RHYTHM — EmArcy 36034 (1956) **$45.**

JAM SESSION IN PARIS — EmArcy 36035 (1956) **$45.**

HOT MALLETS — RCA Victor 1000 (1954) silver label with dog on top **$50.**

JAZZ FLAMENCO — RCA Victor 1422 (1956) dog on top **$35.**

SWING CLASSICS — RCA Victor 2318 (1961) dog on top **$25.**

QUARTET — Clef 142 (1953) 10" **$70**; EP 326, EP 327 (1953) **$35** ea.; *reissued* Clef 673 (1955).

QUARTET — Clef 611 (1953) **$70**; EP 204, EP 203 (1953) **$35** ea.

QUINTET — Clef 628 (1954) **$65**; EP 226 (1954) **$35.**

QUINTET — Clef 642 (1954) **$65;** EP 295, EP 296, EP 297 (1954) **$35** ea.

QUARTET/QUINTET — Clef 667 (1955) **$65.**

BIG BAND — Clef 670 (1955) **$65;** EP 370 (1955) **$30;** *reissued* Verve 8019 (1957).

HAMP — Clef 673 (1955) **$65;** *reissued* Clef 738 (1956) **$60;** *reissued* Verve 8114 (1957) with Verve Records, Inc. on bottom of label **$45;** *reissues of* Clef 142.

FLYING HOME — Clef 735 (1956) **$60;** *reissued* Verve 8112 (1957) with Verve Records, Inc. on bottom of label **$45.**

SWINGING WITH HAMP — Clef 736 (1956) **$50;** *reissued* Verve 8113 (1957) with Verve Records, Inc. on bottom of label **$40.**

HAMP'S BIG FOUR — Clef 744 (1956) **$50;** *reissued* Verve 8117 (1957) with Verve Records, Inc. on bottom of label **$40.**

THE LIONEL HAMPTON, ART TATUM, BUDDY RICH TRIO — Clef 709 (1955) **$60;** *reissued* Verve 8093 (1957) with Verve Records, Inc. on bottom of label **$45.**

ROCKIN' AND GROOVIN' — Blue Note 5046 (1953) 10" **$90.**

HAMP AND GETZ/with Stan Getz — Norgran 1037 (1955) **$95;** *EP 139 (1955)* **$45;** *reissued* Verve 8128 (1957) with Verve Records, Inc. on bottom of label **$75.**

AND HIS GIANTS — Norgran 1080 (1955) **$80;** *reissued* Verve 8170 (1957) with Verve Records, Inc. on bottom of label **$50.**

APOLLO HALL CONCERT 1954 — Epic 3190 (1956) **$35.**

MANY SPLENDORED VIBES — Epic 16027/17027 (1962) **$25.**

SWINGS — Perfect 12002 (1959) **$50.**

WAILIN' AT THE TRIANON — Columbia 711 (1956) red label with 3 black logos on each side **$40;** EP 1997, EP 1998 (1956) **$20** ea.

GOLDEN VIBES — Columbia 1304/8110 (1959) red label with 3 black logos on each side **$30.**

SILVER VIBES — Columbia 1486/8277 (1960) red label with 3 black logos on each side **$20.**

SOFT VIBES — Columbia 1661/8461 (1961) red label with 3 black logos on each side **$15.**

SWINGS IN PARIS — Contemporary 3502 (1955) yellow label **$50.**

THE SWINGING JAZZ OF — American Recording Society 403 (1956) with booklet **$75.**

LIONEL — Audio Fidelity 1849/5849 (1957) **$20.**

HAMP'S BIG BAND — Audio Fidelity 1913/5913 (1959) **$20.**

HAMP IN HI FI — Harmony 7115 (1958) **$25.**

ONE AND ONLY — Harmony 7281 (1961) **$15.**

WITH THE JUST JAZZ ALL STARS — Gene Norman Presents 15 (1957) **$45.**

PLAYS LOVE SONGS — Verve 2018 (1956) with Verve Records, Inc. on bottom of label **$45.**

TRAVLIN' BAND — Verve 8019 (1957) **$45;** *reissue* of Clef 670 (1955) 45.

KING OF THE VIBES — Verve 8105 (1957) with Verve Records, Inc. on bottom of label **$30.**

AIR MAIL SPECIAL — Verve 8106 (1957) with Verve Records, Inc. on bottom of label **$30.**

GENIUS — Verve 8215 (1957) with Verve Records, Inc. on bottom of label **$30.**

'58 — Verve 8223 (1958) with Verve Records, Inc. on bottom of label **$25.**

HALLELUJAH HAMP — Verve 8226 (1958) with Verve Records, Inc. on bottom of label **$25.**

HIGH AND THE MIGHTY — Verve 8228 (1958) with Verve Records, Inc. on bottom of label **$25.**

JIVIN' THE VIBES — Camden 402 (1958) **$25.**

MANY SIDES — Glad Hamp 1001 (1961) **$15.**

EXCITING HAMP IN EUROPE — Glad Hamp 1003 (1962) **$15.**

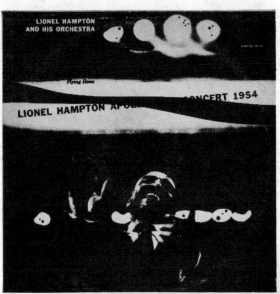

ALL THAT TWISTIN' JAZZ — Glad Hamp 3050 (1962) **$15.**

BOSSA NOVA JAZZ — Glad Hamp 1004 (1963) **$15.**

IN JAPAN — Glad Hamp 1006 (1964) **$15.**

EAST MEETS WEST — Glad Hamp 1007 (1965) **$15.**

TASTE OF HAMP — Glad Hamp 1009 (1965) **$15.**

THE GREAT HAMP AND LITTLE T./with Charlie Teagarden — Coral 57438/75743 (1963) **$20.**

YOU BETTER KNOW IT/with Ben Webster — Impulse 78 (1965) orange label **$35**

SLIDE HAMPTON

trombone, tuba, composer - born 1932 Jeannette, PA

A left handed trombone player and very respected arranger Hampton played with several name big bands in the late 50's. H started his own octet in the early 60's and moved to Europe in the lat 60's, where he has lived, worked and recorded since with only rar visits or appearances in the U.S.

HIS HORN OF PLENTY/with George Coleman — Strand 1006 (1959) **$60.**

TWO SIDES OF/with George Coleman — Charlie Parker 803 (1961) **$45.**

DRUM SUITE/with Yusef Lateef — Epic 16030/17030 (1962) **$45.**

SISTER SALVATION/with George Coleman — Atlantic 1339 (1960) with logo c right side **$35.**

SOMETHIN' SANCTIFIED/with George Coleman — Atlantic 1362 (1960) with lo on right side **$35.**

JAZZ WITH A TWIST/with George Coleman — Atlantic 1379 (1961) with logo on right side **$30.**

XPLOSION!/with Joe Farrell — Atlantic 1396 (1962) with logo on right side **$30.**

HERBIE HANCOCK
piano, composer - born 1940 Chicago, IL

AKIN' OFF/with Dexter Gordon — Blue Note 4109/84109 (1962) with NY on label **$50**; with A Division of Liberty on label **$30.**

MY POINT OF VIEW/with Hank Mobley — Blue Note 4126/84126 (1963) with NY on label **$50**; with A Division of Liberty on label **$30.**

INVENTIONS & DEMENTIONS — Blue Note 4147/84147 (1963) with NY on label **$30**; with A Division of Liberty on label **$20.**

MPYREAN ISLES/with Freddie Hubbard — Blue Note 4175/84175 (1964) with NY on label **$45**; with A Division of Liberty on label **$30.**

MAIDEN VOYAGE/with George Coleman — Blue Note 4195/84195 (1965) with NY on label **$45**; with A Division of Liberty on label **$30.** Ⓐ

JOHN HANDY III
soprano, alto, tenor, baritone saxes - born 1933 Dallas, TX

IN THE VER-NAC'U-LAR — Roulette 52042 (1960) light and dark orange roulette wheel **$30.**

NO COAST JAZZ — Roulette 52088 (1960) light and dark orange roulette wheel **$30.**

ROLAND HANNA
piano - born 1932 Detroit, MI

DESTRY RIDES AGAIN — Atco 33108 (1959) **$30.**

EASY TO LOVE — Atco 33121 (1960) **$30.**

WILBUR HARDEN
fluegelhorn, trumpet - born 1925 Birmingham, AL

MAINSTREAM 1958/with John Coltrane — Savoy 12127 (1958) maroon label **$65.**

JAZZ WAY OUT/with John Coltrane — Savoy 12131/13004 (1958) maroon label **$65.**

THE KING AND I/with Tommy Flanagan — Savoy 12134/13002 (1958) maroon label **$45.**

TANGANYIKA STRUT/with John Coltrane — Savoy 12136 (1958) maroon label **$65.**

BILL HARDMAN
trumpet - born 1933 Cleveland, OH

Hardman spent the 50's with Art Blakey's Jazz Messengers, Horace Silver and Charlie Mingus and began working with Lou Donaldson in the early 60's. Soon he was back with Blakey once again as well as Charlie Mingus and finally formed a group of his own. Hardman has recorded with many of these well known musicians at one time or another and is well known for his abilities on the trumpet.

QUINTET/with Sonny Red — Savoy 12170 (1961) maroon label **$35.**

HERBIE HARPER
trombone - born 1920 Salina, KS

Worked with many names including Benny Goodman, Charlie Barnet and Gene Krupa during the 40's before moving to the West Coast for work with small groups and increasing involvement in studio work for television and radio.

QUINTET/with Bob Gordon — Nocturne 1 (1953) 10" **$100**; EP 1, EP 2 (1953) **$50 ea.**

HERBIE HARPER/with Bud Shank — Nocturne 7 (1954) 10" **$100**; EP 11, EP 12 (1954) **$50 ea.**; *reissued* Liberty 6003 (1956).

HERBIE HARPER/with Charlie Mariano — Bethlehem 1025 (1955) 10" **$80.**

HERBIE HARPER/with Bud Shank and Bob Gordon — Liberty 6003 (1956) blue label **$60.**

SEXTET/with Jay Corre — Mode 100 (1957) **$65.**

QUINTET/with Bob Enevoldsen — Tampa 11 (1957) **$50**; EP 123, EP 124 (1957) **$25 ea.**

TONI HARPER
vocals

TONI — Verve 2001 (1956) with Verve Records, Inc. on bottom of label **$40.**

LADY LONELY/with Marty Paich — RCA Victor 2092 (1959) dog on top **$35.**

NIGHT MOOD — RCA Victor 2253 (1960) dog on top **$35.**

JOE HARRIOTT
alto, baritone, tenor saxes - born 1928 Jamaica, B.W.I

SOUTHERN HORIZONS — Jazzland 37/937 (1961) **$35.**

FREE FORM — Jazzland 49/949 (1961) **$35.**

BARRY HARRIS
piano - born 1929 Detroit, MI

BREAKIN' IT UP — Argo 644 (1958) **$35.**

AT THE JAZZ WORKSHOP — Riverside 326/1177 (1960) with Bill Grauer Pro. **$35.**

PREMINADO — Riverside 354/9354 (1961) with Bill Grauer Pro. **$30.**

LISTEN TO — Riverside 392/9392 (1961) with Bill Grauer Pro. **$30.**

NEWER THAN NEW/with Charlie McPherson — Riverside 413/9413 (1961) with Bill Grauer Pro. **$45.**

CHASIN' THE BIRD — Riverside 435/9435 (1962) with Bill Grauer Pro. **$30.**

BILL HARRIS
guitar - born 1925 Nashville, NC

BILL HARRIS GUITAR — EmArcy 36097 (1956) with drummer logo **$35.**

HARRIS TOUCH — EmArcy 36113 (1957) **$35**; *reissued* Mercury 20552/60120 (1960) **$25.**

GREAT GUITAR SOUNDS — Wing 12220/16220 (1960) **$30.**

BILL HARRIS
trombone - born 1916 Philadelphia, PA died 1973

Through his work with Woody Herman in the mid-40's, which included his recording of Bijou, Harris was known as an exciting musician with a distinctive style. After extensive tours with JATP during the 50's, he worked in Las Vegas in the 60's retiring to Florida where he died in 1973.

COLLATES/with Ralph Burns — Clef 125 (1952) 10" **$125**; EP 135, EP 162 (1952) **$45 ea.**; *reissued* Norgran 1062 (1956).

HERD — Norgran 1062 (1956) **$75**; *reissued* Verve 8152 (1957) with Verve Records, Inc. on bottom of label **$60**.

AND FRIENDS/with Ben Webster — Fantasy 3263 (1957) **$45**.

THE EX-HERMANITES/with Terry Gibbs — Mode 129 (1957) **$60**; *reissued* Premier 2006 (1963) **$30**.

EDDIE HARRIS
tenor sax, composer - born 1934 Chicago, IL

EXODUS TO JAZZ — Vee Jay 3016 (1961) with Chicago Style on cover **$45**.

MIGHTY LIKE A ROSE — Vee Jay 3025 (1961) with Chicago Style on cover **$45**.

JAZZ FOR BREAKFAST AT TIFFANY'S — Vee Jay 3027 (1961) with Chicago Style on cover **$40**.

A STUDY IN JAZZ — Vee Jay 3028 (1962) with Chicago Style on cover **$40**.

GOES TO THE MOVIES — Vee Jay 3031 (1963) **$30**.

BOSSA NOVA — Vee Jay 3034 (1963) **$30**.

COOL SAX, WARM HEART — Columbia 2168/8968 (1964) with one white logo on each side **$25**.

COOL SAX FROM HOLLYWOOD TO BROADWAY — Columbia 2295/9095 (1964) with one white logo on each side **$25**.

HAROLD HARRIS
piano

HERE'S HAROLD — Vee Jay 3018 (1961) **$30**.

AT THE PLAYBOY CLUB — Vee Jay 3036 (1963) **$25**.

NANCY HARROW
vocals

YOU NEVER KNOW/with Phil Woods — Atlantic 8075 (1963) with logo on right side **$45**.

WILD WOMEN DON'T HAVE THE BLUES/with Buddy Tate — Candid 8008/9008 (1962) **$45**.

JOHNNY HARTMAN
vocals - died 1983

Originally worked with Earl "Fatha" Hines and Dizzy Gillespie in the late 40's. From that time on, Hartman worked mostly as a single with pick-up groups through appearances and various recordings. Some of his best and most popular work can be found on the LP with John Coltrane.

SONGS FROM THE HEART — Bethlehem 43 (1956) maroon label **$35**.

ALL OF ME - THE DEBONAIR MR. HARTMAN — Bethlehem 6014 (1958) maroon label **$35**.

JUST YOU, JUST ME — Regent 6014 (1956) green label **$45**.

JOHN COLTRANE AND JOHNNY HARTMAN — Impulse 40 (1963) orange label **$45**.

DROPPED BY TO SAY HELLO — Impulse 57 (1964) orange label **$30**.

THE VOICE THAT IS — Impulse 74 (1965) orange label **$30**.

HAMPTON HAWES
piano - born 1928 Los Angeles, CA died 1977

HAMPTON HAWES — Vantage 1 (1954) 10" **$75**.

HAMPTON HAWES — Prestige 212 (1955) 10" **$70**.

PIANO EAST/PIANO WEST/with Freddie Redd — Prestige 7067 (1956) yellow label **$60**.

TRIO — Contemporary 3505 (1955) yellow label **$35**.

TRIO — Contemporary 3515 (1956) yellow label **$35**.

EVERYBODY LIKES — Contemporary 3523 (1956) yellow label **$35**.

ALL NIGHT SESSION #1 — Contemporary 3545 (1958) yellow label **$30**.

ALL NIGHT SESSION #2 — Contemporary 3546 (1958) yellow label **$30**.

ALL NIGHT SESSION #3 — Contemporary 3547 (1958) yellow label **$30**.

FOUR — Contemporary 3553 (1959) yellow label **$25**.

FOR REAL — Contemporary 3589/5789 (1961) yellow label **$25**.

THE GREEN LEAVES OF SUMMER — Contemporary 3614/7614 (1962) yellow label **$25**.

COLEMAN HAWKINS
tenor sax - born 1904 St. Joseph, MO died 1969

Widely recognized as the first significant jazz tenor stylist, Hawkins fame began in the 20's. He made world famous recordings in the late 30's and was a powerful influence on all who played the instrument. Another remarkable fact about Hawkins was his continuing evolution as a jazz artist, incorporating elements of newer styles popularized by musicians for whom he had originally been an inspiration. His career continued in the U.S., abroad and through recordings until his death in 1969.

COLEMAN HAWKINS ALL STARS/with Miles Davis — Aladdin EP 516 (1953) **$50**.

REUNION/with Don Redman — Repertory EP 17 (1962) **$20**.

ALL STARS/with Dizzy Gillespie — Apollo 101 (1954) 10" **$200**; *reissued* Grand Award 33-316 (1955).

THE BEAN/with Roy Eldridge — EmArcy 26013 (1954) 10" **$200**; EP 1-6029 (1954) with drummer logo **$50**.

AND THE TRUMPET KINGS/with Buck Clayton and Charlie Shavers — EmArcy 26011 (1965) gray label with EmArcy emblems in a circle (early recording from the 40's) **$30**.

KING OF THE TENOR SAX — Commodore 20025 (1950) 10" **$225**; *reissued* Mainstream 56037/6037 (1965).

JAZZ CONCERT/with Howard McGee — Stinson 22 (1950) 10" **$225**.

TENOR SAX — Brunswick 58030 (1953) 10" **$150**; *reissued* Contact 3 (1965).

THE BIG SOUND OF/with Ben Webster — Brunswick 54016 (1956) one side only **$60**.

CLASSICS IN JAZZ/with Howard McGee — Capitol H327 (1952) 10" **$85**; EP 327 (1952) 2 records **$45**.

PRESTIGE 7149

COLEMAN HAWKINS

the hawk flies high

GILDED HAWK/with Strings — Capitol T819 (1957) $50.

TENOR SAX STYLINGS — Coral 9-7030 (1952) 7" 4 record box set $25.

HAWK TALKS — Savoy 15039 (1953) 10" $150.

HAWK RETURNS — Savoy 12013 (1955) maroon label $50.

JAZZ CONCERT — Grand Award 33-316 (1955) $50; reissue of Apollo 101.

ACCENT ON TENOR/with Ernie Royal — Urania 1201 (1955) $65.

HAWK TALKS — Decca 8127 (1955) $65.

HAWK IN PARIS/with Nick Travis — Vik 1059 (1956) $55.

TIMELESS JAZZ/with Billy Taylor — Jazztone 1201 (1956) $50.

DOCUMENTARY — Riverside 12-117/8 (1956) Hawkins narrates, white label with Bill Grauer Pro. $50.

THE HAWK FLIES HIGH/with Idrees Sulieman — Riverside 12-233 (1957) white label with Bill Grauer Pro. $75; reissued (1958) blue label with Bill Grauer Pro. $45.

SAXOPHONE SECTION/with Frank Wess and Frank Foster — World Wide 2001 (1958) $45.

THE HIGH AND MIGHTY HAWK — Felsted 2005/7005 (1958) $45.

HAWK IN FLIGHT/with Fats Navarro — RCA Victor 1017 (1954) dog on top $60.

HAWK IN HI FI — RCA Victor 1281 (1956) dog on top $50.

SONNY MEETS HAWK/with Sonny Rollins — RCA Victor 2712 (1963) dog on top $45.

SOUL/with Kenny Burrell — Prestige 7149 (1958) yellow label $45; reissued Swingsville 2038 (1961) $30.

HAWK EYES/with Charlie Shavers — Prestige 7156 (1959) yellow label $45; reissued Swingsville 2039 (1961) $30.

BEAN BAGS/with Milt Jackson — Atlantic 1316 (1959) with logo at right side $35.

COLEMAN HAWKINS/with Thad Jones — Crown 206/5181 (1960) $25.

THE HAWK SWINGS/with Thad Jones — Crown 224/5207 (1960) $25.

ON THE BEAN — Continental 16006 (1962) $25.

JAZZ REUNION/with Pee Wee Russell — Candid 8020/9020 (1962) $35.

MEDITATIONS/with Cootie Williams — Mainstream 56037/6037 (1965) $25.

BACK IN BEAN'S BAG/with Clark Terry — Columbia 8791/1991 (1963) one white logo on each side of label $20.

JAZZ AT THE METROPOLE — Philips 600-022/200-022 (1962) $25.

THE HAWK AND THE HUNTER/with Frank Hunter — Mira 3003 (1965) $20.

ALL STARS AT NEWPORT/with Roy Eldridge — Verve 8240 (1957) with Verve Records, Inc. on bottom of label $60; with MGM on bottom of label $35.

AT THE OPERA HOUSE/with Roy Eldridge — Verve 8266/6028 (1957) with Verve Records, Inc. on bottom of label $60; with MGM on bottom of label $35.

THE GENIUS OF — Verve 8261/6033 (1958) with Verve Records, Inc. on bottom of label $50; with MGM on bottom of label $30.

AND HIS CONFRERES — Verve 8346/6110 (1959) with Verve Records, Inc. on bottom of label $45; with MGM on bottom of label $30.

ENCOUNTERS/with Ben Webster — Verve 8327/6066 (1959) with Verve Records, Inc. on bottom of label $45; with MGM on bottom of label $30.

HAWKINS ALIVE! AT THE VILLAGE GATE — Verve 8509/68509 (1963) with MGM on bottom of label $30.

ESSENTIAL — Verve 8568/68568 (1964) with MGM on bottom of label $25.

WITH RED GARLAND — Swingsville 2001 (1960) $45.

ALL STARS/with Joe Thomas — Swingsville 2005 (1960) $35.

NIGHT HAWK/with Eddie "Lockjaw" Davis — Swingsville 2016 (1961) $45.

THINGS AIN'T WHAT THEY USED TO BE — Swingsville 2024 (1961) $30.

AT EASE/with Tommy Flanagan — Moodsville 7 (1960) $45.

THE HAWK RELAXES/with Kenny Burrell — Moodsville 15 (1961) $45.

GOOD OLD BROADWAY/with Tommy Flanagan — Moodsville 23 (1962) $40.

JAZZ VERSION OF NO STRINGS/with Tommy Flanagan — Moodsville 25 (1962) $40.

MAKE SOMEONE HAPPY — Moodsville 31 (1963) $40.

DESAFINADO/with Manny Albam — Impulse 28 (1963) orange label $35.

TODAY AND NOW/with Major Holley — Impulse 34 (1963) orange label $35.

WRAPPED TIGHT/with Bill Berry — Impulse 87 (1965) orange label $30.

LOUIS HAYES
drums - born 1937 Detroit, MI

LOUIS HAYES — Vee Jay 3010 (1960) $45.

MARTHA HAYES
vocals

A HAYES NAMED MARTHA — Jubilee 1023 (1956) blue label with silver lettering $45.

TUBBY HAYES
flute, alto, tenor, baritone saxes - born 1935 London, England

As a famous jazz musician in England, Hayes worked with many U.S. musicians who eventually encouraged him to try his luck in America. He appeared here every few years for tours and performances through the 60's and gained a position as a highly respected tenorman but with only a few recordings on American labels.

CHANGING THE JAZZ AT BUCKINGHAM PALACE/with Dizzy Reece — Savoy 12111 (1957) maroon label $65.

THE COURIERS OF JAZZ/with Ronnie Scott — Carlton 12/116 (1959) $50.

MESSAGE FROM BRITAIN/with Ronnie Scott — Jazzland 34/934 (1961) **$35.**

INTRODUCING TUBBS — Epic 16019/17019 (1962) **$45.**

TUBBY THE TENOR — Epic 16023/17023 (1962) **$45.**

TUBBY'S BACK IN TOWN — Smash 27026/67026 (1962) **$40.**

LITTLE GIANT OF JAZZ — Imperial 9046 (1957) **$35.**

ROY HAYNES
drums - born 1926 Roxbury, MA

BUSHMAN'S HOLIDAY/with Sahib Shibab — EmArcy 26048 (1954) 10" **$85;** EP 1-6124, EP 1-6125 (1954) **$45 ea.;** reissued EmArcy 36083 (1956).

JAZZ ABROAD/with Quincy Jones — EmArcy 36083 (1956) one side of LP is Jones **$60.**

WE THREE — New Jazz 8210 (1958) **$35.**

JUST US — New Jazz 8245 (1960) **$35.**

CRACKIN'/with Booker Ervin — New Jazz 8286 (1962) **$45.**

CYMBALISM/with Frank Strozier — New Jazz 8287 (1962) **$45.**

OUT OF THE AFTERNOON/with Roland Kirk — Impulse 23 (1962) orange label **$35.**

PEOPLE/with Frank Strozier — Pacific Jazz 82 (1964) **$35.**

PAT HEALY

JUST DAWN — World Pacific 409 (1958) **$40.**

J. C. HEARD
drums - born 1917 Dayton, OH

THIS IS ME J.C. — Argo 633 (1958) **$35.**

JIMMY HEATH
tenor, alto, baritone saxes, composer
born 1926 Philadelphia, PA

Being a member of a musical family, Heath started gaining acknowledgement in the 40's with many of the best groups of the time. With increasing activity as a composer and arranger during the 50's and 60's, he co-led a quintet with Art Farmer in the mid-60's and became involved with teaching.

THE THUMPER/with Curtis Fuller — Riverside 314/1160 (1960) with Bill Grauer Pro. **$55.**

REALLY BIG/with Clark Terry — Riverside 333/1188 (1960) with Bill Grauer Pro. **$50.**

THE QUOTA/with Freddie Hubbard — Riverside 372/9372 (1961) with Bill Grauer Pro. **$50.**

TRIPLE THREAT/with Freddie Hubbard — Riverside 400/9400 (1962) with Bill Grauer Pro. **$45.**

SWAMP SEED/with Donald Byrd — Riverside 465/9465 (1963) with Bill Grauer Pro. **$45.**

ON THE TRAIL/with Kenny Burrell — Riverside 486/9486 (1965) with Bill Grauer Pro. **$35.**

BILL HENDERSON
vocals - born 1930 Chicago, IL

A good singer with a unique sound, Henderson recorded early on with Horace Silver during late 50's, and with Oscar Peterson in the 60's and then spent a couple of years as vocalist with the Count Basie Band. Afterwards he moved into a career in television and motion pictures, performing most usually as an actor and occasionally as singer.

SINGS — Vee Jay 1015 (1960) **$35.**

BILL HENDERSON — Vee Jay 1031 (1960) **$35.**

WITH THE OSCAR PETERSON TRIO — MGM 4128 (1963) **$25.**

WHEN MY DREAMBOAT COMES HOME — Verve 8619/68619 (1965) with MGM on bottom of label **$20.**

JOE HENDERSON
tenor, soprano saxes, flute, composer - born 1937
Lima, OH

Henderson's hard bop-originated style was exercised in working with Kenny Dorham and Horace Silver in the early 60's, followed by jobs with Freddie Hubbard and Herbie Hancock in the late 60's.

PAGE ONE/with Kenny Dorham — Blue Note 4140/84140 (1963) with NY on label **$40;** with A Division of Liberty on label **$20.**

OUR THING/with Andrew Hill — Blue Note 4152/84152 (1963) with NY on label **$40;** with A Division of Liberty on label **$25.**

IN AND OUT/with Kenny Dorham — Blue Note 4166/84166 (1964) with NY on label **$35;** with A Division of Liberty on label **$20.**

INNER URGE/with McCoy Tyner — Blue Note 4189/84189 (1964) with NY on label **$35;** with A Division of Liberty on label **$20.**

JON HENDRICKS
vocals, songwriter, drums - born 1921 Newark, OH

A great vocalist with an exceptional ability to write lyrics to jazz solos, Hendricks' talents were best demonstrated through his work in the late 50's with Dave Lambert and Annie Ross. Their recordings of Basie tunes and many different jazz compositions were very popular and the group won many awards. Since the group disbanded Hendricks has continued to write, record and tour with groups often including his wife and daughter.

A GOOD GIT-TOGETHER/with Cannonball Adderley — World Pacific 1283 (1959) **$50.**

EVOLUTION OF THE BLUES/with Ben Webster and Pony Poindexter — Columbia 1583/8383 (1961) red label with 3 black logos on each side **$45.**

FAST LIVIN' BLUES/with Billy Mitchell and Pony Poindexter — Columbia 1805/8605 (1961) red label with 3 black logos on each side **$45.**

SALUD — Reprise 20167/6089 (1963) **$25.**

RECORDED IN PERSON AT THE TRIDENT/with Noel Jewkes — Smash 27069/67069 (1965) **$30.**

ERNIE HENRY
alto sax - born 1926 Brooklyn, NY died 1957

Joined the Tadd Dameron group in the late 40's and continued on with name bands of the era through the mid-50's. Henry is best known for his work with Dizzy Gillespie and produced a few recordings under his own name. He died at a young age and on the verge of a seemingly successful career.

PRESENTING/with Kenny Dorham — Riverside 12-222 (1956) white label with Bill Grauer Pro. **$75;** Riverside 12-222 (1958) blue label with Bill Grauer Pro. **$45.**

SEVEN STANDARDS AND A BLUES — Riverside 12-248 (1957) with Bill Grauer Pro. $45.

LAST CHORUS — Riverside 12-266 (1958) with Bill Grauer Pro. $45.

EDDIE HIGGINS
piano - born 1932 Cambridge, MA

EDDIE HIGGINS/with Frank Foster — Vee Jay 3017 (1961) $45.

SOULERO — Atlantic 1446 (1965) with logo on right side $20.

DONNA HIGHTOWER
vocals

TAKE ONE/with Joe Wilder — Capitol 1133 (1959) black label with logo on left side $40.

GEE BABY AIN'T I GOOD TO YOU? — Capitol 1273 (1959) black label with logo on left side $40.

DAVE HILDINGER
piano

THE YOUNG MODERNS — Baton 1204 (1957) $45.

ANDREW HILL
piano, composer - born 1937 Port au Prince, Haiti

BLACK FIRE/with Joe Henderson — Blue Note 4151/84151 (1963) with NY on label $40; with A Division of Liberty on label $20.

JUDGMENT/with Bobby Hutcherson — Blue Note 4159/84159 (1964) with NY on label $30; with A Division of Liberty on label $20.

SMOKESTACK — Blue Note 4160/84160 (1964) with NY on label $30; with A Division of Liberty on label $25.

POINT OF DEPARTURE/with Eric Dolphy — Blue Note 4167/84167 (1964) with NY on label $35; with A Division of Liberty on label $20.

QUINTET/with John Gilmore — Blue Note 4203/84203 (1965) with NY on label $35; with A Division of Liberty on label $20.

COMPULSION/with John Gilmore — Blue Note 4217/84217 (1965) with NY on label $35; with A Division of Liberty on label $20.

EARL "FATHA" HINES
piano - born 1905 Duquesne, PA died

"Fatha" Hines is, in many ways, the father of jazz piano playing. His recordings of the 20's with Louis Armstrong revealed him to be the most influential piano player of this decade. He gained additional fame leading a radio broadcast big band in the 30's which led to a great many famous and aspiring musicians of the bop era working with him during the 40's. In the 50's, Hines worked with smaller groups or as a single and, at times, managed his own night club. Renewed interest through the 60's allowed him to continue to record and tour with undiminished enthusiasm until his death.

EARL HINES AND ALL STARS — Mercury 25018 (1950) 10" $150.

PIANO MOODS — Columbia 6171 (1950) 10" $60.

FATS WALLER MEMORIAL SET/with Nat Jaffe — Advance 4 (1951) 10" $60; *reissued* Brunswick 58034 (1954) 10" $50.

FAMOUS QRS SOLOS — Atlantic 120 (1952) 10" $60.

EARL HINES TRIO — Dial 303 (1952) 10" $60.

EARL HINES ALL STARS — Dial 306 (1952) 10" $150.

JAZZ ROYALTY/with Count Basie — EmArcy 26023 (1954) 10" $50.

EARL "FATHA" HINES — Nocturne 5 (1954) 10" $80; EP 7, EP 8 (1954) $30 ea.

PIANO SOLOS — Label X 3023 (1954) 10" $50.

EARL FATHA HINES WITH BILLY ECKSTINE — RCA Victor LPT 20 (1953) 10" $50.

UP TO DATE/with Budd Johnson — RCA Victor 3380 (1965) dog on top $25.

FATHA PLAYS FATS/with Eddie Duran — Fantasy 3-217 (1956) $45.

SOLO — Fantasy 3-238 (1956) $30.

OH, FATHER! — Epic 3223 (1956) $40.

EARL "FATHA" HINES — Epic 3501 (1958) $30.

"FATHA"/with Jerome Richardson — Tops 1599 (1958) $40; *reissued* Craftsmen 8041 (1960).

COZY'S CARAVAN - EARL'S BACKROOM/with Cozy Cole — Felsted 7002 (1959) $45.

SWINGIN' AND SINGIN'/with Jerome Richardson — Craftsmen 8041 (1960) $30.

EARL'S PEARLS/with Calvin Newborn — MGM 3832 (1960) $30.

ALL STARS/with Eddie Smith — Jazz Panorama 7 (1961) $35.

A MONDAY'S DATE/with James Archey — Riverside 398/9398 (1961) with Bill Grauer Pro. $35.

EARL "FATHA" HINES!/with Orchestra — Capitol 1971 (1963) black label with logo on top $30.

SPONTANEOUS EXPLORATIONS — Contact 2 (1964) $20.

REAL IN CONCERT — Focus 335 (1964) $30.

"FATHA": THE NEW EARL HINES TRIO — Columbia 2320 (1965) $20.

GRAND REUNION/with Coleman Hawkins — Limelight 2020/86020 (1965) $30.

GRAND REUNION - Vol 2/with Roy Eldridge — Limelight 2028/86028 (1965) $30.

MILT HINTON
bass - born 1910 Vicksburg, MS

EAST COAST JAZZ — Bethlehem 1020 (1955) $80.

THE RHYTHM SECTION — Epic 3271 (1956) yellow label $60.

JUTTA HIPP
piano - born 1925 Leipzeg, Germany

Hipp came to America in the mid-50's. Her early works revealed a personal style which was later influenced and lost. However, she does have a few recordings of interest.

QUINTET, NEW SOUND FROM GERMANY — Blue Note 5056 (1954) 10" $100.

AT THE HICKORY HOUSE #1 — Blue Note 1515 (1956) with NY address on label $65; with NY on label $45.

AT THE HICKORY HOUSE #2 — Blue Note 1516 (1956) with NY address on label $65; with NY on label $45.

JUTTA HIPP/with Zoot Sims — Blue Note 1530 (1957) with NY address on label $85; with NY on label $45.

COOL EUROPE — MGM 3157 (1955) with 2 tunes by Albert Hall and 2 tunes by Johnny Dankworth **$80**.

ANDRE HODEIR
composer - born 1921 Paris, France

AMERICAN JAZZMEN PLAY ANDRE HODEIR'S ESSAIS — Savoy 12104 (1957) maroon label **$45**.

THE PARIS SCENE: THE JAZZ GROUP OF PARIS — Savoy 12113 (1958) maroon label **$45**.

JAZZ ET JAZZ — Philips 200-073/600-073 (1964) **$30**.

JOHNNY HODGES
alto sax - born 1906 Cambridge, MA died 1970

Hodges was with Duke Ellington since 1928, with relatively short interruptions to form bands of his own, until his death in 1970. During his time, Hodges was considered to be one of the important influences on alto sax. He recorded extensively with Ellington's band, with members of Ellington's band under various names, and under his own name with Ellington sidemen as well as other jazz greats.

JOHNNY HODGES — Atlantic EP 524 (1954) **$40**.

ALTO SAX — RCA Victor 3000 (1952) 10" **$175**; EP BT3000 (1952) 2 records **$70**.

COLLATES #1/with Al Sears — Clef 111 (1951) 10" **$225**; EP 128, EP 163 (1951) **$50 ea**.

COLLATES #2/with Al Sears — Clef 128 (1952) 10" **$225**; EP 164 (1951) **$50**.

SWING WITH — Norgran 1 (1953) 10" **$200**.

MEMORIES OF ELLINGTON — Norgran 1004 (1954) **$150**; EP 27 (1953) **$50**.

MORE OF — Norgran 1009 (1954) **$150**; EP 63, EP 64, EP 65 (1954) **$50 ea.**; EP 2001-2 (1954) 2 records **$75**.

DANCE BASH/with Flip Phillips — Norgran 1024 (1954) **$125**; EP 117, EP 118, EP 119 (1954) **$40 ea.**; *reissued* Norgran 1091 (1956) **$85**; *reissued* Verve 8176 (1956) **$75**.

CREAMY/with Harry Carney — Norgran 1045 (1955) **$100**; *reissued* Verve 8136 (1957) with Verve Records, Inc. on bottom of label **$70**.

CASTLE ROCK — Norgran 1048 (1955) **$85**; *reissued* Verve 8139 (1957) with Verve Records, Inc. on bottom of label **$70**.

ELLINGTONIA '56/with Harry Carney — Norgran 1055 (1956) **$75**; *reissued* Verve 8145 (1957) with Verve Records, Inc. on bottom of label **$65**.

IN A TENDER MOOD — Norgran 1059 (1956) **$75**; *reissued* Verve 8149 (1957) with Verve Records, Inc. on bottom of label **$65**.

USED TO BE DUKE — Norgran 1060 (1956) **$75**; *reissued* Verve 8150 (1957) with Verve Records, Inc. on bottom of label **$65**.

THE BLUES — Norgran 1061 (1956) **$75**; *reissued* Verve 8151 (1957) with Verve Records, Inc. on bottom of label **$65**.

PERDIDO — Verve 8179 (1957) with Verve Records, Inc. on bottom of label **$60**; *reissue* of Norgran 1024.

IN A MELLOW TONE — Verve 8180 (1957) with Verve Records, Inc. on bottom of label **$60**; *reissue* of Norgran 1004.

DUKE'S IN BED/with Clark Terry — Verve 8203 (1956) with Verve Records, Inc. on bottom of label **$75**; *reissued* American Recording Society 421 (1957) **$65**.

BIG SOUND/with Harry Carney — Verve 8271/6017 (1958) with Verve Records, Inc. on bottom of label **$75**; with MGM on bottom of label **$30**.

PLAYS THE PRETTIEST GERSHWIN/with Strings — Verve 8314/6048 (1959) with Verve Records, Inc. on bottom of label **$60**; with MGM on bottom of label **$30**.

BACK TO BACK/with Duke Ellington — Verve 8317/6055 (1959) with Verve Records, Inc. on bottom of label **$60**.

SIDE BY SIDE/with Ben Webster — Verve 8345/6109 (1959) with Verve Records, Inc. on bottom of label **$60**.

SAVOY MG 12104

american jazzmen play Andre Hodeir

DONALD BYRD
IDREES SULIEMAN
FRANK REHACK
BOBBY JASPAR
HAL McKUSICK
JAY CAMERON
EDDIE COSTA
GEORGE DUVIVIER
BOBBY DONALDSON
and ANNIE ROSS

STEREO

BLUE PYRAMID
JOHNNY HODGES
WILD BILL DAVIS

NOT SO DUKISH/with Roy Eldridge — Verve 8355/68355 (1960) with Verve Records, Inc. at bottom of label **$50**; with MGM on bottom of label **$30**.

BLUES A PLENTY/with Ben Webster — Verve 8358/68358 (1960) with Verve Records, Inc. on bottom of label **$45**; with MGM on bottom of label **$30**.

MULLIGAN MEETS HODGES/with Gerry Mulligan — Verve 8367/68367 (1961) with MGM on bottom of label **$45**.

BLUE HODGES/with Wild Bill Davis — Verve 8406/68406 (1961) with MGM on bottom of label **$40**.

WITH BILLY STRAYHORN — Verve 8452/68452 (1962) with MGM on bottom of label **$35**.

THE ELEVENTH HOUR/with Oliver Nelson — Verve 8492/68492 (1962) with MGM on bottom of label **$40**.

SANDY'S GONE/with Wild Bill Davis — Verve 8561/68561 (1963) with MGM on bottom of label **$35**.

MESS OF BLUES/with Wild Bill Davis — Verve 8570/68570 (1963) with MGM on bottom of label **$35**.

BLUE RABBIT/with Wild Bill Davis — Verve 8599/68599 (1964) with MGM on bottom of label **$35**.

JOE'S BLUES/with Wild Bill Davis — Verve 8617/68617 (1965) with MGM on bottom of label **$35**.

WINGS AND THINGS/with Wild Bill Davis — Verve 8630/68630 (1965) with MGM on bottom of label **$30**.

BLUE PYRAMID/with Wild Bill Davis — Verve 8635/68635 (1965) with MGM on bottom of label **$30**.

HODGES' PODGE — Epic 3105 (1955) *reissue* of his Vacalion 78 RPM days **$60** EP 7073 (1955) **$30**.

ELLA, LENA AND BILLIE/with Ella Fitzgerald and Lena Horne — Columbia 2531 (1956) 10" **$75**; *reissued* Harmony 7125 (1958) with Sarah Vaughan added to 12" LP **$35**.

LADY IN SATIN/with Ray Ellis — Columbia 1157 (1958) red label with 3 black logos on each side **$65**; EP 11571 (1958) **$35**.

THE GOLDEN YEARS — Columbia C3L-21 (1962) red label with 3 black logos on each side, 3 record box set with booklet **$60**.

EVENING WITH BILLIE/with Paul Quinichette — Clef 144 (1953) 10" **$200**; EP 165 (1952) **$50**; *reissued* Clef 686 (1955).

FAVORITES/with Flip Phillips — Clef 118 (1953) 10" **$200**; EP 145, EP 144 (1952) **$50 ea.**; *reissued* Clef 690 (1956).

FAVORITES/with Charlie Shavers — Clef 161 (1954) 10" **$175**; EP 224, EP 225 (1954) **$50 ea.**; *reissued* Clef 686 (1956).

JAZZ AT THE PHILHARMONIC/with Buck Clayton — Clef 169 (1954) 10" **$175**; EP 298, EP 299 (1954) **$50 ea.**; *reissued* Clef 718 (1956).

MUSIC FOR TORCHING/with Benny Carter — Clef 669 (1955) **$95**; EP 368, EP 369 (1955) **$40 ea.**; *reissued* Verve 8026 (1957) with Verve Records, Inc. on bottom of label **$65**; with MGM on bottom of label **$30**.

A RECITAL — Clef 686 (1955) **$95**; *reissued* Verve 8027 (1957) with Verve Records, Inc. on bottom of label **$65**; with MGM on bottom of label **$30**; *reissue* of Clef 161 (1954).

SOLITUDE — Clef 690 (1956) **$90**; *reissued* Verve 8074 (1957) with Verve Records, Inc. on bottom of label **$65**; with MGM on bottom of label **$30**.

VELVET MOODS/with Benny Carter — Clef 713 (1956) **$90**; *reissued* American Recording Society 409 (1956) **$85**; *reissued* Verve 8096 (1957) with Verve Records, Inc. on bottom of label **$65**; with MGM on bottom of label **$30**.

JAZZ RECITAL — Clef 718 (1956) **$80**; *reissued* Verve 8098 (1957) with Verve Records, Inc. on bottom of label **$50**; with MGM on bottom of label **$30**; *reissue* of Clef 169 (1954).

LADY SINGS THE BLUES/with Tony Scott — Clef 721 (1956) **$80**; *reissued* American Recording Society 431 (1956) **$75**; *reissued* Verve 8099 (1956) with Verve Records, Inc. on bottom of label **$60**; with MGM on bottom of label **$30**.

LOVER MAN — Decca 5345 (1952) 10" **$175**; Decca 9-250 7" 4 record box set (1952) **$45**.

THE LADY SINGS — Decca 8215 (1956) black label with silver lettering **$80**; EP 2031 (1956) **$40**.

BLUES ARE BREWIN' — Decca 8701 (1958) black label with silver lettering **$80**.

SINGS THE BLUES/with Tiny Grimes — Score 4014 (1957) **$75**.

BODY & SOUL/with Ben Webster — Verve 8197 (1957) with Verve Records, Inc. on bottom of label **$45**; with MGM on bottom of label **$30**.

SONGS FOR DISTINGUE' LOVERS — Verve 8257/6021 (1959) with Verve Records, Inc. on bottom of label **$45**; with MGM on bottom of label **$25**.

STAY WITH ME/with Tony Scott — Verve 8302 (1959) with Verve Records, Inc. on bottom of label **$45**; with MGM on bottom of label **$25**.

UNFORGETTABLE LADY DAY — Verve 8338/2 (1960) 2 LP's with Verve Records, Inc. on bottom of label **$50**; with MGM on bottom of label **$40**.

THE ESSENTIAL/with Coleman Hawkins — Verve 8410 (1961) with MGM on bottom of label **$35**. (A)

BILLIE HOLIDAY/with Jimmy Cleveland — MGM 3764 (1959) **$50**.

SINGS — Jazztone 1209 (1956) **$45**; *reissue* of Commodore 20005.

LADY LOVE/with Buddy DeFranco — United Artists 14014/15014 (1962) with silhouette of sax player **$45**.

RARE LIVE RECORDING/with Buster Harding — Ric 2001 (1964) recording of a concert done in 1951 **$20**.

BILLIE HOLIDAY — Metro 515 (1965) **$20** *reissue* of her Clef and Verve days.

ONCE UPON A TIME — Mainstream 6022/56022 (1965) **$25** *reissue* of Commodore 20006.

COMMODORE RECORDINGS — Mainstream 6000/56000 (1965) **$25**; *reissue* of Commodore 20005.

AND THE ELLINGTON ALL STARS — American Recording Society 421 (1957) **$65**; *reissue* of Verve 8203 (1956).

WITH LAWRENCE WELK'S ORCHESTRA — Dot 3682/25682 (1965) **$25**.

BILLIE HOLIDAY
vocals - born 1915 Baltimore, MD died 1959

A supreme jazz singer whose recording debut in 1933 with Benny Goodman was just the beginning of a very successful, publicized and very tragic career. "Lady Day" worked through the 30's with Benny Goodman, Count Basie and Artie Shaw and also recorded with The Teddy Wilson Orchestra. She continued to work through the 40's with numerous engagements as soloist and into the 50's in concerts across the U.S. and abroad. The Bessie Smith influence is somewhat noticeable in Billie's style and the voice/tenor integration she and "Prez" (Lester Young) achieved is a milestone in jazz musical history. Billie Holiday is by far one of the most "feeling" vocalist of all times. Unfortunately, but inevitably, her battle with a narcotics addiction robbed Billie of much of her vocal qualities and finally lead to her early and untimely death.

BILLIE HOLIDAY — Vol 1/with Eddie Heywood — Commodore 20005 (1950) 10" **$150**; *reissued* Commodore 30011 (1959) **$65**.

BILLIE HOLIDAY — Vol 2/with Eddie Heywood — Commodore 20006 (1950) 10" **$150**; *reissued* Commodore 30008 (1959) **$65**.

BILLIE AND STAN/with Stan Getz — Dale 25 (1951) 10" **$200**.

BILLIE HOLIDAY/with Lester Young — Jolly Rogers 5020 (1954) 10" **$100**.

SINGS — Columbia 6129 (1950) 10" **$200**.

FAVORITES — Columbia 6163 (1950) 10" **$200**.

LADY DAY — Columbia 637 (1954) red label with Columbia in gold at top **$95**; *reissued* Columbia 637 (1956) red label with 3 black logos on each side **$65**.

JOE HOLIDAY
tenor sax - born 1925 Agira, Sicily

JOE HOLIDAY — Federal EP 256 (1951) **$50.**

NEW SOUNDS FROM NEWARK/with Jordan Fordin — Prestige 131 (1952) 10" **$150.**

MAMBO JAZZ/with Billy Taylor — Prestige 171 (1953) 10" **$125;** EP 1302 (1953) **$45.**

HOLIDAY FOR JAZZ/with Art Farmer — Decca 8487 (1957) black label with silver lettering **$65.**

RED HOLLOWAY
tenor sax - born 1927 Helena, AK

BURNER/with George Butcher — Prestige 7299 (1964) yellow label **$45;** *reissued* Prestige 7299 (1965) blue label with logo on right side **$30.**

COOKIN' TOGETHER/with Jack McDuff — Prestige 7325 (1964) black label with logo on top **$35.**

SAX, STRINGS, SOUL/with Strings — Prestige 7390 (1964) blue label with logo on right side **$30.**

SOUL/with George Benson — Prestige 7473 (1965) blue label with logo on right side **$30.**

BILL HOLMAN
tenor sax, composer, arranger - born 1927 Olive, CA

Holman played in and arranged for many great bands such as Charlie Barnet and Stan Kenton through the 50's, and with Shorty Rogers, Mel Lewis and Gerry Mulligan through the 60's. Since this time, Holman's efforts have been applied to writing and arranging for many of the best singers and big bands.

KENTON PRESENTS/with Bob Gordon — Capitol H6500 (1954) 10" **$80;** EP HL6500 (1954) 2 records **$40.**

GREAT BIG BAND/with Bill Perkins — Capitol 1464 (1960) black label with logo on left side **$30.**

THE FABULOUS/with Charlie Mariano — Coral 57188 (1957) maroon label with silver lettering **$65.**

IN A JAZZ ORBIT/with Jack Sheldon — Andex 3004 (1958) **$45.**

JIVE FOR FIVE/with Mel Lewis — Andex 3005 (1958) **$60.**

WEST COAST JAZZ IN HI FI/with Frank Rosolino — Hi Fi Jazz 609 (1959) **$45.**

RICHARD "GROOVE" HOLMES
organ - born 1931 Camden, NJ

LES McCANN PRESENTS THE DYNAMIC JAZZ ORGAN OF/with Ben Webster — Pacific Jazz 23 (1961) **$45.**

GROOVIN' WITH JUG/with Gene Ammons — Pacific Jazz 32 (1961) **$35.**

SOMETHIN' SPECIAL/with Les McCann — Pacific Jazz 51 (1962) **$25.**

AFTER HOURS — Pacific Jazz 59 (1962) **$25.**

BOOK OF THE BLUES/with Onzy Matthews — Warner Brothers 1553 (1964) **$20**

RED HOLT
drums - born 1932 Rosedale, MS

LOOK OUT, LOOK OUT/with Wallace Burton — Argo 696 (1961) **$45.**

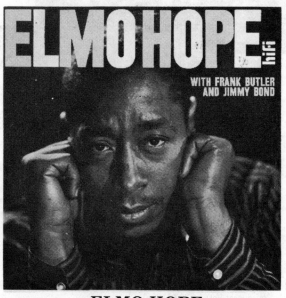

ELMO HOPE
piano, composer - born 1923 New York City, NY
died 1967

Hope's style was reminiscent of a longtime friend, Bud Powell, but as demonstrated on his recordings under his own name and as a sideman, he most definitely had his own very unique and tasteful approach.

TRIO — Blue Note 5029 (1953) 10" **$75.**

QUINTET/with Frank Foster — Blue Note 5044 (1954) 10" **$150.**

MEDITATIONS TRIO — Prestige 7010 (1955) yellow label **$60.**

HOPE MEETS FOSTER/with Frank Foster — Prestige 7021 (1956) yellow label **$100.**

WAIL, FRANK, WAIL/with Elmo Hope — Prestige 7021 (1957) yellow label **$75;** *reissue* of Prestige 7021 (1956).

SEXTET "INFORMAL JAZZ"/with John Coltrane and Hank Mobley — Prestige 7043 (1956) yellow label **$100.**

ELMO HOPE/with Frank Butler and Jimmy Bond — Hi Fi Jazz 616 (1960) **$45.**

JAZZ MESSENGER/ELMO HOPE — Pacific Jazz 33 (1962) **$60.**

HOMECOMING/with Jimmy Heath and Frank Foster — Riverside 12-381 (1961) with Bill Grauer Pro. **$60.**

HOPE-FULL/with Bertha Hope — Riverside 408/9408 (1961) with Bill Grauer Pro. **$30.**

HIGH HOPES — Beacon 401 (1961) **$45.**

TRIO/with Paul Chambers — Celebrity 209 (1962) **$30.**

SOUNDS FROM RIKER'S ISLAND/with John Gilmore — Audio Fidelity 2119/ 6119 (1963) **$45.**

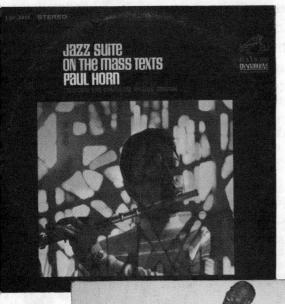

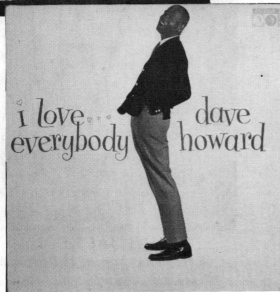

PAUL HORN
flute, alto sax, composer - born 1930 New York City, NY

While much in demand for studio work the young, well-trained Horn began working and recording with Chico Hamilton in the late 50's. His success here led to his forming his own group which appeared, toured and recorded most of the 60's.

HOUSE OF HORN/with Dick Marx — Dot 3091 (1957) **$60.**

PLENTY OF HORN/with Shelly Manne — Dot 9002 (1958) **$50.**

IMPRESSIONS/with John Pisano — World Pacific 1266 (1959) **$45.**

SOMETHING BLUE/with Emil Richards — Hi Fi Jazz 615 (1960) **$35.**

THE SOUND/with Emil Richards — Columbia 1677/8477 (1961) red label with 3 black logos on each side **$30.**

PROFILE OF A JAZZ MUSICIAN/with Emil Richards — Columbia 1922/8722 (1962) red label with 3 black logos on each side **$30.**

IMPRESSIONS OF CLEOPATRA/with Victor Feldman — Columbia 2050/ 8850 (1963) red label with one white logo on each side **$25.**

JAZZ SUITE ON THE MASS TEXTS/with Frank Rosolino — RCA Victor 3414 (1965) dog on top **$25.**

SHIRLEY HORN
vocals, piano - born 1934 Washington, DC

EMBERS AND ASHES — Stereocraft 16 (1961) **$20.**

LOADS OF LOVE/with Kenny Burrell — Mercury 20761/60761 (1963) black label **$35.**

WITH HORN — Mercury 20835/60835 (1964) black label **$35.**

TRAVELIN' LIGHT/with Frank Wess and Jerome Richardson — ABC Paramount 538 (1965) **$45.**

DAVE HOWARD
vocals - born San Francisco, CA

I LOVE EVERYBODY/with Bud Shank — Choreo 5 (1961) **$45.**

FREDDIE HUBBARD
trumpet, fluegelhorn - born 1938 Indianapolis, IN

Hubbard became popular quite rapidly in the early 60's working and recording with many musicians and groups in an increasingly avantgarde style. He was first heard with Art Blakey and Quincy Jones and was soon recording under his own name and on sessions with Eric Dolphy and Ornette Coleman.

OPEN SESAME/with Tina Brooks — Blue Note 4040/84040 (1960) with NY address on label **$50**; with NY on label **$35**; with A Division of Liberty on label **$20.**

GOIN' UP/with Hank Mobley — Blue Note 4056/84056 (1960) with NY address on label **$50**; with NY on label **$35**; with A Division of Liberty on label **$20.**

HUB CAP/with Jimmy Heath — Blue Note 4073/84073 (1961) with NY address on label **$45**; with NY on label **$35**; with A Division of Liberty on label **$20.**

READY FOR FREDDIE/with Wayne Shorter — Blue Note 4085/84085 (1961) with NY address on label **$45**; with NY on label **$35**; with A Division of Liberty on label **$20.**

HUB TONES/with James Spaulding — Blue Note 4115/84115 (1962) with NY on label **$40**; with A Division of Liberty on label **$20.**

HERE TO STAY/with Wayne Shorter — Blue Note 4135/84135 (1962) with NY on label **$40**; with A Division of Liberty on label **$20.**

BREAKING POINT/with James Spaulding — Blue Note 4172/84172 (1964) with NY on label **$35**; with A Division of Liberty on label **$20.**

BLUE SPIRITS/with Joe Henderson — Blue Note 4196/84196 (1965) with NY on label **$35**; with A Division of Liberty on label **$20.**

THE ARTISTRY OF/with John Gilmore — Impulse 27 (1962) orange label **$35.**

THE BODY AND SOUL/with Eric Dolphy — Impulse 38 (1963) orange label **$35.**

LANGSTON HUGHES
narrater

THE STORY OF JAZZ — Folkways 7312 (1954) 10" with pamphlet **$10.**

THE STORY OF JAZZ FOR CHILDREN AND YOUNG PEOPLE AND OTHERS — Folkways 712 (1954) 10" with pamphlet **$10.**

THE WEARY BLUES/with Charlie Mingus and Red Allen — MGM 3697 (1958) **$45.**

HELEN HUMES
vocals - born 1913 Louisville, KY died 1981

Originally recorded with James P. Johnson in the late 20's but is best known as a vocalist with Count Basie from 1935 to 1942. Humes' big hit was Be-baba-leba in 1945 and she continued to work on the West Coast and tour along side Red Norvo through the late 50's. Her career continued at a slower pace, picked up in the 70's with appearances, tours and some recordings which were very well received.

HELEN HUMES — Dootone EP 206 (1955) **$40.**

TAIN'T NOBODY'S BIZ'NESS IF I DO/with Benny Carter — Contemporary 3571/7571 (1960) yellow label **$45.**

SONGS I LOVE TO SING/with Art Pepper — Contemporary 3582/7582 (1961) yellow label **$40.**

SWINGIN' WITH HUMES/with Teddy Edwards — Contemporary 3598/7598 (1961) yellow label **$40.**

LURLEAN HUNTER
vocals - born 1928 Clarksdale, MS

LONESOME GAL — RCA Victor 1151 (1955) dog on top **$50**.

NIGHT LIFE — Vik 1061 (1956) **$45**.

STEPPING OUT — Vik 1116 (1958) **$45**.

BLUE AND SENTIMENTAL — Atlantic 1344 (1960) with logo on right side **$35**.

BOBBY HUTCHERSON
vibes - born 1941 Los Angeles, CA

DIALOGUE — Blue Note 4198/84198 (1965) with NY on label **$30**; with A Division of Liberty on label **$20**.

SOLOMON ILORI
vocals, drums, guitar - born Nigeria

AFRICAN HIGH LIFE/with Hosea Taylor — Blue Note 4136/84136 (1963) with NY on label **$35**; with A Division of Liberty on label **$20**.

PETER IND
bass - born 1928 Oxbridge, Middlesex, England

LOOKING OUT/with Sheila Jordan — Wave 1 (1961) **$20**.

ISLES OF JAZZ
Deuchar, Rendell, Christie, Smith

ISLES OF JAZZ BRITAINS BEST — Discovery 2010 (1954) 10″ **$50**.

CHUBBY JACKSON
bass, songwriter - born 1918 New York City, NY

Jackson worked as sidemen in many name bands but is most prominently known for his work with Woody Herman from the early 40's into the 50's. He has led his own trio as early as the late 40's and continued off and on through the 60's during which time he wrote and taught music and did work through the television media.

CHUBBY JACKSON/BILL HARRIS — Norgran EP 57 (1953) **$50**.

ALL STARS — Prestige 105 (1950) 10″ **$200**; EP 1318, EP 1323 (1950) **$50** ea.

JAZZ JOURNEY/with Bill Harris — Mercury 25076 (1951) 10″ **$125**.

CHUBBY JACKSON — Rainbow 708 (1954) 10″ **$100**.

& ALL STARS QUARTET — Columbia 756 (1956) red label with 3 black logos on each side **$80**.

CHUBBY'S BACK/with Sandy Mosse — Argo 614 (1958) **$45**.

I'M ENTITLED TO YOU/with Sandy Mosse — Argo 625 (1958) **$45**.

CHUBBY TAKES OVER/with Bob Brookmeyer — Everest 5009/1009 (1959) **$35**.

THE BIG THREE/with Marty Napoleon — Everest 5029/1029 (1960) **$35**.

JAZZ THEN TILL NOW/with Marty Napoleon — Everest 5041/1041 (1959) **$35**.

THE BIG THREE — Stereo Craft 108 (1958) **$35**.

CHUBBY JACKSON DISCOVERS MARIA MARSHALL/with Sam Taylor — Crown 208/5183 (1960) **$20**.

TWIST CALLING — Laurie 2011 (1962) **$30**.

FRED JACKSON
tenor sax

HOOTIN' & TOOTIN' — Blue Note 4094/84094 (1962) with NY on label **$45**; with Division of Liberty on label **$20**.

MILT JACKSON
vibes, piano - born 1923 Detroit, MI

Beginning in the mid-40's with Dizzy Gillespie, Jackson established himself as a modern master vibes player. He worked with Tadd Dameron, Thelonious Monk and Woody Herman before becoming a founding member of the Modern Jazz Quartet. The MJQ was a highly successful group for 22 years including subsequent reunions. Before during and after his career with the MJQ, Jackson has had many recordings with many other major musicians and stands as a significant influence on his instrument throughout his career.

MILT JACKSON — Dee Gee 1002 (1951) 10″ **$200**.

WIZARD OF THE VIBES/with Lou Donaldson — Blue Note 5011 (1952) 10″ **$150** *reissued* Blue Note 1509 (1956).

MILT JACKSON AND THELONIOUS MONK/with Lou Donaldson — Blue Note 1509 (1956) with NY address on label **$80**; with NY on label **$45**; with A Division of Liberty on label **$20**; *reissue* of Blue Note 5011.

QUINTET/with Henry Bozier — Prestige 183 (1954) 10″ **$100**; EP 1356, EP 1-36 (1954) **$40** ea.

QUARTET/with Horace Silver — Prestige 7003 (1955) yellow label **$60**; *reissue* Prestige 7224 (1962).

SOUL PIONEERS — Prestige 7224 (1962) yellow label **$45**; *reissue* of Prestige 7003.

MILT JACKSON/with Billy Mitchell — Savoy 15058 (1950) 10″ **$100**; *reissue* Savoy 12061 (1956).

OPUS DE JAZZ/with Frank Wess — Savoy 12036 (1955) maroon label **$60**.

ROLL 'EM BAGS/with Lucky Thompson — Savoy 12042 (1956) maroon label **$60**.

THE QUARTET/with John Lewis — Savoy 12046 (1956) maroon label **$45**.

MEET MILT JACKSON/with Lucky Thompson — Savoy 12061 (1956) maroon label **$50**; *reissue* of Savoy 15058 (1950).

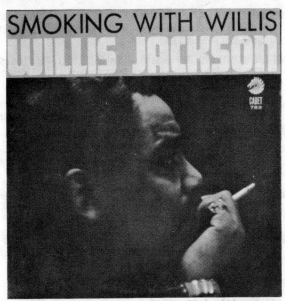

JAZZ SKYLINE/with Lucky Thompson — Savoy 12070 (1956) maroon label **$50**.

JACKSONVILLE/with Lucky Thompson — Savoy 12080 (1956) maroon label **$50**.

BALLADS & BLUES/with Lucky Thompson — Atlantic 1242 (1956) black label **$50**; EP 601 (1956) **$20**; *reissued* Atlantic 1242 with logo on right side **$25**.

PLENTY, PLENTY SOUL/with Frank Foster and Cannonball Adderley — Atlantic 1269 (1957) black label **$45**; *reissued* Atlantic 1269 with logo on right side **$25**.

BAGS & FLUTES/with Bobby Jaspar and Frank Wess — Atlantic 1294 (1958) **$45**.

BEAN BAGS/with Coleman Hawkins — Atlantic 1316 (1959) with logo on right side **$35**.

BALLAD ARTISTRY/with Quincy Jones — Atlantic 1342 (1960) with logo on right side **$25**.

BAGS & TRANE/with John Coltrane — Atlantic 1368 (1961) with logo on right side **$35**.

VIBRATIONS/with Jimmy Heath — Atlantic 1417 (1964) with logo on right side **$25**.

BAGS OPUS/with Benny Golson — United Artists 4022/5022 (1959) red label **$45**.

BAGS MEETS WES/with Wes Montgomery — Riverside 407/9407 (1961) with Bill Grauer Pro. **$35**.

BIG BAGS/with All Star Orchestra — Riverside 429/9429 (1962) with Bill Grauer Pro. **$25**.

INVITATION/with Kenny Dorham — Riverside 446/9446 (1963) with Bill Grauer Pro. **$35**.

FOR SOMEONE IN LOVE — Riverside 478/9478 (1965) with Bill Grauer Pro. **$25**.

STATEMENTS/with Paul Chambers — Impulse 14 (1961) orange label **$35**.

JAZZ N' SAMBA — Impulse 70 (1964) orange label **$25**.

IN A NEW SETTING/with Jimmy Heath — Limelight 82006/86006 (1965) fold out cover **$35**.

WILLIS JACKSON
tenor sax

PLEASE MR. JACKSON/with Bill Jennings — Prestige 7162 (1959) yellow label **$60**; *reissued* Prestige 7162 (1965) blue label with logo on right side **$25**.

COOL GATOR/with Bill Jennings — Prestige 7172 (1960) yellow label **$60**; *reissued* Prestige 7172 (1965) blue label with logo on right side **$25**.

BLUE GATOR/with Bill Jennings — Prestige 7183 (1961) yellow label **$50**; *reissued* Prestige 7183 (1965) blue label with logo on right side **$25**.

REALLY GROOVIN'/with Jimmy Neely — Prestige 7196 (1961) yellow label **$50**; *reissued* Prestige 7196 (1965) blue label with logo on right side **$25**.

COOKIN' SHERRY/with Bill Jennings — Prestige 7211 (1962) yellow label **$45**; *reissued* Prestige 7211 (1965) blue label with logo on right side **$25**.

THUNDERBIRD/with Bill Jennings — Prestige 7232 (1962) yellow label **$45**; *reissued* Prestige 7232 (1965) blue label with logo on right side **$25**.

BOSSA NOVA PLUS/with Kenny Burrell — Prestige 7260 (1962) yellow label **$40**; *reissued* Prestige 7260 (1965) blue label with logo on right side **$20**.

NEAPOLITAN NIGHTS/with Bucky Pizzarelli — Prestige 7264 (1962) yellow label **$45**; *reissued* Prestige 7264 (1965) blue label with logo on right side **$25**.

LOOSE/with Bill Jones — Prestige 7273 (1963) yellow label **$45**; *reissued* Prestige 7273 (1965) blue label with logo on right side **$25**.

GREASE N' GRAVY/with Pat Azzara — Prestige 7285 (1963) yellow label **$45**; *reissued* blue label with logo on right side **$25**.

THE GOOD LIFE/with Jimmy Neely — Prestige 7296 (1964) yellow label **$40**.

MORE GRAVY/with Pat Azzara — Prestige 7317 (1964) yellow label **$40**.

BOSS SHOUTIN'/with Pat Azzara — Prestige 7329 (1965) blue label with logo on right side **$35**.

JACKSON'S ACTIONS/with Pat Azzara — Prestige 7348 (1965) blue label with logo on right side **$35**.

IN MY SOLITUDE/with Richard Wyands — Moodsville 17 (1962) **$45**.

SMOKING WITH WILLIS/with Vincent Corrao — Cadet 763 (1965) dark blue and light blue label with Cadet on top in pink and white **$25**.

WILLIS JACKSON — Verve 8782 (1964) with MGM on bottom of label **$35**.

ILLINOIS JACQUET
tenor sax - born 1922 Broussard, LA

Jacquet had a tremendous hit in Flying Home when with the Lionel Hampton Band in the early 40's. In the following years he joined with Cab Calloway and Count Basie before starting his own group in the late 40's. He toured with JATP extensively during the 50's and has remained active in the U.S. and Europe with tours, festivals and recordings.

ILLINOIS JACQUET JAM SESSION — Apollo 104 (1950) 10" **$200**; EP 602 (1950) **$70**.

BATTLE OF THE SAXES/with Lester Young — Aladdin 701 (1954) 10" **$150**; EP 501 (1953) **$50**.

AND HIS TENOR SAX/with Miles Davis — Aladdin 708 (1954) 10" **$150**; EP 504, EP 511 (1953) **$50** ea.

AND HIS TENOR SAX — Aladdin 803 (1956) **$80**; *reissue* in part of Aladdin 701.

COLLATES #1 — Clef 112 (1951) 10" **$100**; EP 126, EP 143 (1951) **$50** ea.

COLLATES #2 — Clef 129 (1952) 10" **$100**; EP 166, EP 167 (1952) **$50** ea.

JAZZ MOODS — Clef 622 (1954) **$100**; EP 207 (1954) **$50**.

AND HIS ORCHESTRA — Clef 676 (1955); EP 374 (1955) **$80**; *reissued* Verve 8061 (1957) with Verve Records, Inc. on bottom of label **$60**; with MGM on bottom of label **$25**.

KID AND THE BRUTE/with Ben Webster — Clef 680 (1955) **$75**; *reissued* Verve 8065 (1957) with Verve Records, Inc. on bottom of label **$50**; with MGM on bottom of label **$25**.

JAZZ MOODS — Clef 700 (1956) **$60**; EP 207 (1956) **$35**; *reissued* Verve 8084 (1957) with Verve Records, Inc. on bottom of label **$45**; with MGM on bottom of label **$25**; *reissue* in part of Clef 112.

PORT OF RICO/with Count Basie — Clef 701 (1956) **$60**; *reissued* Verve 8085 (1957) with Verve Records, Inc. on bottom of label **$45**; with MGM on bottom of label **$25**.

GROOVIN' WITH JACQUET — Clef 702 (1956) **$65**; EP 245 (1956) **$35**; *reissued* Verve 8086 (1957) with Verve Records, Inc. on bottom of label **$45**; with MGM on bottom of label **$25**.

SWINGS THE THING — Clef 750 (1956) **$60**; *reissued* Verve 8023 (1957) with Verve Records, Inc. on bottom of label **$45**; with MGM on bottom of label **$25**.

TENOR SAX/with Emmett Berry — Savoy 15024 (1950) 10" **$100**.

FLIES AGAIN/with Budd Johnson — Roulette 52035 (1959) **$45**.

ILLINOIS JACQUET/with Leo Parker — Epic 16033/17033 (1962) yellow label **$45**.

FLYING HOME — Imperial 9184 (1962) **$45**; *reissue* of Aladdin recording days.

BLACK VELVET/with J.J. Johnson — RCA 3236 (1964) dog on top **$60**; EPB 3236 (1964) **$20**.

MESSAGE/with Kenny Burrell — Argo 722 (1963) **$40**.

DESERT WINDS/with Kenny Burrell — Argo 735 (1964) **$40**.

PLAYS COLE PORTER/with Benny Golson — Argo 746 (1965) **$35**.

SPECTRUM/with Ernie Royal — Argo 754 (1965) **$35**.

RUSSELL JACQUET
trumpet, vocals - born 1917 Broussard, LA

RUSSELL JACQUET/with Sonny Stitt — King 295 (1954) 10" **$100**; EP 308, EP 309 (1954) **$50** ea.

AHMAD JAMAL
piano - born 1930 Pittsburgh, PA

TRIO — Epic 3212 (1956) **$35**.

CHAMBER MUSIC OF NEW JAZZ — Argo 602 (1956) **$40**.

COUNT 'EM 88 — Argo 610 (1956) **$40**.

AT THE PERSHING — Argo 628 (1958) **$35**.

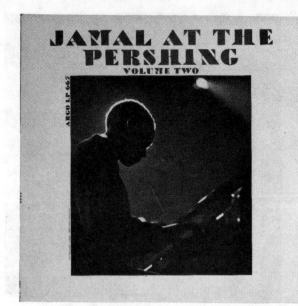

TRIO — VOL 4 — Argo 636 (1958) **$35**.

PORTFOLIO OF — Argo 638 (1958) 2 record special limited edition **$50**.

AT THE PENTHOUSE — Argo 646 (1959) **$35**.

HAPPY MOOD — Argo 662 (1960) **$30**.

AT THE PERSHING — VOL 2 — Argo 667 (1961) **$20**.

LISTEN TO THE — Argo 673 (1961) **$20**.

ALHAMBRA — Argo 685 (1961) **$20**.

ALL OF YOU — Argo 691 (1962) **$15**.

AT THE BLACKHAWK — Argo 703 (1962) **$15**.

MACANUDO — Arco 712 (1963) **$15**.

POIN'CI-AN'A — Argo 719 (1963) **$15**.

NAKED CITY THEME — Argo 733 (1964) **$15**.

THE ROAR OF THE GREASEPAINT — Argo 751 (1965) **$15**.

EXTENSIONS — Argo 758 (1965) **$15** during Argo to Cadet changeover with Cadet chess horse and Argo on cover.

BOB JAMES
piano, composer - born 1939 Marshall, MO

BOLD CONCEPTIONS — Mercury 20768/60768 (1963) **$25**.

EXPLOSIONS — ESP 1009 (1965) **$20**.

BOBBY JASPAR
tenor sax, flute, clarinet - born 1926 Liege, Belgium died 1963

Widely known and recorded in Paris in the early 50's, Jaspar came to America in 1956 and worked with many great artists such as Miles Davis, J.J. Johnson, Chet Baker and Donald Byrd amongst many others. Jaspar was an outstanding tenorman who also recorded with groups of his own but, unfortunately, the larger portion of his recordings were not American issues. Jaspar's career was cut short suddenly when he died of heart problems in 1963.

AND HIS ALL STARS/with Rene Urtreger — EmArcy 36105 (1957) with drummer logo **$75**.

TENOR AND FLUTE/with Idrees Sulieman — Riverside 12-240 (1957) blue label **$60**; *reissued* after 1965 with same cover but black label with #SMJ 6156M on left side and Victor Musical Industories on bottom of label.

FLUTE FLIGHT/with Herbie Mann — Prestige 7124 (1957) yellow label **$75**.

JAZZ BROTHERS
Gap Mangione and Chuck Mangione

JAZZ BROTHERS — Riverside 335/9335 (1960) blue label with Bill Grauer Pro. **$50**.

EY BABY — Riverside 371/9371 (1961) blue label with Bill Grauer Pro. **$50.**

PRING FEVER/with Sal Nistico — Riverside 405/9405 (1962) blue label with Bill Grauer Pro. **$50.**

THE JAZZ COURIERS
Dave Pike, Eugene Russell, John Goodman, Reed Vaughan

HE JAZZ COURIERS — Whippet 700 (1956) **$60.**

JAZZ CRUSADERS
Wilton Fedler, Joe Sample, Wayne Henderson Nesbert "Sticks" Hooper

REEDOM SOUND/with Roy Gaines and Jimmy Bond — Pacific Jazz 27 (1961) **$45.**

OOKIN' BACK/with Roy Gaines and Jimmy Bond — Pacific Jazz 43 (1961) **$45.**

T THE LIGHTHOUSE/with Victor Gaskin — Pacific Jazz 57 (1962) yellow vinyl **$45.**

OUGH TALK/with Bobby Haynes — Pacific Jazz 68 (1963) **$40.**

EAT WAVE/with Bobby Haynes — Pacific Jazz 76 (1963) **$40.**

AZZ WALTZ/with Les McCann and Bobby Haynes — Pacific Jazz 81 (1964) **$35.**

TRETCHIN' OUT/with Joe Pass and Monk Montgomery — Pacific Jazz 83 (1964) **$35.**

HE THING/with Monk Montgomery and Victor Gaskin — Pacific Jazz 87 (1964) **$35.**

HILE CON SOUL/with Hubert Laws and Clare Fischer — Pacific Jazz 20092/10092 (1965) **$30.**

JAZZ EXPONENTS
Elliott, Jack Gridley, Norm Diamond, Dick Riorda

THE JAZZ EXPONENTS — Argo 622 (1958) **$30.**

JAZZ FIVE
Barry Klein, Vic Arch, Brian Dee Bill Eyden, Malcolm Cacil

THE HOOTER — Riverside 361/9361 (1960) blue label with Bill Grauer Pro. **$35.**

JAZZ LABORATORY

JAZZ LABORATORY SERIES NO. 2/with Phil Woods — Signal 102 (1955) **$75.**

THE JAZZ MAKERS
Ronnie Ross, Art Ellefson, Sam Jones Stan Wasser, Allan Ganley

THE JAZZ MAKERS — Atlantic 1333 (1960) logo on right side **$45.**

JAZZ MEN DETROIT
Pepper Adams, Kenny Burrell, Tommy Flanagan Paul Chambers, Kenny Clarke

JAZZ MEN DETROIT — Savoy 12083 (1955) maroon label **$65.**

THE JAZZ MODES
Julius Watkins and Charlie Rouse

JAZZVILLE/with Art Blakey — Dawn 1101 (1956) **$80.**

LES JAZZ MODES/with Paul Chambers — Dawn 1108 (1956) **$80.**

MOOD IN SCARLET/with Ron Jefferson — Dawn 1117 (1956) **$80** *reissued* Seeco 466 (1960).

THE MOST HAPPY FELLA — Atlantic 1280 (1958) black label **$50.**

THE JAZZ MODES — Atlantic 1306 (1958) black label **$50.**

SMART JAZZ FOR THE SMART SET — Seeco 466 (1960) **$25;** *reissue* of Dawn 1117.

JAZZ STUDIO

ONE/with Frank Foster and Paul Quinichette — Decca 8058 (1954) black label with silver lettering **$85;** EP 2130 (1953) **$40.**

SIX/THE AMRAM-BARROW QUARTET — Decca 8558 (1957) black label with silver lettering **$40.**

THE JAZZPICKERS

FOR MODERNS ONLY/with Buddy Collette — EmArcy 36111 (1957) drummer logo $60.

COMMAND PERFORMANCE/with Red Norvo — EmArcy 36123 (1958) drummer logo $45.

THE JAZZTET
Art Farmer and Benny Golson

MEET THE JAZZTET/with Curtis Fuller — Argo 664 (1960) $40.

BIG CITY SOUNDS/with Tom McIntosh — Argo 672 (1960) $40.

AND JOHN LEWIS — Argo 684 (1961) $45.

AT BIRDHOUSE/with Cedar Walton — Argo 688 (1961) $40.

HERE AND NOW/with Gracham Moncur — Mercury 20698/60698 (1962) black label $50.

ANOTHER GIT TOGETHER/with Harold Mabern — Mercury 20737/60737 (1962) black label $50.

EDDIE JEFFERSON
vocals - born 1918 Pittsburgh, PA died 1979

Jefferson is credited with being the originator of the concept of setting lyrics to what had been solos on recordings, a concept later expanded and popularized by Lambert, Hendricks and Ross, the great jazz vocal group. Jefferson worked through the 40's as a vocalist and in the 50's became manager of the James Moody Band and remained through the 60's.

LETTER FROM HOME/with Johnny Griffin — Riverside 411/9411 (1962) blue label with Bill Grauer Pro. $45.

RON JEFFERSON
drums - born 1926 New York City, NY

LOVE LIFTED ME/with Wilbur Brown — Pacific Jazz 36 (1962) $45.

JOHN JENKINS
alto sax - born 1931 Chicago, IL

JAZZ EYES/with Donald Byrd — Regent 6056 (1957) green label $60.

JOHN JENKINS/with Kenny Burrell — Blue Note 1573 (1958) with NY address on label $55; with NY on label $30; with A Division of Liberty on label $20.

JOHN JENKINS, CLIFF JORDAN, BOBBY TIMMONS — New Jazz 8232 (1960) $35.

BILL JENNINGS
guitar

BILL JENNINGS QUARTET — King EP 342, EP 356 (1955) $50.

BILLY IN THE LION'S DEN/with Leo Parker — King 527 (1958) $85; EP 341 (1958) $40.

GUITAR, VIBES — Audio Lab 1514 (1959) $70.

ENOUGH SAID/with Jack McDuff — Prestige 7164 (1959) yellow label $65.

GLIDE ON/with Jack McDuff — Prestige 7177 (1960) yellow label $65.

JFK QUINTET

NEW JAZZ FRONTIERS FROM WASHINGTON — Riverside 396/9396 (1962) blue label with Bill Grauer Pro. $30.

YOUNG IDEAS — Riverside 424/9424 (1962) blue label with Bill Grauer Pro. $30.

ANTONIO CARLOS JOBIM
composer, guitar, piano - born 1927 Rio de Janeiro, Brazil

THE COMPOSER OF "DESAFINADO" PLAYS — Verve 8547/68547 (1963) with MGM on bottom of label $20.

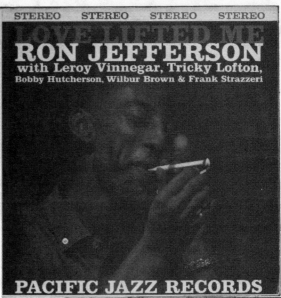

BUDD JOHNSON
tenor, alto, baritone saxes, clarinet, composer born 1910 Dallas, TX

Johnson gained a great deal of recognition with Earl Hines in the 30 and 40's and served as an important member of many of the pionee groups that helped bring bop into being. He has continued to wor with name bands and groups of his own for tours and man recordings as well as becoming active in lecturing and clinics.

BLUES A LA MODE/with Joe Newman — Felsted 2007/7007 (1958) $65.

AND THE FOUR BRASS GIANTS/with Nat Adderley, Harry Edison, Clark Terr and Ray Nance — Riverside 343/9343 (1960) blue label with B Grauer Pro. $60.

LET'S SWING/with Tommy Flanagan — Prestige Swingsville 2015 (1961) $4

FRENCH COOKIN'/with Kenny Burrell — Argo 721 (1963) $35.

YA! YA!/with Al Williams — Argo 736 (1964) $35.

OFF THE WALL/with Joe Newman — Argo 748 (1965) $35.

DICK JOHNSON
alto sax, clarinet - born 1925 Brockton, MA

MUSIC FOR SWINGING MODERNS/with Bill Havemann — EmArcy 36081 (195 drummer logo $65.

MOST LIKELY/with Dave McKenna — Riverside 12-253 (1957) blue label with B Grauer Pro. $50.

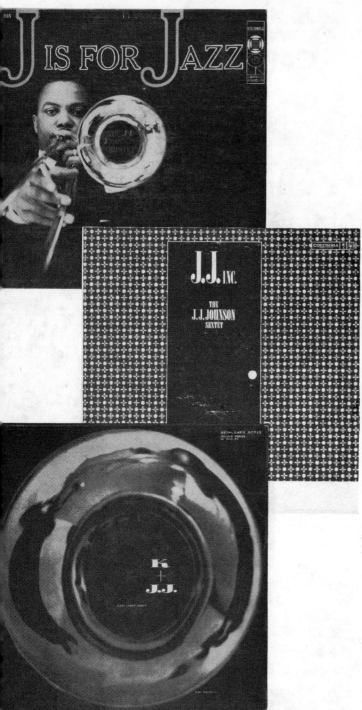

J. J. JOHNSON
trombone, composer - born 1924 Indianapolis, IN

Through the development of be-bop, J.J. Johnson was the first trombonist to play with the facility required. He worked with many great bands in the 40's, namely Bennie Carter and Count Basie and, in the 50's, collaborated in a very successful group and series of recordings with Kai Winding. The late 50's exposed Johnson's composing abilities and, though he continued to play, he devoted more time and energy to composing and concentrated on arranging, conducting and compositions for movies and television.

JAY AND KAI/with Kai Winding — Savoy 15038 (1954) 10" **$100**; *reissued* in part Savoy 12010 (1955).

JAY AND KAI — VOL 2/with Kai Winding and Leo Parker — Savoy 15048 (1954) 10" **$125**; *reissued* in part Savoy 12010 (1955).

JAY AND KAI — Vol 3/with Kai Winding and Sonny Rollins — Savoy 15049 (1954) 10" **$125**; *reissued* Savoy 12106 (1957).

JAY AND KAI — Savoy 12010 (1955) **$80**; *reissue* of Savoy 15038 and 15048.

JAZZ QUINTET/with Cecil Payne and Sonny Rollins — Savoy 12106 (1957) **$100**; *reissue* of Savoy 15049.

J.J. JOHNSON ALL STARS/with Clifford Brown — Blue Note 5028 (1954) 10" **$125**; *reissued* Blue Note 1505 (1956).

THE EMINENT/with Wynton Kelly — Blue Note 5057 (1954) 10" **$100**; *reissued* in part Blue Note 1505 (1955) and Blue Note 1506 (1956).

J.J. JOHNSON — Vol 3/with Hank Mobley — Blue Note 5070 (1954) 10" **$100**; *reissued* Blue Note 1506 (1956).

THE EMINENT — Blue Note 1505 (1956) with NY address on label **$80**; with NY on label **$40**; with A Division of Liberty on label **$20**.

THE EMINENT - Vol 2 — Blue Note 1506 (1956) with NY address on label **$80**; with NY on label **$40**; with A Division of Liberty on label **$20**.

MODERN JAZZ TROMBONES/with Kai Winding — Prestige 109 (1952) 10" **$150**.

MODERN JAZZ TROMBONES/with Bennie Green — Prestige 123 (1952) 10" **$150**; EP 1332 (1952) **$50**; *reissued* Prestige 7030 (1956).

JAY AND KAI — Prestige 195 (1954) 10" **$100**; EP 1362, EP 1368 (1954) **$45** ea.; *reissued* Prestige 7253 (1962).

TROMBONE BY THREE/with Kai Winding and Bennie Green — Prestige 7030 (1956) yellow label, four songs by Green **$90**; *reissue* of Prestige 123.

LOOKING BACK — Prestige 7253 (1962) yellow label **$60**; *reissue* of Prestige 195.

KAI WINDING AND J.J. JOHNSON — Bethlehem 13 (1955) **$60**; EP 115, EP 116 **$30** ea.; *reissued* Bethlehem 6001 (1956).

K + JJ EAST COAST JAZZ 7/with Kai Winding — Bethlehem 6001 (1956) **$45**.

JAZZ WORKSHOP — TROMBONE RAPPORT/with Kai Winding, Bennie Green and Willie Dennis — Debut 5 (1954) 10" **$125**.

THE QUINTET — Debut 124 (1958) **$75**.

FOUR TROMBONES — Debut 126 (1958) **$60**; *reissue* of Debut 5.

AFTERNOON AT BIRDLAND/with Kai Winding — Vik 1040 (1957) **$60**.

JAZZ SOUTH PACIFIC — Regent 6001 (1956) green label **$45**.

FOUR TROMBONES — Fantasy 6008 (1963) **$45**; *reissue* of Debut 5.

J.J.!/with Jimmy Cleveland — RCA 3350 (1965) dog on top **$35**.

JAY AND KAI/with Kai Winding — Columbia 2573 (1956) 10" **$60**; EP B9731 (1956) **$20**; *reissued* Columbia 973 (1957).

TROMBONE FOR TWO/with Kai Winding — Columbia 742 (1955) red label with 3 black logos on each side **$50**; with one white logo on each side **$20**.

J.J. JOHNSON — KAI WINDING + 6 — Columbia 892 (1956) red label with 3 black logos on each side **$50**; with one white logo on each side **$20**.

JAY AND KAI/with Kai Winding — Columbia 973 (1957) red label with 3 black logos on each side **$45**; with one white logo on each side **$20**; *reissue* of Columbia 2573.

J IS FOR JAZZ/with Bobby Jaspar — Columbia 935 (1956) red label with 3 black logos on each side **$50**; with one white logo on each side **$20**.

JAY & KAI AT NEWPORT/with Kai Winding — Columbia 932 (1956) red label with 3 black logos on each side **$40**; with one white logo on each side **$20**; LP has Dave Brubeck on one side.

FIRST PLACE/with Paul Chambers — Columbia 1030 (1957) red label with 3 black logos on each side **$45**; with one white logo on each side **$20**.

DIAL J.J./with Bobby Jaspar — Columbia 1084 (1957) red label with 3 black logos on each side **$50**; with one white logo on each side **$20**.

J.J. IN PERSON/with Nat Adderley — Columbia 1161/8009 (1958) red label with 3 black logos on each side **$45**; with one white logo on each side **$20**.

BLUE TROMBONE/with Tommy Flanagan — Columbia 1303/8109 (1959) red label with 3 black logos on each side **$40**; with one white logo on each side **$20**.

REALLY LIVIN'/with Bobby Jaspar — Columbia 1383/8178 (1959) red label with 3 black logos on each side **$50**; with one white logo on each side **$20**.

J.J., INC./with Clifford Jordan — Columbia 1606/8406 (1960) red label with 3 black logos on each side **$45**; with one white logo on each side **$20**.

A TOUCH OF SATIN/with Victor Feldman — Columbia 1737/8537 (1960) red label with 3 black logos on each side **$35**; with one white logo on each side **$20**.

TROMBONE & VOICES — Columbia 1547/8347 (1960) red label with 3 black logos on each side **$30**; with one white logo on each side **$20**.

THE GREAT KAI & J.J./with Kai Winding — Impulse 1 (1961) orange label **$35**. Ⓐ

PROOF POSITIVE/with Harold Mabern — Impulse 68 (1964) orange label **$30**. Ⓐ

OSIE JOHNSON
drums, composer, vocals - born 1923 Washington, D.C.

THE HAPPY JAZZ OF/with Frank Wess — Bethlehem 66 (1957) maroon label **$60**.

A BIT OF THE BLUES/with Al Cohn — RCA Victor 1369 (1957) dog on top **$65**.

SWINGIN' SOUNDS/with Frank Wess — Jazztone 1234 (1956) **$60**.

PETE JOLLY
piano - born 1932 New Haven, CT

JOLLY JUMPS IN/with Jimmy Giuffre — RCA Victor 1105 (1955) dog on top **$60**.

THE FIVE/with Bill Perkins — RCA Victor 1121 (1955) dog on top **$60**.

DUO, TRIO, QUARTET — RCA Victor 1125 (1955) dog on top **$45**.

WHEN LIGHTS ARE LOW — RCA Victor 1367 (1957) dog on top **$45**.

IMPOSSIBLE/with Ralph Pena — Metrojazz 1014 (1958) **$45**.

GASSES EVERYBODY/with Buddy Collette — Charlie Parker 825 (1962) **$35**.

AND FRIENDS "LITTLE BIRD"/with Harold Roberts — Ava 22 (1963) **$30**.

SWEET SEPTEMBER — Ava 39 (1963) **$30**.

TOO MUCH BABY — Columbia 2397/9197 (1965) red label one white logo on each side **$20**.

CARMELL JONES
trumpet, composer - born 1936 Kansas City, MO

Jones worked and recorded with several fine West Coast jazz bands in the early 60's, most frequently with Harold Land. He then formed his own group with which he recorded until the mid-60's when he moved to Europe where he continues to work.

THE REMARKABLE/with Harold Land — Pacific Jazz 29 (1961) **$45**.

BRASS BAG/with Tricky Lofton — Pacific Jazz 49 (1962) **$40**.

BUSINESS MEETIN'/with Harold Land — Pacific Jazz 53 (1962) **$40**.

JAY HAWK TALK/with Jimmy Heath — Prestige 7401 (1965) blue label with logo on right side **$35**.

ELVIN JONES
drums - born 1927 Pontiac, MI

ELVIN!/with Frank Wess and Frank Foster — Riverside 409/9409 (1962) blue label with Bill Grauer Pro. **$45**.

TOGETHER/with Philly Joe Jones — Atlantic 1428 (1964) with logo on right side **$35**.

AND THEN AGAIN/with Frank Wess — Atlantic 1443 (1965) with logo on right side **$30**.

ILLUMINATION/with Charles Davis — Impulse 49 (1963) orange label **$35**.

DEAR JOHNNY C./with Charlie Mariano — Impulse 88 (1965) orange label **$30**.

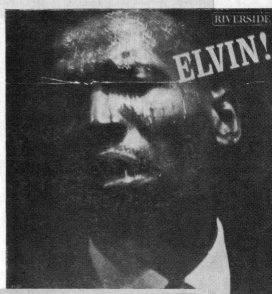

ETTA JONES
vocals - born 1928 Aiken, SC

A very genuine and consistent jazz vocalist, Jones began her professional career with the Buddy Johnson band and moved on to gig with J.C. Heard in 1948 and Earl Hines from 1949 to 1952. Etta received the Gold Record Award for her overwhelming hit Don't Go To Strangers on the Prestige label. Influenced by the great Billie

Holiday, Jones possesses the rare ability to put real feeling into her words and music and continues to record and tour to date.

SINGS — King 544 (1958) **$85**; *reissued* King 707 (1959) black label **$75**.

DON'T GO TO STRANGERS/with Frank Wess — Prestige 7186 (1960) yellow label **$65**; *reissued* Prestige 7186 (1965) blue label with logo on right side **$35**.

SOMETHING NICE/with Oliver Nelson — Prestige 7194 (1961) yellow label **$65**; *reissued* Prestige 7194 (1965) blue label with logo on right side **$35**.

O WARM/with Oliver Nelson — Prestige 7204 (1961) yellow label $60; *reissued* Prestige 7204 (1965) blue label with logo on right side $30.

ROM THE HEART/with Oliver Nelson — Prestige 7214 (1962) yellow label $50; *reissued* Prestige 7214 (1965) blue label with logo on right side $30.

ONELY AND BLUE — Prestige 7241 (1962) yellow label $50; *reissued* Prestige 7241 (1965) blue label with logo on right side $30.

OVE SHOUT/with Jerome Richardson — Prestige 7272 (1963) yellow label $45; *reissued* Prestige 7272 (1965) blue label with logo on right side $30.

OLLER/with Oliver Nelson — Prestige 7284 (1963) yellow label $45; *reissued* Prestige 7284 (1965) blue label with logo on right side $30.

TTA JONES AND SYLVIA SIMS — Grand Prix 420 $15; *reissue* of 1944-45 recordings.

HANK JONES
piano - born 1918 Pontiac, MI

ANK JONES (Solo) — Clef 100 (1951) 10" $90; EP 181 (1950) $40.

RBANITY/with Johnny Smith — Clef 707 (1956) $80; *reissued* Verve 8091 (1957) with Verve Records, Inc. on bottom of label $60; both are *reissues* of Clef 100 excluding 4 tunes.

RIO/with Kenny Clarke — Savoy 12023 (1955) maroon label $40.

UARTET-QUINTET/with Donald Byrd — Savoy 12037 (1955) maroon label $70.

LUE BIRD/with Jerome Richardson — Savoy 12053 (1955) maroon label $70.

AVE YOU MET (Solo) — Savoy 12084 (1956) maroon label $40.

UARTET/with Bobby Jaspar — Savoy 12087 (1956) maroon label $60.

WINGS GIGI/with Barry Galbraith — Golden Crest 3042/5002 (1958) $45.

HE TALENTED TOUCH/with Barry Galbraith — Capitol 1044 (1958) black label with logo on left side $40.

ORGY & BESS/with Kenny Burrell — Capitol 1175 (1959) black label with logo on left side $35.

RRIVAL TIME — RCA Victor 2570 (1962) dog on top $25.

ERE'S LOVE/with Kenny Burrell — Argo 728 (1963) $25.

HIS IS RAGTIME NOW — ABC Paramount 496 (1964) $15.

JO JONES
drums - born 1911 Chicago, IL

PECIAL/with Lucky Thompson — Vanguard 8503 (1956) $50.

LUS TWO/with Ray Bryant — Vanguard 8525 (1959) $35.

RIO/with Ray Bryant — Everest 5023/1023 (1959) $25; EP 108 (1959) $15.

AMP TILL READY/with Jimmy Forrest — Everest 5099/1099 (1960) $45.

ERCUSSION & BASS/with Milt Hinton — Everest 5110/1110 (1960) $20.

JONES BROTHERS
Thad Jones, Hank Jones, Elvin Jones, Eddie Jones

KEEPIN' UP WITH THE JONESES — Metrojazz 1003 (1959) $45.

PHILLY JOE JONES
drums - born 1923 Philadelphia, PA

BLUES FOR DRACULA/with Johnny Griffin — Riverside 12-282 (1958) blue label with Bill Grauer Pro. $60.

DRUMS AROUND THE WORLD/with Cannonball Adderley — Riverside 12-302/1147 (1959) blue label with Bill Grauer Pro. $50.

SHOWCASE/with Bill Barron — Riverside 12-313/1159 (1959) blue label with Bill Grauer Pro. $45.

PHILLY JOE'S BEAT/with Bill Barron — Atlantic 1340 (1960) with logo on right side $35.

QUINCY JONES
trumpet, composer, arranger - born 1933 Chicago, IL

Early recordings brought Jones out as a superb trumpet master early in his career and he performed with many big jazz names. The next step to his great success was his development and concentration on his arranging and composing abilities. He demonstrated his combined musical talents in the 50's with Lionel Hampton and Dizzy Gillespie, eventually leading a group of his own on world-wide tours. His abilities were such that it was easier for Jones to write for the many groups who wanted him than it was to keep together a band of his own. In the years since he has made a tremendous number of recordings with various major performers, won an incredible number of awards and gained the respect of many for the quality of his work.

SWEDEN — AMERICAN ALL STARS/with Arne Domnerus and Lars Gullin — Prestige 172 (1953) 10" $225.

THIS IS HOW I FEEL ABOUT JAZZ/with Lucky Thompson — ABC Paramount 149 (1956) $80.

GO WEST, MAN!/with Bill Perkins — ABC Paramount 186 (1957) $80.

JAZZ ABROAD/with Roy Haynes — EmArcy 36083 (1956) $60.

BIRTH OF A BAND/with Phil Woods — Mercury 20444/60129 (1959) black label $50.

THE GREAT WIDE WORLD OF/with Nick Travis — Mercury 20561/60221 (1960) black label $40.

I DIG DANCERS/with Jerome Richardson — Mercury 20612/60612 (1960) black label $40.

AROUND THE WORLD/with Clark Terry — Mercury 2014/6014 (1961) black label $35.

AT NEWPORT '61/with Curtis Fuller — Mercury 20653/60653 (1961) black label $30.

BOSSA NOVA/with Roland Kirk — Mercury 20751/60751 (1962) black label **$20**.

PLAYS HIP HITS/with Joe Newman — Mercury 20799/60799 (1963) black label **$25**.

EXPLORES THE MUSIC OF HENRY MANCINI/with Urbie Green — Mercury 20863/60863 (1964) red label **$15**.

GOLDEN BOY/with Frank Foster — Mercury 20938/60938 (1964) red label **$15**.

THE PAWNBROKER/with Oliver Nelson — Mercury 21011/61011 (1964) red label **$25**.

THE QUINTESSENCE/with Freddie Hubbard — Impulse 11 (1961) orange label **$30**.

RUFUS JONES
drums - born 1936 Charleston, SC

FIVE ON EIGHT/with Tommy Turrentine — Cameo 1076 (1964) **$30**.

SAM JONES
bass - born 1924 Jacksonville, FL

SOUL SOCIETY/with Jimmy Heath — Riverside 12-324/1172 (1960) blue label with Bill Grauer Pro. **$50**.

CHANT/with Cannonball Adderley — Riverside 358/9358 (1961) blue label with Bill Grauer Pro. **$45**.

DOWN HOME/with Frank Strozier — Riverside 432/9432 (1962) blue label with Bill Grauer Pro. **$45**.

THAD JONES
cornet, trumpet, composer - born 1923 Pontiac, MI

THE FABULOUS/with Frank Wess — Debut 12 (1954) 10" **$100**; *reissued* Debut 127 (1958); *reissued* Fantasy 8004/6004 (1962).

JAZZ COLLABORATIONS/with Charlie Mingus — Debut 17 (1955) 10" **$100**; *reissued* Debut 127 (1958); *reissued* Fantasy 8004/6004 (1962).

THAD JONES — Debut 127 (1958) **$80**.

THE FABULOUS — Fantasy 8004/6004 (1962) red vinyl **$40**.

MAD THAD/with Frank Wess — Period 1208 (1957) **$65**.

MOTOR CITY SCENE/with Billy Mitchell — United Artists 4025/5025 (1959) red label **$50**.

DETROIT — NEW YORK JUNCTION/with Billy Mitchell — Blue Note 1513 (1956) with NY address on label **$75**; with NY on label **$40**; with A Division of Liberty on label **$20**.

THE MAGNIFICENT/with Billy Mitchell — Blue Note 1527 (1956) with NY address on label **$65**; with NY on label **$40**; with A Division of Liberty on label **$20**.

THE MAGNIFICENT/with GiGi Gryce — Blue Note 1546 (1957) with NY address on label **$60**; with NY on label **$40**; with A Division of Liberty on label **$20**.

CLIFFORD JORDAN
tenor sax - born 1931 Chicago, IL

Beginning in the late 50's with Horace Silver, Jordan evolved toward freer forms of jazz but with a strong blues feeling. During the 60's he led groups with Kenny Dorham, Max Roach, and Charlie Mingus touring extensively.

CLIFFORD JORDAN/with Lee Morgan — Blue Note 1565 (1957) with NY address on label **$75**; with NY on label **$40**; with A Division of Liberty on label **$20**.

CLIFF CRAFT/with Art Farmer — Blue Note 1582 (1957) with NY address on label **$70**; with NY on label **$40**; with A Division of Liberty on label **$20**.

SPELLBOUND/with Cedar Walton — Riverside 340/9340 (1960) blue label with Bill Grauer Pro. **$40**.

A STORY TALE/with Sonny Red — Jazzland 40/940 (1961) **$35**.

STARTING TIME/with Kenny Dorham — Jazzland 52/952 (1961) **$35**.

BEARCAT/with Cedar Walton — Jazzland 69/969 (1962) **$35**.

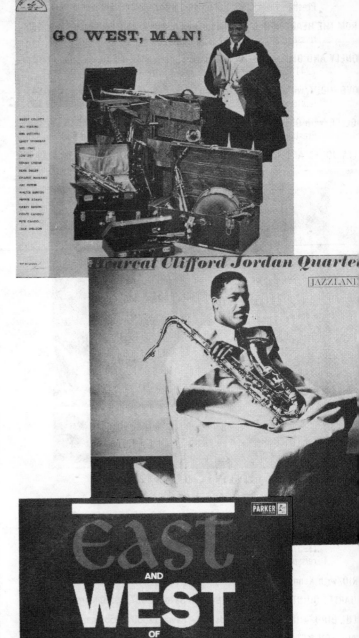

DUKE JORDAN
piano - born 1922 Brooklyn, NY

JAZZ LABORATORY — Signal 101 (1955) **$75**; *reissued* Savoy 12145 (1958) **$4**

TRIO-QUINTET — Signal 1202 (1956) **$75**.

FLIGHT TO JORDAN/with Stanley Turrentine — Blue Note 4046 (1960) with address on label **$65**; with NY on label **$40**; with A Division of Liber on label **$20**.

EAST AND WEST OF JAZZ/with Sadik Hakim — Charlie Parker 805 (1962) o side of LP each **$25**.

LES LIAISONS DANGEREUSES/with Charlie Rouse — Charlie Parker 813 (196 **$25**.

Jazz collector's dream

Collectable, Rare & Valuable

**JUST 20 OF THE 6052
RECORDS LISTED IN
VOL. I MAINSTREAM**

Jazz

**1949-1965 RECORD
COLLECTORS PRICE GUIDE**

LUCY ANN POLK - Lucky Lucy Ann (1957)
An original Mode release that has been out of print for 25 years. This label put out some of the best jazz of the 50's.

BILL PERKINS - 2° East - 3° West (1956)
This is the original on Pacific Jazz black label considered to be Perkins at his best and is a rare record.

HAL McKUSICK - Jazz Workshop (1957)
Another very collectible that has been out of print for 24 years.

PAUL QUINICHETTE - The Kid From Denver (1956)
An original Dawn record that has been out of [print for] years. Dawn records are hard to come by and [are a] production of Seeco Records.

**BILLIE HOLIDAY - Blues Are Brewin'
(1958)**
Released on original Decca black label with silver lettering and represents works from 1946 and 1949. It is a rarity to find original LPs of Ms. Holiday's in good condition.

**OSCAR PETERSON - At Carnegie
(1952)**
A 10" production of his 1950 Carnegie Hall show and an original Mercury/Clef record. The LP cover is the work of artist David Stone Martin. Clef Records discontinued production in 1956 and this LP can be considered a true collector's item.

**GERRY MULLIGAN, [SHORTY]
ROGERS - Modern [Sounds]
(1956)**
Released on the [original] Capitol green lab[el. It is a] combination of tw[o of the] best 10" LPs of the e[ra.] The title of the albu[m is] the Shorty Rogers [and] the Mulligan 10" w[as Gerry Mulligan] And His Tentette. T[his] label has been out [of print] since 1958.

LAMBERT, HENDRICKS & ROSS - The Swingers (1959)
An original World Pacific record that has been out of print since 1964. This is the only LP they did with Zoot Sims and is the hardest to find.

**CHICO HAMILTON - C[hico]
Hamilton Trio (1955)**
This is Chico's first LP a[nd is] an original Pacific Jazz [record.] Pacific Jazz stopped re[cord]ing 10" recordings in [1956] and went to 12" records.

LUCKY THOMPSON - Lucky Thompson - Vol 1 (1956)
This LP has been out of print for the past 22 years and is
an original Am-Par Records production.

BOBBY TROUP - Escapade (1957)
An interview with six jazz artists that has not
been issued for 21 years.

SPECTRA-SONIC-SOUND...THE ULTIMATE IN HIGH FIDELITY

SL 9005

LIBERTY

Escapade
REVIEWS THE
JAZZ SCENE

a symposium in sound
featuring

BOBBY TROUP
JACK TEAGARDEN
ZIGGY ELMAN
HOWARD RUMSEY
JACK COSTANZO
JOHNNY OTIS

the GENE KRUPA sextet

**...UPA - The Gene
...xtet #1 (1953)**
...original 10"
...g with side-
...Webster and
...er done by
...David Stone

SUPERVISED BY
NORMAN GRANZ

CLEF RECORDS

BETHLEHEM BCP 1002

CHRIS CONNOR
Sings Lullabys For Lovers

CHRIS CONNOR - Sings Lullabys For Lovers (1954)
A 10" that is an original
that was reissued and
comprised half of a 12"
release titled Lullabys Of
Birdland. This is Connor's
second LP and considered
very rare.

VI REDD - Bird Call
(1962)
On the original Uni-
ted Artists jazz label
with the silhouette
of a sax player. This
label was discon-
tinued in 1964.

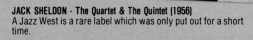

Vi
Redd
Bird
Call

JAZZ-WEST-MLP-6

JACK SHELDON THE QUARTET THE QUINTET
with ZOOT SIMS, WALTER NORRIS, RALPH PENA, GENE GAMMAGE, LAWRENCE MARABLE & BOB WHITLOCK

JACK SHELDON - The Quartet & The Quintet (1956)
A Jazz West is a rare label which was only put out for a short
time.

SHORTY ROGERS - Martians Come Back (1956)
On the original Atlantic black label with silver lettering that is rare and difficult to find.

ABBEY LINCOLN - Affair (1956)
Another very rare record that has not been issued for 25 years.

JOE NEWMAN - I'm Still Swinging (1956)
This record has been out of print for 24 years and is hard to find.

PAT MORRISSEY - I'm Pat Mo
(1956)
This particular LP was issued 23 years ago.

BUDDY COLLETTE - Buddy's Best (1957)
This is an original Dooto recording. The Dooto label was most commonly known for comedy releases but did produce some good jazz and is not easy to find.

O'Sullivan
Woodside &

2218 E. Magnolia • Phoenix, Arizona

SHIELA JORDAN
vocals - born 1929 Detroit, MI

Jordan came to the attention of George Russell who helped her with her first recording in 1962. The record was a critical success and she continued to work alongside Russell and on her own. She is most popular in Europe where she has done considerable touring and performing.

PORTRAIT OF — Blue Note 9002/89002 (1962) with NY address on label $60; with NY on label $40.

TAFT JORDAN
trumpet, vocals - born 1915 Florence, SC

THE MOODS OF — Mercury 20429/60101 (1959) black label $25.

MOOD INDIGO — Moodsville 21 (1961) $35.

RICHIE KAMUCA
tenor sax - born 1930 Philadelphia, PA died 1977

Kamuca worked and recorded extensively on the West Coast with a number of name bands including Stan Kenton, Chet Baker, Maynard Ferguson, Shelly Manne and the Lighthouse All Stars during the 50's. In the 60's he joined with Gerry Mulligan and continued appearances, recordings and studio work into the 70's until his death in 1977.

THE BROTHERS/with Al Cohn and Bill Perkins — RCA Victor 1162 (1956) dog on top $60.

QUARTET/with Carl Perkins — Mode 102 (1957) $60.

TENORS HEAD ON/with Bill Perkins — Liberty 3051 (1957) $50.

JAZZ EROTICA — Hi Fi 604 (1959) $40.

KEESTER PARADE — Pacific Jazz 42 (1962) $40.

DICK KATZ
piano, composer - born 1924 Baltimore, MD

PIANO AND PIN/with Jimmy Raney — Atlantic 1314 (1959) with logo on right side $30.

FRED KATZ
composer, cello, piano - born 1919 Brooklyn, NY

4-5-6 TRIO — Decca 9213/79213 (1958) black label $25.

AND JAMMERS — Decca 9217/79217 (1958) black label $25.

SOUL CELLO — Decca 9202/79202 (1958) black label $25.

FRED KAZ
piano

EASTERN EXPOSURE — Atlantic 1335 (1960) with logo on right side $20.

JOHNNY KEATING
trombone, composer, arranger - born 1927 Edinburgh, Scotland

ENGLISH JAZZ/with Ronnie Ross — Bally 12001 (1956) $45.

SWINGING SCOTS — Dot 3066 (1957) $35.

ROGER KELLAWAY
piano, composer - born 1939 Waban, MA

PORTRAITS — Regina 298 (1964) $25.

THE TRIO — Prestige 7399 (1965) blue label with logo on right side $25.

ALLEN KELLER
A NEW LOOK AT THE WORLD/with Kai Winding — Charlie Parker 817 (1963) $25.

HAL KELLER
piano - born Chicago, IL

DEBUT — Sand 7 (1957) $45; *reissued* Sound 602 (1959) $30.

BEVERLY KELLY
vocals - born 1934 Rittman, OH

SINGS/with Moran — Audio Fidelity 1874/5874 (1958) $35.

LOVE LOCKED OUT/with Jerome Richardson — Riverside 328/9328 (1959) blue label with Bill Grauer Pro. $45.

IN PERSON — Riverside 345/9345 (1960) blue label with Bill Grauer Pro. $40.

WYNTON KELLY
piano, composer - born 1931 Jamaica, B.W.I. died 1971

Early experience in rhythm and blues bands led to work with Lester Young, Dizzy Gillespie and others during the 50's. In the late 50's, Kelly worked with Miles Davis and, in the mid-60's, with members of the Davis group. Kelly can be found on many recordings with Davis, with his own group and other big jazz personalities.

TRIO/with Fred Skeets — Blue Note 5025 (1951) 10" $90.

WYNTON KELLY/with Kenny Burrell — Riverside 12-254 (1958) blue label with Bill Grauer Pro. $45; *reissued* Jazzland 83 (1962).

KELLY BLUE/with Bobby Jaspar — Riverside 12-298/1142 (1959) blue label with Bill Grauer Pro. $60.

WHISPER NOT — Jazzland 83 (1962) **$25**.

KELLY GREAT/with Lee Morgan — Vee Jay 1016 (1959) **$40**.

KELLY AT MIDNIGHT/with Paul Chambers — Vee Jay 3011 (1960) **$30**.

WYNTON KELLY/with Paul Chambers — Vee Jay 3022 (1961) **$30**.

THE BEST OF — Vee Jay 1086 (1963) **$25**.

COMIN' IN THE BACK DOOR/with Kenny Burrell — Verve 8576/68576 (1963) with MGM on bottom of label **$20**.

IT'S ALRIGHT/with Candido — Verve 8588/68588 (1964) with MGM on bottom of label **$20**.

UNDILUTED/with Paul Chambers — Verve 8622/68622 (1965) with MGM on bottom of label **$20**.

CHARLIE KENNEDY
alto, tenor saxes, clarinet, flute
born 1927 Staten Island, NY

CHARLIE KENNEDY/with Bill DeArango — Regent 6047 (1957) green label **$50**.

*STAN KENTON
leader, composer, piano - born 1912 Wichita, KS
died 1979

Kenton formed his first group around 1941 which included musicians and vocalists of unmeasurable talent. His success could be primarily the result of these artists including such eventual greats as Art Pepper, Conte Candoli, Lee Konitz, Ann Richards and June Christy, just to name a few. His style of music fluctuated according to his arrangers and Kenton experienced periods of classical and commercial music but is best known for his jazz contributions. The latter recordings will be the ones listed herein.

ENCORES/with Art Pepper — Capitol 155 (1952) 10" **$90**; EP 155 (1952) 2 records **$25**; *reissued* Capitol T155 (1955) green label **$70**.

ARTISTRY IN RHYTHM/with Vido Musso — Capitol 167 (1952) 10" **$90**; EP 167 (1952) 2 records **$25**; *reissued* Capitol T167 (1955) green label **$70**.

A PRESENTATION OF PROGRESSIVE JAZZ/with Art Pepper — Capitol 172 (1952) 10" **$85**; EP 172 (1952) 2 records **$25**; *reissued* Capitol T172 (1955) green label **$65**. (A)

MILESTONES — Capitol 190 (1952) 10" **$80**; EP 190 (1952) 2 records **$25**; *reissued* Capitol T190 (1955) green label **$60**.

PRESENTS/with Art Pepper and June Christy — Capitol 248 (1952) 10" **$80**; EP 248 (1952) 3 records **$40**; *reissued* Capitol T248 (1955) green label **$60**.

CLASSICS/with Art Pepper — Capitol 358 (1953) 10" **$75**; EP 358 (1953) 2 records **$20**; *reissued* Capitol T358 (1955) green label **$55**.

CITY OF GLASS/with Art Pepper — Capitol 353 (1953) 10" **$75**; EP 353 (1953) 2 records **$20**; *reissued* Capitol T353 (1955) green label **$55**.

PROLOGUE "THIS IS AN ORCHESTRA"/with Lee Konitz — Capitol 386 (1953) 10" **$75**; EP 386 (1953) **$25**.

PORTRAITS OF STANDARDS/with Art Pepper — Capitol 462 (1954) 10" **$70**; *reissued* Capitol T462 (1955) green label **$50**.

SHOWCASE/with Bill Russo — Capitol 525 (1954) 10" **$70**; *reissued* Capitol W524 (1955) green label **$50**.

SHOWCASE/with Bill Holman — Capitol 526 (1954) 10" **$70**; *reissued* Capitol W524 (1955) green label **$50**.

DUET/with June Christy — Capitol 656 (1956) green label **$45**; EP 1-656, EP 2-656, EP 3-656 (1956) **$20 ea**.

CONTEMPORARY CONCERTS/with Charlie Mariano — Capitol 666 (1956) green label **$45**.

IN HI FI/with Perkins — Capitol 724 (1956) green label **$40**.

CUBAN FIRE/with Perkins — Capitol 731 (1956) green label **$35**.

ADVENTURES IN JAZZ — Capitol 1796 (1963) black label with logo on top **$25**.

*The only LP's within the scope of this book.

JACK KEROVAC
BLUES HAIKUS/with Al Cohn and Zoot Sims — Hanover 5006 (1959) **$60**.

BARNEY KESSEL
guitar - born 1923 Muskogee, OK

Kessel was greatly influenced by Charlie Christian but has maintained his own recognizable sound since his work with many bands in the 40's. He toured and recorded with Oscar Peterson in the early 50's and, beginning in the late 50's to date, has combined and alternated studio work with working in jazz groups into the 60's. Kessel is considered to be one of the very best in jazz guitar.

BARNEY KESSEL/with Shelly Manne — Clef EP 182 (1953) **$50**.

BARNEY KESSEL - Vol. 1/with Bud Shank — Contemporary 2508 (1953) 10" **$250**; *reissued* Contemporary 3511 (1956).

BARNEY KESSEL - Vol. 2/with Bob Cooper — Contemporary 2514 (1954) 10" **$250**; EP 4009, EP 4010 (1954) **$50 ea.**; *reissued* Contemporary 3512 (1956).

EASY LIKE — Contemporary 3511 (1956) yellow label **$100**.

KESSEL PLAYS STANDARDS — Contemporary 3512 (1956) yellow label **$100**.

TO SWING OR NOT TO SWING/with Bill Perkins — Contemporary 3513 (1956) yellow label **$100**.

MUSIC TO LISTEN TO/with Buddy Collette — Contemporary 3521 (1957) yellow label **$95**; *reissued* Contemporary 7001 (1958) black label, stereo **$85**.

THE POLL WINNERS/with Shelly Manne and Ray Brown — Contemporary 3535 (1957) yellow label **$60**; *reissued* Contemporary 7010 (1958) black label, stereo **$50**.

THE POLL WINNERS RIDE AGAIN — Contemporary 3556/7029 (1957) yellow label **$60**.

PLAYS CARMEN/with Buddy Collette — Contemporary 3563/7563 (1958) yellow label mono; black label stereo **$85**.

SOME LIKE IT HOT/with Art Pepper — Contemporary 3565/7565 (1958) yellow label mono; black label stereo **$85.**

POLL WINNERS THREE — Contemporary 3576/7576 (1958) yellow label **$50.**

THE POLL WINNERS: EXPLORING THE SCENE — Contemporary 3581 (1958) yellow label **$50.**

WORKIN' OUT/with Marvin Jenkins — Contemporary 3585/7585 (1958) yellow label mono; black label stereo **$40.**

LET'S COOK/with Ben Webster — Contemporary 3603/7603 (1958) yellow label mono; black label stereo **$60.**

SWINGIN' PARTY/with Marvin Jenkins — Contemporary 3613/7613 (1960) yellow label mono; black label stereo **$40.**

BREAKFAST AT TIFFANY'S/with Bud Shank — Reprise 6019/9-6019 (1962) **$30.**

BOSSA NOVA: PLUS BIG BAND — Reprise 6049/9-6049 (1962) **$30.**

KESSEL/JAZZ/with Paul Horn — Reprise 6073/9-6073 (1963) **$30.**

ON FIRE/with Frank Capp — Emerald 2401 (1965) **$50.**

MORGANA KING
vocals - born 1930 Pleasantville, NY

FOR YOU, FOR ME, FOREVER MORE — EmArcy 36079 (1956) drummer logo **$50.**

SINGS THE BLUES — Mercury 20231 (1958) black label **$40.**

MORE MORGANA KING — Wing 12307/16307 (1965) **$20.**

FOLK SONGS A LA KING — United Artists 3028/6028 (1960) **$45;** *reissued* Ascot 13020 (1965).

LET ME LOVE YOU — United Artists 30020 (1960) **$45;** *reissued* Ascot 13019 (1965).

THE GREATEST SONGS EVER SWUNG — Camden 543 (1959) **$35.**

THE WINTER OF MY DISCONTENT — Ascot 13014/16014 (1965) **$30.**

THE END OF A LOVE AFFAIR — Ascot 13019/16019 (1965) **$15;** *reissue* of United Artists 30020.

EVERYBODY LOVES SATURDAY NIGHT — Ascot 13020/16020 (1965) **$15;** *reissue* of United Artists 3028.

TEDDI KING
vocals - born 1929 Boston, MA

'ROUND MIDNIGHT — Storyville 302 (1954) 10" **$150.**

STORYVILLE PRESENTS — Storyville 314 (1954) 10" **$150.**

NOW IN VOGUE — Storyville 903 (1956) **$100.**

ALL THE KING'S SONGS — Coral 57278/757278 (1959) maroon and silver label **$60.**

BIDIN' MY TIME — RCA Victor 1147 (1956) dog on top **$75.**

TO YOU FROM — RCA Victor 1313 (1957) dog on top **$60.**

A GIRL AND HER SONGS — RCA Victor 1454 (1957) dog on top **$60.**

TONY KINSEY
drums, piano - born 1927 Birmingham, England

KINSEY COMES ON/with Ronnie Ross — London 1672 (1957) **$70.**

JOHN KIRBY
bass, leader - born 1908 Baltimore, MD

INTIMATE SWING/with Charlie Shavers — Harmony 7124 (1958) red label **$35.**

*ANDY KIRK
leader - born 1898 Newport, KY

A MELLOW BIT OF RHYTHM/with Al Cohn and Ernie Royal — RCA Victor 1302 (1957) dog on top **$45.**

The only LP's within the scope of this book.

RAHSAAN ROLAND KIRK
*tenor, alto saxes, flute, reeds, trumpet, composer
born 1936 Columbus, OH died 1977*

Kirk was a musician with a tremendous scope of expression and command of the entire range of history of what he called "black classical music." He was capable, from early in his career, of playing two and even three horns at once. Kirk's playing was also noted for its incorporation of whistles, horns, sirens and many other sounds. The initial reaction he received was critical, but eventually his considerable talent was recognized and he worked and recorded with groups of his own in the late 50's. Kirk continued to record, tour and appear extensively, expanding all his talents including writing, multi-horn playing and recording an LP in which he demonstrated his phenominal control of circular breathing in a continuous non-stop solo of over 20 minutes. Kirk was sightless, but his ear for music far exceeds many.

TRIPLE THREAT/with James Madison — King 539 (1956) **$90;** *reissued* Bethlehem 6064 (1960) **$45.**

INTRODUCING/with Ira Sullivan — Argo 669 (1960) **$35.**

KIRK'S WORK/with Jack McDuff — Prestige 7210 (1961) yellow label **$45;** *reissued* blue label with logo on right side (1965) **$20.**

WE FREE KINGS/with Hank Jones — Mercury 60679/20679 (1961) black label **$35.**

DOMINO/with Wynton Kelly — Mercury 20748/60748 (1962) black label **$35.**

REEDS AND DEEDS/with Virgil Jones — Mercury 20800/60800 (1963) black label **$25.**

MEETS THE BENNY GOLSON ORCHESTRA — Mercury 20844/60844 (1963) black label **$25.**

IN COPENHAGEN/with Tate Montoliu — Mercury 20894/60894 (1963) black label **$25.**

GIFTS AND MESSAGES/with Horace Parlan — Mercury 20939/60939 (1964) black label **$25.**

I TALK WITH THE SPIRITS/with Horace Parlan — Limelight 82008/86008 (1964) fold out cover **$20.**

ROLAND KIRK FEATURING ELVIN JONES — Limelight 82027/86027 (1965) fold out cover **$20.**

AL KLINK
tenor sax, flute - born 1915 Danbury, CT

PROGRESSIVE JAZZ/with Bob Alexander — Grand Award 33-525 (1956) **$45.**

JIMMY KNEPPER
trombone - born 1927 Los Angeles, CA

Knepper has been highly regarded since his work in the 50's in a number of bands of varying sizes. He began working and recording with Charlie Mingus in 1957 until 1961 and worked many broadway shows through the 60's as well as playing with the Thad Jones-Mel Lewis Orchestra.

NEW FACES — Debut 129 (1958) **$50.**

PEPPER-KNEPPER QUINTET/with Pepper Adams — Metrojazz 1004 (1958) **$40.**

A SWING INTRODUCTION TO — Bethlehem 77 (1957) maroon label **$40.**

FREE BLOWN JAZZ/with Tony Scott — Carlton 12-113 (1959) **$40.**

MOE KOFFMAN
flute, alto sax, composer - born 1928 Toronto, Ontario, Canada

COOL AND HOT SAX — Jubilee 1037 (1957) **$35.**

THE SHEPHERD SWINGS AGAIN — Jubilee 1074 (1958) **$35.**

TALES OF KOFFMAN — United Artists 14029/15029 (1963) **$25.**

HANS KOLLER
tenor, baritone saxes, clarinet - born 1921 Vienna, Austria

HANS KOLLER — Discovery 2005 (1954) **$75.**

HANS ACROSS THE SEA — Vanguard 8509 (1956) **$45.**

LEE KONITZ
alto sax - born 1927 Chicago, IL

Konitz has been well known since the late 40's during which time he played with Miles Davis and intermittently with Lennie Tristano with whom he remained through the 50's and 60's. During this time he also worked on his own and with various musicians for tours and recordings while maintaining his own style and further promoting "cool" jazz.

LEE KONITZ/with Lennie Tristano — Presitge 101 (1950) **$200;** EP 1314 (1950) **$50;** *reissued* Prestige 7004 (1955).

LEE KONITZ/with Miles Davis — Prestige 116 (1952) 10" **$250.**

THE NEW SOUNDS OF LEE KONITZ/with Billy Bauer — Prestige 108 (1950) 10" **$200;** EP 1315 (1950) **$50;** *reissued* Prestige 7004 (1955).

GROUPS — Prestige 7004 (1955) yellow label **$100;** *reissued* Prestige 7250 (1962) yellow label **$60.**

ORIGINALEE/with Stan Levey — Roost 416 (1953) **$175.**

AT STORYVILLE/with Ronnie Ball — Storyville 304 (1954) 10" **$160;** EP 403, EP 404 (1954) **$50 ea.;** *reissued* Storyville 901 (1956) **$90.**

KONITZ/with Peter Ind — Storyville 313 (1954) 10" **$160;** EP 418, EP 419 (1954) **$50 ea.**

IN HARVARD SQUARE/with Ronnie Ball — Storyville 323 (1955) 10" **$150;** EP 438, EP 439 (1955) **$45 ea.**

LEE KONITZ WITH WARNE MARSH — Atlantic 1217 (1955) black label **$90;** *reissued* Atlantic 1217 with logo on right side **$45.**

INSIDE HI-FI/with Billy Bauer — Atlantic 1258 (1956) black label **$85;** *reissued* Atlantic 1258 with logo on right side **$45.**

THE REAL/with Billy Bauer — Atlantic 1273 (1957) black label **$85;** *reissued* Atlantic 1273 with logo on right side **$45.**

VERY COOL/with Don Ferrara — Verve 8209 (1957) with Verve Records, Inc. on bottom of label **$80;** with MGM on bottom of label **$45.**

TRANQUILITY/with Billy Bauer — Verve 8281 (1957) with Verve Records, Inc. on bottom of label **$80;** with MGM on bottom of label **$45.**

AN IMAGE — Verve 8286 (1958) with Verve Records, Inc. on bottom of label **$70;** with MGM on bottom of label **$35.**

MEETS JIMMY GIUFFRE/with Warne Marsh — Verve 8335/6073 (1959) with Verve Records, Inc. on bottom of label **$70;** with MGM on bottom of label **$35.**

YOU & LEE/with Bob Brookmeyer — Verve 8362/6131 (1959) with Verve Records, Inc. on bottom of label **$70;** with MGM on bottom of label **$35.**

MOTION/with Elvin Jones — Verve 8399/68399 (1961) with MGM on bottom of label **$35.**

LEE KONITZ PLAYS WITH THE GERRY MULLIGAN QUARTET — Pacific Jazz 2 (1953) 10" **$150;** EP 4-3 (1953) **$50;** *reissued* World Pacific 406/1273 (1958) **$65;** *reissued* Pacific Jazz 38 (1962) **$45.**

IRENE KRAL
vocals - born 1932 Chicago, IL

Kral began singing at an early age and credits her brother, Roy Kral, as being her inspiration. She worked with Woody Herman, Maynard Ferguson, Stan Kenton and Shelly Manne among others during the 50's and 60's and recorded considerably during that time but has only a few recordings under her own name.

THE BAND AND I/with Herb Pomeroy — United Artists 4016/5016 (1959) **$80.**

STEVE IRENE O!/with Al Cohn — United Artists 3052/6052 (1959) **$60.**

BETTER THAN ANYTHING/with Junior Mance — Ava 33 (1963) **$40.**

WONDERFUL LIFE/with Russ Freeman — Mainstream 56058/6058 (1965) **$25.**

GENE KRUPA
drums, leader - born 1909 Chicago, IL

Krupa was an innovator early on. He played with name bands for several years and became famous with Benny Goodman in the late 30's with Sing, Sing, Sing among other recordings. He led his own big band from 1938 through 1951, played with groups of smaller sizes and joined with JATP through the 50's. A misleading movie was made of his career in late 1959 in which he played the drum score. Krupa is recognized by most jazz fans as the first jazz drummer to draw attention to the drums as an instrument.

FAVORITES — Columbia B138 (1949) 7" 4 record set **$40.**

GENE KRUPA/with Anita O'Day — Columbia 6017 (1949) 10" **$150;** EP 1616 **$35.**

DANCE PARADE/with Charlie Ventura — Columbia 6066 (1949) 10" **$150** EP 2520, EP 2519 **$25 ea.**

AT JATP/with Charlie Ventura — Clef 600 (1954) **$100**; *reissued* Verve 8031 (1957) with Verve Records, Inc. on bottom of label **$60**; with MGM on bottom of label **$35**.

ROCKING MR. KRUPA/with Eddie Shu — Clef 627 (1954) **$150**; EP 222, EP 223 (1953) **$50 ea.**; *reissued* Verve 8190 (1957).

SEXTET #3/with Eddie Davis — Clef 631 (1954) **$150**; EP 247, EP 248 (1954) **$50 ea.**; *reissued* Verve 8107 (1957).

QUARTET/with Eddie Shu — Clef 668 (1955) **$100**; EP 366 (1955) **$50**.

KRUPA AND RICH/with Buddy Rich — Clef 684 (1956) **$100**; *reissued* Verve 8069 (1957) with Verve Records, Inc. on bottom of label **$80**; with MGM on bottom of label **$35**.

THE EXCITING — Clef 687 (1956) **$80**; *reissued* Verve 8071 (1957) with Verve Records, Inc. on bottom of label **$60**; with MGM on bottom of label **$35**; *reissues* of Clef 147 (1953).

DRUM BOOGIE — Clef 703 (1956) **$80**; *reissued* Verve 8087 (1957) with Verve Records, Inc. on bottom of label **$60**; with MGM on bottom of label **$35**; *reissues* of Clef 121 (1952).

DRUMMER MAN/with Anita O'Day — Verve 2008 (1956) with Verve Records, Inc. on bottom of label **$50**; with MGM on bottom of label **$35**; *reissued* American Recording Society 427 (1957) **$65**.

THE DRIVING — Verve 8107 (1956) with Verve Records, Inc. on bottom of label **$50**; with MGM on bottom of label **$35**; *reissue* of Clef 631 (1954).

SING, SING, SING — Verve 8190 (1957) with Verve Records, Inc. on bottom of label **$50**; with MGM on bottom of label **$35**; *reissue* of Clef 627 (1954).

JAZZ RHYTHMS/with Eddie Shu — Verve 8204 (1957) with Verve Records, Inc. on bottom of label **$50**; with MGM on bottom of label **$35**; *reissue* of American Recording Society 411 (1956).

KRUPA ROCKS — Verve 8276 (1959) with Verve Records, Inc. on bottom of label **$45**; with MGM on bottom of label **$35**.

PLAYS GERRY MULLIGAN ARRANGEMENTS/with Phil Woods — Verve 8292/6008 (1959) with Verve Records, Inc. on bottom of label **$45**; with MGM on bottom of label **$35**.

HEY! HERE'S/with Eddie Shu — Verve 8300 (1959) with Verve Records, Inc. on bottom of label **$50**; with MGM on bottom of label **$35**.

BIG NOISE FROM WINNETKA/with Eddie Wasserman — Verve 8310/6042 (1959) with Verve Records, Inc. on bottom of label **$50**; with MGM on bottom of label **$35**.

GENE KRUPA STORY (Soundtrack)/with Benny Carter — Verve 15010/6105 (1959) with Verve Records, Inc. on bottom of label **$60**.

PRECUSSION KING/with Jimmy Cleveland — Verve 8414/68414 (1961) with MGM on bottom of label **$30**.

THE ORIGINAL DRUM BATTLE — Verve 8484/68484 (1962) with MGM on bottom of label **$25**; *reissue* of Clef 684 (1956).

NEW QUARTET/with Charlie Ventura — Verve 8584/68584 (1964) with MGM on bottom of label **$25**.

GENE KRUPA QUARTET/with Eddie Shu — American Recording Society L111 (1956) **$65**; *reissued* Verve 8204 (1957).

GENE KRUPA — Metro 518 (1965) **$15**.

CHARLES KYNARD
organ, piano, composer - born 1933 St. Louis, MO

WHERE IT'S AT/with Clifford Scott — Pacific Jazz 72 (1963) **$40**.

CHARLES KYNARD — World Pacific 1823 (1964) **$35**.

STEVE LACY
soprano sax - born 1934 New York City, NY

SOPRANO SAXOPHONE — Prestige 7125 (1957) yellow label **$80**.

REFLECTIONS — New Jazz 8206 (1958) **$50**.

EVIDENCE — New Jazz 8271 (1961) **$50**.

THE STRAIGHT HORN OF — Candid 8007/9007 (1960) **$50**.

DRUMMER MAN/with Anita O'Day — Columbia 2515 (1956) 10" **$60**.

GENE KRUPA/with Anita O'Day — Columbia 753 (1956) with 3 black logos on each side **$75**.

SIDEKICKS/with Anita O'Day — Columbia 641 (1955) red label with 3 black logos on each side **$75**.

DRUMMER MAN — Columbia C2L29 (1962) red label with 3 black logos on each side, 2 LP box set with 16 page booklet **$60**.

STORY IN MUSIC/with Anita O'Day — Harmony 7252 (1960) **$35**.

KRUPA-VENTURA TRIO/with Charlie Ventura — Commodore 20,028 (1950) 10" **$200**.

SWINGIN' WITH KRUPA/with Urbie Green — Camden 340 (1958) **$35**.

COLLATES/with Charlie Ventura — Clef 121 (1952) 10" **$200**; EP 140 (1952) **$50**; *reissued* Clef 703 (1956).

SEXTET/with Ben Webster — Clef 147 (1953) 10" **$200**; EP 193, EP 194 (1953) **$50 ea.**; *reissued* Clef 687 (1956).

SEXTET #2/with Charlie Shavers — Clef 152 (1953) 10" **$200**; *reissued* Clef 687 (1956).

GENE KRUPA — Clef 500 (1953) 10" **$150**.

TRIO — Clef 514 (1953) 10" **$150**.

DAVE LAMBERT

vocals, arranger - born 1917 Boston, MA died 1966

Lambert worked and recorded with Gene Krupa in the mid-40's and went on to lead a vocal group in a broadway show and into recording. In the early 50's Lambert organized groups and did arrangements for several name groups and vocalists. He was one of the originals of the Lambert, Hendricks and Ross vocal trio, remaining with them through many recordings, tours, awards and the change from Annie Ross to Yolande Bavan. Lambert finally departed the group in 1964 but continued to work until his death by accident in 1966.

SING AND SWINGS ALONE — United Artists 3084/6084 (1959) red label **$45.**

LAMBERT, HENDRICKS AND BAVAN

Dave Lambert, Jon Hendricks, Yolande Bavan
vocal group

LIVE AT BASIN STREET EAST/with Pony Poindexter — RCA Victor 2635 (1963) dog on top **$35.**

AT NEWPORT/with Coleman Hawkins — RCA Victor 2747 (1963) dog on top **$25.**

AT THE VILLAGE GATE/with Booker Ervin — RCA Victor 2861 (1964) dog on top **$25.**

LAMBERT, HENDRICKS AND ROSS

Dave Lambert, Jon Hendricks, Annie Ross

By using ideas developed during the 40's by themselves and others, the members of this vocal group took advantage of new recording techniques and became extremely popular and respected for their interpretations of jazz recordings, arrangements and solos. They made many recordings and appearances and were easily regarded the very best in their line of work, as is believed by many to date. It appears that even twenty years after the group disbanded their popularity, unique style and influence in the jazz world continue.

SING A SONG OF BASIE/with Count Basie — ABC Paramount 223 (1957) **$75.**

THE SWINGERS/with Zoot Sims — World Pacific 1264 (1959) **$95.**

THE HOTTEST NEW GROUP IN JAZZ/with the Ike Isaacs Trio — Columbia 1403/8198 (1959) red label with 3 black logos on each side **$75;** *reissued* Impulse 83 (1965) orange label **$35.**

SING ELLINGTON/with the Ike Isaacs Trio — Columbia 1510/8310 (1960) red label with 3 black logos on each side **$60.**

HIGH FLYING WITH/with the Ike Isaacs Trio — Columbia 1675/8475 (1961) red label with 3 black logos on each side **$50.**

SING ALONG WITH BASIE/with Count Basie and Joe Williams — Roulette 52018 (1958) white label with multicolored pinwheel **$40.**

HAROLD LAND

tenor sax - born 1928 Houston, TX

A West Coast musician by location but not necessarily a "cool" player, beginning in the 50's Land worked with name bands, recording with them and on his own. He is known for his work with the Gerald Wilson Orchestra with whom he worked extensively. Land has also played his part in the area of studio work for movies, backing vocalists and many well known musicians over the years.

IN THE LAND OF JAZZ/with Carl Perkins — Contemporary 3550 (1958) yellow label **$60;** *reissued* Contemporary 7550 (1959).

GROOVEYARD — Contemporary 7550 (1959) stereo **$50;** *reissue* of Contemporary 3550 (1958).

THE FOX/with Elmo Hope — Hi Fi 612 (1959) **$45.**

WEST COAST BLUES/with Wes Montgomery — Jazzland 20/920 (1960) **$45.**

IN NEW YORK/with Kenny Dorham — Jazzland 33/933 (1960) **$40.**

JAZZ IMPRESSIONS OF FOLK MUSIC/with Carmell Jones — Imperial 9247/12247 (1963) black label **$35.**

HEAR YE!/with Red Mitchell — Atlantic 1376 (1962) with logo on right side **$35.**

RONNIE LANG

alto sax, flute - born 1927 Chicago, IL

MODERN JAZZ/with Dave Pell — Tops 1521 (1958) **$25.**

*ELLIS LARKINS

piano - born 1923 Baltimore, MD

BLUES IN THE NIGHT — Decca 5391 (1951) 10" **$25.**

PERFUME AND RAIN — Storyville 316 (1954) 10" **$25;** EP 424, EP 425 (1954) **$10 ea.**

DO NOTHIN' TILL YOU HEAR FROM ME — Storyville 913 (1955) **$25.**

INVENTIONS/with Ruby Braff — Vanguard 8019 (1954) 10" **$50.**

INVENTIONS - Vol 2/with Ruby Braff — Vanguard 8020 (1954) 10" $50.

TWO BY TWO/with Ruby Braff — Vanguard 8502 (1956) maroon and silver label $35.

*The only LP's within the scope of this book.

PETE LA ROCA
drums, composer - born 1938 New York City, NY

BASRA/with Joe Henderson — Blue Note 4205/84205 (1965) with NY on label $35; with A Division of Liberty on label $20.

PRINCE LASHA
flute, composer - born 1929 Fort Worth, TX

THE CRY — Contemporary 3610/7610 (1963) yellow label $30.

YUSEF LATEEF
flute, tenor sax, oboe, composer, leader born 1921 Chatanooga, TN

Lateef played with Roy Eldridge and Dizzy Gillespie in the late 40's in Detroit and was soon leading his own group. When he first arrived in New York City in the early 60's he teamed up with Charlie Mingus, Babtundi Olatunji and "Cannonball" Adderley afterwhich he once again formed his own group of musicians. Lateef has continued to play and record in the years following, gaining recognition for his varied and unusual instrumentations and compositions.

JAZZ MOOD/with Curtis Fuller — Savoy 12103 (1956) maroon label $45.

JAZZ FOR THE THINKER/with Curtis Fuller — Savoy 12109 (1956) maroon label $45.

PRAYER TO THE EAST/with Wilbur Harden — Savoy 12117 (1957) maroon label $45.

JAZZ AND THE SOUNDS OF NATURE/with Wilbur Harden — Savoy 12120 (1957) maroon label $45.

THE DREAMER/with Terry Pollard — Savoy 12139/13007 (1958) maroon label $40.

THE FABRIC OF JAZZ/with Terry Pollard — Savoy 12140/13008 (1958) maroon label $40.

BEFORE DAWN/with Hugh Lawson — Verve 8217 (1957) with Verve Records, Inc. on bottom of label $85; with MGM on bottom of label $35.

THE SOUNDS OF/with Hugh Lawson — Prestige 7122 (1957) yellow label $80; *reissued* New Jazz 8261 (1961) $35.

OTHER SOUNDS/with Wilber Harden — New Jazz 8218 (1959) $40.

CRY! TENDER/with Wilbur Harden — New Jazz 8234 (1960) $40.

INTO SOMETHING/with Elvin Jones — New Jazz 8272 (1961) $40.

THE THREE FACES OF/with Hugh Lawson — Riverside 12-325/1176 (1960) blue label with Bill Grauer Pro. $50.

THE CENTAUR AND THE PHOENIX/with Clark Terry — Riverside 337/9337 (1960) blue label with Bill Grauer Pro. $50.

LOST IN SOUND/with Vincent Pitts — Charlie Parker 814 (1962) $30.

EASTERN SOUNDS/with Barry Harris — Moodsville 22 (1961) $45.

JAZZ AROUND THE WORLD/with Richard Williams — Impulse 56 (1963) orange label $35.

LIVE AT PEP'S/with Richard Williams — Impulse 69 (1964) orange label $25.

1984/with Mike Nock — Impulse 84 (1965) orange label $25.

LATIN ALL STARS
Buddy Collette, Tommy Tedesco, Eddie Cano Tony Reyes, Carlos Mejia, Darias

JAZZ HEAT BONGO BEAT — Crown 187 (1958) with liner notes on cover $15.

LATIN JAZZ QUINTET

CARIBE/with Eric Dolphy — New Jazz 8251 (1960) $35.

HOT SAUCE/with Bobby Capers — Trusound 15003 (1962) $30.

LATIN JAZZ QUINTET/with Bobby Capers — Trusound 15012 (1962) $30.

LATIN JAZZ QUINTET — United Artists 4071/5071 (1963) $25.

ELLIOT LAWRENCE
piano, leader, composer - born 1925 Philadelphia, PA

COLLEGE PROM — Decca 5274 (1950) 10" $40.

MOONLIGHT OF THE CAMPUS — Decca 5353 (1951) 10" $40.

PLAYS GERRY MULLIGAN ARRANGEMENTS — Fantasy 3-206 (1956) $45.

PLAYS TINY KAHN & JOHNNY MANDEL ARRANGEMENTS — Fantasy 3-219 (1956) $45.

DREAM — Fantasy 3-226 (1956) $30.

SWINGING AT THE STEEL PIER/with Al Cohn — Fantasy 3-236 (1956) $50.

DREAM ON, DREAM ON — Fantasy 3261 (1958) $30.

JAZZ GOES BROADWAY/with Zoot Sims — Vik 1113 (1958) $50.

MUSIC FOR TRAPPING — Top Rank 304/604 (1959) $30.

HUBERT LAWS
flute, composer - born 1939 Houston, TX
THE LAWS OF JAZZ — Atlantic 1432 (1965) with logo on right side $25.

DEE LAWSON
vocals - born Long Island, NY

'ROUND MIDNIGHT/with Jimmy Cleveland — Roulette 52017 (1958) white label with multicolored pinwheel $75.

SAM LAZAR
organ - born 1933 St. Louis, MO

SPACE FLIGHT/with Grant Green — Argo 4002 (1960) **$40.**

PLAYBACK/with Miller Brisker — Argo 4015 (1961) **$40.**

SOUL MERCHANT/with Miller Brisker — Argo 714 (1962) **$35.**

BARBARA LEA
vocals

A WOMAN IN LOVE/with Johnny Windhurst — Riverside 2518 (1955) 10" **$95.**

BARBARA LEA/with Johnny Windhurst — Prestige 7065 (1956) yellow label **$60.**

LEA IN LOVE — Prestige 7100 (1957) yellow label **$50.**

DAVID LEE

BELGIAN JAZZ — Bally 12005 (1956) **$40.**

JULIA LEE

vocals, piano - born 1902 Kansas City, MO died 1958
Coming from the influence of a musical family, Lee was a well known vocalist and pianist in Kansas City and Chicago whose style was quite similar to the male blues performers and big band singers from those areas. She worked extensively, recording quite regularly with all star bands but has only one LP to her credit.

PARTY TIME — Capitol 228 (1952) 10" **$150;** *reissued* Capitol T228 (1955) green label **$100.**

*PEGGY LEE

vocals - born 1922 Jamestown, ND
Lee was first heard with Benny Goodman in the early 40's and was successful thereafter as a performer and as composer of many of her hits. Lee also fared quite well in movie and television, especially with Pete Kelly's Blues in 1956. Since that time she has enjoyed many collaborations on numerous recordings with musicians such as Duke Ellington and Quincy Jones. Lee is known for her bluesy, feeling vocal quality which she maintains through continued television and personal appearances.

REDEZVOUS — Capitol 155 (1952) 10" **$60;** EP 151 (1952) 2 records **$40;** *reissued* Capitol T151 (1955) green label **$50;** *reissued* Capitol 1743.

MY BEST TO YOU — Capitol 204 (1952) 10" **$60;** *reissued* Capitol 1743.

THE MAN I LOVE — Capitol 864 (1956) green label **$50;** EP 1-864, EP 2-864, EP3-864 (1956) **$20 ea.**

JUMP FOR JOY — Capitol 975 (1957) green label **$40;** *reissued* Capitol 975 (1958) black label with logo on left side **$35.**

THINGS ARE SWINGIN' — Capitol 1049 (1959) black label with logo on left side **$40;** EP 1-1049 (1959) **$20.**

I LIKE MEN — Capitol 1131 (1959) black label with logo on left side **$35;** EP 1-1131 (1959) **$20.**

FEVER — Capitol EP 1-1052 (1959) **$30.**

BEAUTY AND THE BEAT/with George Shearing — Capitol 1219 (1960) black label with logo on left side **$40.**

ALL AGLOW AGAIN — Capitol 1366 (1960) black label with logo on left side **$30.**

BASIN STREET EAST/with Stan Levey — Capitol 1520 (1960) black label with logo on left side **$35.**

BLUES CROSS COUNTRY/with Quincy Jones — Capitol 1671 (1961) black label with logo on left side **$45.**

IF YOU GO/with Quincy Jones — Capitol 1630 (1961) black label with logo on left side **$35.**

SUGAR AND SPICE/with Benny Carter — Capitol 1772 (1962) black label with logo on top **$30.**

BEWITCHING LEE — Capitol 1743 (1962) **$30;** *reissue* of Capitol 151 and 204 (1952).

MINK JAZZ/with Jack Sheldon — Capitol "Dimensions in Jazz" 1850 (1963) tan and black label **$35.**

I'M A WOMAN/with Stan Levey — Capitol 1857 (1963) **$25.**

IN LOVE AGAIN/with Bill Holman — Capitol 1969 (1963) **$25.**

BIG SPENDER/with Bill Holman — Capitol 2475 (1965) black label with logo on top **$25;** EP 2475 (1965) **$15.**

THE JAZZ SINGER — Decca EP 2003 (1952) 1 record **$40.**

SONG IN INTIMATE STYLE — Decca 5539 (1953) 10" **$50.**

BLACK COFFEE — Decca 5482 (1953) 10" **$60;** *reissued* Decca 8358 (1957) black label with silver lettering **$40.**

LADY AND THE TRAMP — Decca 5557 (1955) 10" **$70;** *reissued* Decca 8462 (1957) black label with silver lettering **$40.**

PETE KELLY'S BLUES/with Ella Fitzgerald — Decca 8166 (1955) black label with silver lettering **$80.**

DREAM STREET — Decca 8411 (1956) black label with silver lettering **$40.**

SEA SHELLS — Decca 8591 (1958) black label with silver lettering **$35.**

MISS WONDERFUL — Decca 8816 (1959) black label with silver lettering **$30**

LOVER — Decca 4458/74458 (1964) black label with rainbow strip **$20.**

THE FABULOUS — Decca 4461/74461 (1964) black label with rainbow strip **$20.**

THE BEST OF — Decca DXB 164 (1964) 2 records, black label with rainbow strip **$30.**

SINGS/with Benny Goodman — Harmony 7005 (1958) **$15.**

---

*The only LP's within the scope of this book.

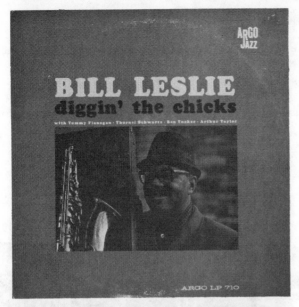

PERRI LEE
organ

A NIGHT AT COUNT BASIE'S — Roulette 52080 (1962) light and dark orange roulette wheel label **$20.**

BILL LESLIE
tenor sax

DIGGIN' THE CHICKS/with Tommy Flanagan — Argo 710 (1962) **$40.**

JOHN LETMAN
trumpet - born 1917 McCormick, SC

THE MANY ANGLES OF — Bethlehem 6053 (1961) maroon label **$35.**

STAN LEVEY
drums - born 1925 Philadelphia, PA

An important and influential drummer in the bop movement from the early 40's, Levey continued to work with artists such as Stan Kenton, Charlie Parker, Dizzy Gillespie and George Auld through the 50's. Levey was considered to be in the front running with drummers such as his good friend Max Roach but gradually moved out of the music business to indulge in the field of photography.

PLAYS/with Zoot Sims — Bethlehem 1017 (1954) 10" **$100;** *reissued* Bethlehem 9 (1955).

WEST COASTING — Bethlehem 9 (1955) maroon label **$80;** *reissue* of Bethlehem 1017.

THIS TIME THE DRUMS ON ME/with Frank Rosolino — Bethlehem 37 (1955) maroon label **$40.**

GRAND STAN/with Richie Kamuca — Bethlehem 71 (1956) maroon label **$40.**

QUARTET/with Bill Perkins — Mode 101 (1957) **$60.**

DRUMMIN' THE BLUES/with Max Roach — Liberty 3064 (1957) green label with lighthouse **$60;** one side each.

RON LEVITT
trombone, composer - born 1929 Portland, OR

DYNAMIC SOUND PATTERNS/with Rolf Ericson — Riverside 471/9471 (1963) blue label with Bill Grauer Pro. **$20.**

IN SIGHT/with Rolf Ericson — RCA Victor 3372 (1965) dog on top **$20.**

LOU LEVY
piano - born 1928 Chicago, IL

TRIO — Nocturne 10 (1954) 10" **$50.**

SOLO SCENE — RCA Victor 1267 (1956) dog on top **$50.**

JAZZ IN FOUR COLORS — RCA Victor 1319 (1957) dog on top **$50.**

A MOST MUSICAL FELLA — RCA Victor 1491 (1957) dog on top **$40.**

WEST COAST WAILERS/with Conte Candoli — Atlantic 1268 (1957) black label **$60.**

BABY GRAND JAZZ — Jubilee 1101 (1959) **$30.**

JOHN LEWIS
piano, composer, arranger - born 1920 LaGrange, IL

Lewis began to demonstrate his considerable skills as a pianist, composer and arranger in the mid-40's with Dizzy Gillespie and, in the late 40's, with the great Miles Davis. Beginning in 1952, Lewis was a co-founder of the Modern Jazz Quartet (MJQ) and through that group and his own projects over the years has come to be regarded as one of the finest jazz composers and arrangers.

AFTERNOON IN PARIS/with Sacha Distel — Atlantic 1267 (1957) black label **50;** *reissued* with logo on right side **$20.**

THE JOHN LEWIS PIANO/with Barney Wilen — Atlantic 1272 (1957) black label **$50;** *reissued* with logo on right side **$20.**

IMPROVISED MEDITATION & EXCURSIONS — Atlantic 1313 (1959) with logo on right side **$20.**

A MILANESE STORY/with Bobby Jaspar — Atlantic 1388 (1962) with logo on right side **$25.**

ANIMAL DANCE/with Albert Mangeldorff — Atlantic 1402 (1962) with logo on right side **$35.**

ESSENCE/with Freddie Hubbard — Atlantic 1425 (1964) with logo on right side **$20.**

THE GOLDEN STRIKER/with Joe Wilder — Atlantic 1334 (1960) with logo on right side **$20.**

ORIGINAL SIN — Atlantic 1370 (1961) with logo on right side **$25.**

WONDERFUL WORLD OF JAZZ/with Eric Dolphy — Atlantic 1375 (1961) with logo on right side **$20.**

EUROPEAN WINDOWS — RCA Victor 1742 (1958) dog on top **$40.**

ODDS AGAINST TOMORROW (Soundtrack) — United Artists 4063/5063 (1959) red label **$50.**

THE JAZZTET AND JOHN LEWIS — Argo 604 (1961) **$45.**

ORCHESTRA U.S.A./with Phil Woods — Colpix 448 (1963) gold label **$35.**

ORCHESTRA U.S.A.; JAZZ JOURNEY/with Coleman Hawkins — Columbia 2247/9047 (1964) red label with 1 white logo on each side **$35.**

MEL LEWIS
drums - born 1929 Buffalo, NY

Big band experience in the 40's helped open the door to work with many groups during the 50's. Lewis played with Gerry Mulligan, Dizzy Gillespie, and Benny Goodman in the early 60's before starting a big band in New York City in 1965 with Thad Jones. This band has proven quite successful with regular appearances, tours and recordings.

GOT 'CHA/with Jerry Coker — San Francisco 2 (1957) **$60.**

SEXTET/with Charlie Mariano — Mode 103 (1957) **$60.**

RAMSEY LEWIS TRIO
piano, composer - born 1925 Chicago, IL
Eldee Young - bass, Red Holt - drums

DOWN TO EARTH — EmArcy 36150/80029 (1958) with EmArcy in Mercury logo **$60.**

GENTLEMAN OF SWING — Argo 611 (1958) **$60.**

GENTLEMAN OF JAZZ — Argo 627 (1958) **$60.**

LEN WINCHESTER AND RAMSEY LEWIS TRIO — Argo 642 (1959) **$55.**

HOUR WITH — Argo 645 (1959) **$55.**

IN CHICAGO — Argo 671 (1960) **$50.**

STRETCHING OUT — Argo 665 (1960) **$50.**

MORE MUSIC FROM THE SOIL — Argo 680 (1961) **$45.**

SOUND OF CHRISTMAS — Argo 687 (1961) **$50;** EP 1084 (1961) **$25.**

THE SOUND OF SPRING — Argo 693 (1962) **$35.**

COUNTRY MEET THE BLUES — Argo 701 (1962) **$45.**

BOSSA NOVA — Argo 705 (1962) **$25.**

POT LUCK — Argo 715 (1962) **$40.**

BAREFOOT SUNDAY BLUES — Argo 723 (1963) **$40.**

BACH TO THE BLUES — Argo 732 (1964) **$35.**

AT THE BOHEMIAN CAVERNS — Argo 741 (1964) **$35.**

MORE SOUND OF CHRISTMAS — Argo 745 (1964) **$45.**

YOU BETTER BELIEVE IT/with Jean DuShon — Argo 750 (1965) **$35.**

CHOICE! THE BEST OF — Argo 755 (1965) **$25.**

THE IN CROWD — Argo 757 (1965) **$35.** (A)

ABBEY LINCOLN
vocals - born 1930 Chicago, IL

Working on the West Coast as a vocalist and actress in clubs and performances during the 50's, Lincoln made her first recording on Capitol under her own name in 1956. Lincoln is definitely a jazz artist with a style unlike that of anyone else in the profession. She continues with occasional recordings and considerable club appearances.

AFFAIR/with Benny Carter — Liberty 3025 (1957) **$70.**

THAT'S HIM/with Sonny Rollins — Riverside 12-251/1107 (1957) blue label with Bill Grauer Pro. **$60.**

IT'S MAGIC/with Benny Golson — Riverside 12-277 (1958) blue label with Bill Grauer Pro. **$60.**

ABBEY'S BLUE/with Kenny Dorham — Riverside 12-308 (1959) blue label with Bill Grauer Pro. **$60.**

STRAIGHT AHEAD/with Coleman Hawkins — Candid 8015/9015 (1961) **$70.**

MELBA LISTON
trombone, composer - born 1926 Kansas City, MO

AND HER BONES/with Slide Hampton — Metrojazz 1013 (1958) **$45.**

BOOKER LITTLE
trumpet, composer - born 1938 Memphis, TN died 1961

A very talented musician with exceptional writing abilities, Little began working and appearing with Max Roach in 1958 but was quickly out working and recording on his own. He was recognized as an innovator on his instrument during his time but his career was unfortunately cut short by his death in 1961.

BOOKER LITTLE 4/with Max Roach — United Artists 4034/5034 (1959) red label **$75.**

BOOKER LITTLE/with Tommy Flanagan — Time 52011/2011 (1960) **$60.**

OUT FRONT/with Eric Dolphy — Candid 8027/9027 (1961) **$60.**

AND FRIENDS/with George Coleman — Bethlehem 6061 (1961) maroon label **$45.**

CHARLES LLOYD

tenor sax, flute, composer - born 1928 Memphis, TN

DISCOVERY!/with Don Friedman — Columbia 2267/9067 (1964) red label with 1 white logo on each side **$15.**

OF COURSE, OF COURSE/with Gabor Szabo — Columbia 2412/9212 (1965) red label with 1 white logo on each side **$15.**

GIUSEPPI LOGAN

tenor, alto saxes, composer - born 1935 Philadelphia, PA

QUARTET — ESP Disk 1007 (1965) **$20.**

*JULIE LONDON

vocals - born 1926 Santa Rosa, CA

JULIE IS HER NAME/with Barney Kessel — Liberty 3027 (1955) green label **$60;** EP 1001 (1955) **$30;** *reissued* Liberty 7027 (1959) stereo, black label with rainbow strip on left side **$40.**

ABOUT THE BLUES/with Russ Garcia — Liberty 3043 (1956) green label **$60;** EP 1-3043, EP 2-3043 (1957) **$30 ea.**

MAKE LOVE TO ME/with Russ Garcia — Liberty 3060 (1956) green label **$50.**

JULIE/with Jimmy Rowles — Liberty 3096 (1957) green label mono **$45;** *reissued* (1958) black label with rainbow strip on left side, stereo **$40.**

JULIE IS HER NAME - Vol 2/with Howard Roberts — Liberty 3100/7100 (1958) **$40.**

SWING ME AN OLD SONG/with Jimmy Rowles — Liberty 3119/7119 (1959) **$35.**

SEND FOR ME/with Jimmy Rowles — Liberty 3171/7171 (1960) **$35.**

ALL THROUGH THE NIGHT/with Bud Shank Quintet — Liberty 7434 (1965) **$30.**

*The only LP's within the scope of this book.

DANNY LONG

piano

JAZZ FURLOUGH — Capitol 1988 (1963) black label with logo on top **$20.**

HARRY LOOKOFSKY

violin, viola - born 1913 Paducha, KY

STRINGSVILLE/with Bob Brookmeyer — Atlantic 1319 (1959) with logo on right side **$35.**

LEE LOVETT

piano, arranger - born 1919 Germantown, PA

JAZZ DANCE PARTY — Strand 1055 (1960) **$35.**

MISTY/with Bob Brown — Strand 1059 (1960) **$40.**

MUNDELL LOWE

guitar, composer, arranger - born 1922 Laurel, MS

A superb guitarist who has worked with several name big bands and a number of combos during the 40's and 50's. Also, during the 50's, Lowe began his work in television numbers and eventually was composing and arranging to the point that, by the 60's, he was almost exclusively involved in studio work on the West Coast.

QUINTET/with Trigger Alpert — RCA Victor 3002 (1954) 10" **$150.**

QUARTET/with Trigger Alpert — Riverside 12-204 (1955) white label with Bill Grauer Pro. **$80;** *reissued* blue label (1958) **$45.**

GUITAR MOODS/with Trigger Alpert — Riverside 12-208 (1956) white label with Bill Grauer Pro. **$80;** *reissued* blue label (1958) **$45.**

NEW MUSIC OF ALEC WILDER/with Joe Wilder — Riverside 12-219 (1956) white label with Bill Grauer Pro. **$80;** *reissued blue label (1958)* **$40;** *reissued* Offbeat 3010/93010 (1960).

A GRAND NIGHT FOR SWINGING/with Gene Quill — Riverside 12-238 (1957) white label with Bill Grauer Pro. **$75;** *reissued* Jazzland 8 (1960).

LOW DOWN GUITAR — Jazzland 8 (1960) **$35;** *reissue* of Riverside 12-238.

TACET FOR NEUROTICS — Offbeat 3010/93010 (1960) **$35;** *reissue* of Riverside 12-219.

PORGY AND BESS/with Ben Webster — Camden 490 (1958) **$40.**

T.V. ACTION JAZZ/with Tony Scott — Camden 522 (1959) **$40.**

T.V. ACTION JAZZ - Vol 2/with Clark Terry — Camden 627 (1960) **$40.**

SATIN IN HIGH HEELS (Soundtrack)/with Al Cohn — Charlie Parker 406 (1961) **$45;** *reissued* Charlie Parker 822 (1962).

BLUES FOR A STRIPPER — Charlie Parker 822 (1962) **$35;** *reissue* of Charlie Parker 822 (1961).

GENE LUDWIG

organ

ORGAN OUT LOUD — Mainstream 56032/6032 (1965) **$15.**

*ARTHUR LYMAN

vibes

LEIS OF JAZZ/with Ethel Azama — Hi Fi 607 (1959) **$35.**

*The only LP's within the scope of this book.

*GLORIA LYNNE

vocals - born 1931 New York City, NY

MISS GLORIA LYNNE/with Harry Edison — Everest 5022/1022 (1959) **$40.**

LONELY AND SENTIMENTAL/with Melba Liston — Everest 5063/1063 (1959) **$40.**

TRY A LITTLE TENDERNESS/with Leroy Holmes — Everest 5090/1090 (1960) $40.

DAY IN DAY OUT/with Ernie Wilkins — Everest 5101/1101 (1960) $30.

I AM GLAD THERE'S YOU — Everest 5126/1126 (1961) $25.

HE NEEDS ME/with Jimmy Jones — Everest 5128/1128 (1962) $25.

AT LAS VEGAS THUNDERBIRD/with Herman Foster — Everest 5208/1208 (1962) $25.

MY FUNNY VALENTINE — Design 177 (1962) $25.

INTIMATE MOMENTS — Fontana 27528/67528 (1964) $20.

SOUL SERENADE — Fontana 67541/27541 (1965) $20.

*The only LP's within the scope of this book.

JOHNNY LYTLE
vibes - born 1932 Springfield, OH

BLUE VIBES/with Milton Harris — Jazzland 22/922 (1960) $30.

HAPPY GROUND/with Milton Harris — Jazzland 44/944 (1961) $30.

NICE AND EASY/with Johnny Griffin — Jazzland 67/967 (1962) $35.

MOON CHILD/with Milton Harris — Jazzland 81/981 (1962) $25.

GOT THAT FEELING/with Milton Harris — Riverside 456/9456 (1963) blue label with Bill Grauer Pro. $20.

THE VILLAGE CALLER/with Milton Harris — Riverside 480/9480 (1965) blue label with Bill Grauer Pro. $20.

TEO MACERO
composer, saxophones - born 1925 Glen Falls, NY

EXPLORATIONS/with Charlie Mingus — Debut 6 (1953) 10" $75.

WHAT'S NEW/with Art Farmer and George Barrow — Columbia 842 (1956) red label with 3 black logos on each side $45 (Bob Prince Group plays five sides on the LP).

WITH THE PRESTIGE JAZZ QUARTET/with Mal Waldron and Teddy Charles — Prestige 7104 (1957) yellow label $45.

MACHITO
leader - born 1912 Tampa, FL

MACHITO AFRO-CUBAN JAZZ SUITE/with Harry Edison and Sol Rabinowitz — Clef 505 (1953) 10" $80.

JAZZ ALBUM FLIP & BIRD/with Flip Phillips and Charlie Parker — Clef 511 (1953) 10" $80.

AFRO CUBAN JAZZ: KENYA/with Cannonball Adderley and Joe Newman — Roulette 52006 (1957) white label with multicolored pinwheel $50.

WITH FLUTE TO BOOT/with Herbie Mann and Johnny Griffin — Roulette 52026 (1958) white label with multicolored pinwheel $50.

MIKE MAINERI
vibes - born 1924 Bronx, NY

BLUES ON THE OTHER SIDE — Argo 706 (1962) $30.

JUNIOR MANCE
piano - born 1928 Chicago, IL

JUNIOR — Verve 8319/6057 (1959) with Verve Records, Inc. on bottom of label $45; with MGM on bottom of label $25.

THE SOULFUL PIANO OF — Jazzland 30/930 (1960) $20.

AT THE VILLAGE VANGUARD — Jazzland 41/941 (1961) $20.

BIG CHIEF — Jazzland 53/953 (1961) $20.

JAZZ SOUL OF HOLLYWOOD — Jazzland 63/963 (1962) $20.

HAPPY TIME — Jazzland 77/977 (1962) $20.

JUNIOR'S BLUES — Riverside 447/9447 (1963) blue label mono; black label stereo with Bill Grauer Pro. $25.

GET READY, SET, JUMP!/with Pete Candoli — Capitol 2092 (1963) black label with logo on top $30.

STRAIGHT AHEAD/with Shelly Manne — Capitol 2218 (1964) black label with logo on top $15.

THAT'S WHERE IT IS — Capitol 2393 (1965) black label with logo on top $15.

HENRY MANCINI
composer, conductor - born 1924 Cleveland, OH

THE MUSIC FROM PETER GUNN/with Pete Candoli and Ted Nash — RCA Victor 1956 (1959) dog on top, rare original has artistic cover with musical instruments in squares by Jason Kirby $45; with artistic cover by Fritz Miller $25; EP 4333 (1959) $10.

MORE MUSIC FROM PETER GUNN/with Pete Candoli and Ronny Lang — RCA Victor 2040 (1959) dog on top $25; EP 4339 (1959) $15.

COMBO! THE ORIGINAL PETER GUNN SOUND/with Art Pepper and Shelly Manne — RCA Victor 2258 (1961) dog on top $35.

GUS MANCUSO
baritone horn - born 1933 Rochester, NY

INTRODUCING/with Cal Tjader and Richie Kamuca — Fantasy 3-223 (1956) red vinyl $75.

MUSIC FROM NEW FACES/with Red Mitchell — Fantasy 3282/8025 (1957) $50.

CHUCK MANGIONE
trumpet, composer - born 1940 Rochester, NY

ECUERDO — Jazzland 84/984 (1962) **$45**.

THE MANHATTAN JAZZ ALL-STARS
*Teddy Charles, Phil Woods, Bob Brookmeyer,
Zoot Sims, Mose Allison, Nick Travis*

WINGING GUYS AND DOLLS — Columbia 1426/8223 (1959) red label with 3 black logos on each side **$40**.

THE MANHATTAN JAZZ SEPTETTE
*Urbie Green, Herbie Mann,
Hal McKusick, Eddie Costa*

HE MANHATTAN JAZZ SEPTETTE — Coral 57090 (1956) maroon label **$60**.

HERBIE MANN
*tenor sax, flute, woodwinds, composer - born 1930
Brooklyn, NY*

Mann's first recordings were with him on tenor but he is best known as one of the first popularizers of the flute in the jazz stream. Throughout his profusely recorded career Mann has continued to volve in style and especially to incorporate his musical ndeavors many influences of both jazz and ethnic musics from around the world. He obtained early critical success followed by wider commercial and popular success through the 50's and 60's.

AST COAST JAZZ-4/with Benny Weeks — Bethlehem 1018 (1954) 10" **$100**; EP 125, EP 127 (1954) **$45** ea.

LAMINGO, MY GOODNESS, 4 FLUTES - Vol 2/with Joe Puma — Bethlehem 24 (1955) maroon label **$60**.

HE HERBIE MANN-SAM MOST QUINTET — Bethlehem 40 (1955) maroon label **$60**.

LAYS — Bethlehem 58 (1956) maroon label **$50**.

OVE AND THE WEATHER/with Orchestra & Strings — Bethlehem 63 (1956) maroon label **$50**.

PITOME OF JAZZ — Bethlehem 6067 (1963) maroon label **$35**.

MANN ALONE (Solo) — Savoy 12107 (1957) maroon label **$30**.

ARDBIRD SUITE/with Phil Woods — Savoy 12108 (1957) maroon label **$45**.

SALUTE TO THE FLUTE/with Joe Wilder — Epic 3395 (1957) yellow and black label **$80**.

HERBIE MANN WITH ILCKEN TRIO — Epic 3499 (1958) **$60**.

ULTRY SERENADE/with Urbie Green — Riverside 12-234 (1957) blue label with Bill Grauer Pro. **$60**.

GREAT IDEAS OF WESTERN MANN/with Jack Sheldon — Riverside 12-245 (1957) blue label with Bill Grauer Pro. **$70**; *reissued* Jazzland 5.

CALIFORNIANS — Jazzland 5 (1960) **$35**.

FLUTE FRATERNITY/with Buddy Collette — Mode 114 (1957) **$65**; *reissued* Interlude 503/1003 (1959) pink label **$45**; *reissued* Premier 2001.

HI FLUTIN'/with Buddy Collette — Premier 2001 (1963) **$25**.

FLUTE SOUFFLE/with Bobby Jaspar — Prestige 7101 (1957) yellow label **$75**.

FLUTE FLIGHT/with Bobby Jaspar — Presitge 7124 (1957) yellow label **$75**.

MANN IN THE MORNING/with Ake Persson — Prestige 7136 (1958) yellow label **$60**.

THE BEST OF — Prestige 7432 (1965) blue label with logo on right side **$25**.

JUST WAILIN'/with Charlie Rouse — New Jazz 8211 (1958) **$45**.

THE MAGIC FLUTE OF/with Laurindo Almeida — Verve 8247 (1957) with Verve Records, Inc. on bottom of label **$45**.

AFRO CUBAN JAZZ/with John Rae — Verve 8336 (1959) with Verve Records, Inc. on bottom of label **$35**.

FLUTE, BRASS, VIBES & PERCUSSION — Verve 8392/68392 (1960) with Verve Records, Inc. on bottom of label **$35**.

SOUND — Verve 8527/68527 (1963) with MGM on bottom of label **$25**.

BRAZIL, BOZZA NOVA AND BLUES/with Willie Bobo — United Artists 14009/15009 (1962) gray label with silhouette of sax player **$35**.

ST. THOMAS — United Artists 14022/15022 (1962) gray label with silhouette of sax player **$35**.

AFRICAN SUITE — United Artists 4042/5042 (1959) red label **$40**.

THE COMMON GROUND — Atlantic 1343 (1960) with logo on right side **$25**.

FAMILY OF MANN — Atlantic 1371 (1961) with logo on right side **$25**.

AT THE VILLAGE GATE — Atlantic 1380 (1962) with logo on right side **$20**.

RIGHT NOW — Atlantic 1384 (1962) with logo on right side **$20**.

DO THE BOSSA NOVA — Atlantic 1397 (1963) with logo on right side **$20**.

RETURNS TO VILLAGE GATE — Atlantic 1407 (1963) with logo on right side **$20**.

LIVE AT NEWPORT — Atlantic 1413 (1963) with logo on right side **$20**.

LATIN FEVER — Atlantic 1422 (1964) with logo on right side **$20**.

NIRVANA/with Bill Evans — Atlantic 1426 (1964) with logo on right side **$25**.

MY KINDA GROOVE — Atlantic 1433 (1965) with logo on right side **$20**.

SHELLY MANNE
drums - born New York City, NY

Well known first as a drummer with big bands such as Stan Kenton, Woody Herman and many others during the 40's, Manne also recorded with smaller groups led by Dizzy Gillespie, Ben Webster, Coleman Hawkins and others while stationed in New York City. His work with Bob Cooper and Art Pepper on The West Coast Sounds is with out a doubt an LP that should not be overlooked by any serious jazz enthusiast. Since the early 50's, Manne has worked primarily on the West Coast. He was much in demand and worked in studios for jazz dates, movie and television and is known for his contribution to the soundtrack, Man With The Golden Arm. In 1956 he once again formed his own group, operated his own club and continued to appear and record in a wide variety of jazz situations. Truly, it can easily be stated that Manne is a front running jazz drummer with overwhelming capabilities.

HERE'S THAT MANNE — Dee Gee 1003 (1952) 10" **$225**.

AND HIS MEN/with Art Pepper and Bob Cooper — Contemporary 2503 (1953) 10" **$225**; EP 4001, EP 4007 (1953) **$50 ea.**; *reissued* Contemporary 3507.

AND HIS MEN - Vol 2/with Bob Enevoldsen — Contemporary 2511 (1953) 10" **$150**.

THE THREE/with Shorty Rogers and Jimmy Giuffre — Contemporary 2516 (1954) 10" **$125**; *reissued* Contemporary 3584.

SHELLY MANNE/RUSS FREEMAN — Contemporary 2518 (1954) 10" **$60**; *reissued* Contemporary 3584.

THE WEST COAST SOUND/with Jimmy Giuffre and Bud Shank — Contemporary 3507 (1956) yellow label **$75**; *reissue* of Contemporary 2503 plus 4 other sides.

SWINGING SOUNDS/with Charlie Mariano — Contemporary 3516 (1956) yellow label **$75**.

MORE SWINGING SOUNDS/with Charlie Mariano — Contemporary 3519 (1956) yellow label **$60**; *reissued* Contemporary 7007 (1958) stereo **$40**.

AND HIS FRIENDS/with Andre Previn and Leroy Vinnegar — Contemporary 3525 (1956) yellow label **$25**.

MY FAIR LADY/with Andre Previn and Leroy Vinnegar — Contemporary 3527 (1956) yellow label **$30**; *reissued* Contemporary 7527 (1958) stereo **$25**.

LIL' ABNER/with Andre Previn and Leroy Vinnegar — Contemporary 3533 (1956) yellow label **$40**; *reissued* Contemporary 7019 (1958) stereo **$35**.

CONCERTO FOR CLARINET AND COMBO/with Jack Montrose and Charlie Mariano— Contemporary 3536 (1957) yellow label **$50**.

THE GAMBIT/with Charlie Mariano — Contemporary 3557 (1958) yellow label mono; Contemporary 7030 black label stereo **$50**.

BELLS ARE RINGING/with Andre Previn and Red Mitchell — Contemporary 3559/7559 (1958) yellow label **$25**.

PLAY PETER GUNN/with Herb Geller and Conte Candoli — Contemporary 3560/7025 (1959) yellow label **$45**.

SON OF GUNN/with Richie Kamuca and Joe Gordon — Contemporary 3566/7566 (1959) yellow label **$45**.

AT THE BLACK HAWK - Vol 1/with Richie Kamuca and Joe Gordon — Contemporary 3577/7577 (1960) yellow label **$40**.

AT THE BLACK HAWK - Vol 2/with Richie Kamuca and Joe Gordon — Contemporary 3578/7578 (1960) yellow label **$40**.

AT THE BLACK HAWK- Vol 3/with Richie Kamuca and Joe Gordon — Contemporary 3580/7580 (1960) yellow label **$40**.

THE THREE AND THE TWO — Contemporary 3584 (1960) yellow label **$40**; *reissue* of Contemporary 2516 and 2518.

THE PROPER TIME/with Russ Freeman — Contemporary 3587/7587 (1960) yellow label **$35**.

AT MANNE-HOLE/with Richie Kamuca and Conte Candoli — Contemporary 3593/7593 (1961) yellow label **$35**.

CHECKMATE/with Richie Kamuca — Contemporary 3599/7599 (1961) yellow label **$35**.

SOUNDS UNHEARD OF — Contemporary 5006/9006 (1962) yellow label **$25**.

MY SON THE DRUMMER — Contemporary 3609/7609 (1963) yellow label **$25**.

2, 3, 4/with Coleman Hawkins — Impulse 20 (1962) orange label **$35**.

PEPPER/MANNE — Charlie Parker 836 (1963) one side each **$35**.

MANNE - THAT'S GERSHWIN — Capitol 2313 (1965) black label with logo on top **$20**.

LAWRENCE MARABLE
drums - born 1929 Los Angeles, CA

WRENCE MARABLE TENORMAN/with James Clay — Jazz West 8 (1956) **$85.**

CHARLIE MARIANO
alto sax - born 1923 Boston, MA

riano worked extensively with name bands and combos in the ly 50's including many recordings with Stan Kenton and Shelly anne. He co-led a group with Toshiko Akiyoski to whom he was rried at the time. Although Mariano has only a few recordings der his own name he is an outstanding musician who has not eived due recognition. Nevertheless, he has continued to record, r and teach through the years with many different groups cluding his own.

ARLIE MARIANO/with Herb Pomeroy — Imperial 3006 (1951) 10" **$300.**

ARLIE MARIANO QUINTET/with Herb Pomeroy — Imperial 3007 (1951) 10" **$300.**

W SOUNDS FROM BOSTON/with Joe Gordon — Prestige 130 (1952) 10" **$250.**

STON ALL STARS/with Herb Pomeroy — Prestige 153 (1953) 10" **$250.**

ARLIE MARIANO SEXTET/with Dick Collins — Fantasy 3-10 (1953) 10" **$200;** EP 4009, EP 4010 (1953) **$50 ea.;** *reissued* Fantasy 3-224 (1956).

ARLIE MARIANO SEXTET AND THE DICK COLLINS-NAT PIERCE NONET — Fantasy 3-224 (1956) **$65.**

CHARLIE MARIANO SEXTET/with Frank Rosolino — Bethlehem 1022 (1954) 10" **$200;** EP 117 (1954) **$50.**

CHARLIE MARIANO - Vol 2/with John Williams — Bethlehem 25 (1955) maroon label **$65.**

CHARLIE MARIANO PLAYS/with John Williams — Bethlehem 49 (1956) maroon label **$65.**

BEAUTIES OF 1918/with Jerr Dodgion — World Pacific 1245/1014 (1958) **$50.**

A JAZZ PORTRAIT OF — Regina 286 (1963) **$35.**

TOSHIKO (AKIYOSHI) MARIANO
(Note: See Toshiko Akiyoshi)

TOSHIKO-MARIANO/with Charlie Mariano — Candid 8015/9015 (1960) **$40.**

JAZZ IN JAPAN/with Charlie Mariano — Vee Jay 2505 (1964) black label **$35.**

DODO MARMAROSA
piano - born 1925 Pittsburgh, PA died

A great pianist of the bop era, from the early 40's to 50's Marmarosa worked and recorded with many name bands including Artie Shaw, Dizzy Gillespie and, most notably, Charlie Parker. Marmarosa appeared to be at the height of his profession during this time but, like many other musicians, faded from the business possibly due to health problems. He reappeared briefly in 1961 for one LP only.

PIANO CONTRASTS/with Harry Babasin and Jackie Mills — Dial 208 (1948) 10" **$85.**

DODO'S BACK/with Richard Evans and Marshall Thompson — Argo 4012 (1961) **$50.**

HANK MARR
organ

LIVE AT THE CLUB 502/with Rusty Bryant — King 899 (1964) artistic cover, King without crown on label **$35.**

WARNE MARSH
tenor sax - born 1927 Los Angeles, CA

A Tristano/Young influence and blending displays the good horn abilities of Marsh. Some of his best works can be found on recordings with Lennie Tristano, with whom he played for sometime. Also, pay particular attention to a 1955 Atlantic recording titled Lee Konitz/Warne Marsh on which Marsh is unquestionably outstanding.

JAZZ OF TWO CITIES/with Ted Brown — Imperial 9027 (1956) **$95.**

WINDS OF MARSH — Imperial 12013 (1959) black label stereo **$60.**

MUSIC FOR PRANCING/with Red Mitchell — Mode 125 (1957) **$80.**

WARNE MARSH/with Paul Chambers — Atlantic 1291 (1958) black label **$80;** *reissued* Atlantic 1291 (1961) with logo on right side **$35.**

ARCH MARTIN
trombone

ARCH MARTIN QUINTET/with Dick Busey — Zephyr 12009 (1959) **$35.**

SABU MARTINEZ
congas - born 1930 New York, NY

PALO CONGO — Blue Note 1561 (1957) with NY address on label **$60.**

SABU'S JAZZ ESPAGNOLE/with Bobby Porcelli and Marty Sheller — Alegre 802 (1961) **$45.**

BILL MARX

piano - born 1937 Los Angeles, CA

JAZZ KALEIDOSCOPE/with Paul Horn — Vee Jay 3032 (1962) black label **$35.**

MY SON THE FOLK SINGER/with Victor Feldman — Vee Jay 3035 (1962) black label **$30.**

NIGHT TIME IS THE RIGHT TIME — Vee Jay 1108 (1964) black label **$25.**

*DICK MARX

piano, composer - born 1924 Chicago, IL

MARX MAKES BROADWAY/with Buddy Collette and Howard Roberts — Omega 1002 (1958) **$60.**

The only LP's within the scope of this book.

THE MASTERSOUNDS

Monk Montgomery - bass, Buddy Montgomery - vibes
Richie Crabtree - piano, Benny Barth - drums

JAZZ SHOWCASE — Pacific Jazz 403 (1957) **$50;** *reissued* World Pacific 1271 (1959) **$30.**

THE KING AND I — Pacific Jazz 405 (1957) **$50;** *reissued* World Pacific 1017/1272 (1959) **$30.**

KISMET/with Wes Montgomery — World Pacific 1243/1010 (1958) **$25.**

FLOWER DRUM SONG — World Pacific 1252/1012 (1958) **$25.**

BALLADS AND BLUES — World Pacific 1260/1019 (1959) **$35.**

IN CONCERT — World Pacific 1269/1026 (1959) **$35.**

HAPPY HOLIDAYS FROM MANY LANDS (Christmas LP) — World Pacific 1280/1030 (1960) **$60.**

PLAY HORACE SILVER — World Pacific 1284 (1960) **$35.**

SWINGIN' WITH — Fantasy 3305/8050 (1960) red vinyl mono; blue vinyl stereo **$30.**

A DATE WITH — Fantasy 3316/8062 (1961) red vinyl mono; blue vinyl stereo **$30.**

ON TOUR — Fantasy 3323/8066 (1961) **$25.**

*MAT MATHEWS

accordion - born 1924 The Hague, Holland

ACCORDION SOLOS/with Herbie Mann and Percy Heath — Brunswick 54013 (1954) **$50.**

THE MODERN ART OF JAZZ/with Art Farmer and Gigi Gryce — Dawn 1104 (1956) **$75.**

The only LP's within the scope of this book.

RONNIE MATHEWS

piano - born 1935 Brooklyn, NY

DOIN' THE THANG/with Freddie Hubbard — Prestige 7303 (1964) yellow label **$30.**

*JOHNNY MATHIS

vocals

JOHNNY MATHIS/with Art Farmer, Nick Travis and Hal McKusick — Columbia 887 (1956) red label with 3 black logos on each side **$45.**

The only LP's within the scope of this book.

LENNIE McBROWNE

drums - born 1933 Brooklyn, NY

AND THE FOUR SOULS/with Don Sleet — Pacific Jazz 1 (1960) **$45.**

EASTERN LIGHTS/with Don Sleet — Riverside 346/9346 (1960) blue label mono; black label stereo with Bill Grauer Pro. **$45.**

MARY ANN McCALL

vocals - born 1919 Philadelphia, PA

SINGS/with Phil Moore Orchestra — Discovery 3011 (1953) 10" **$125.**

AN EVENING WITH/with Charlie Ventura — Norgran 20 (1954) 10" **$100;** EP 3 EP 34 (1954) **$40 ea.;** *reissued* in part Verve 8143.

AN EVENING WITH/with Charlie Ventura — Norgran 1013 (1955) **$80;** EP 7 EP 78 (1955) **$40 ea.;** *reissued* Verve 8143.

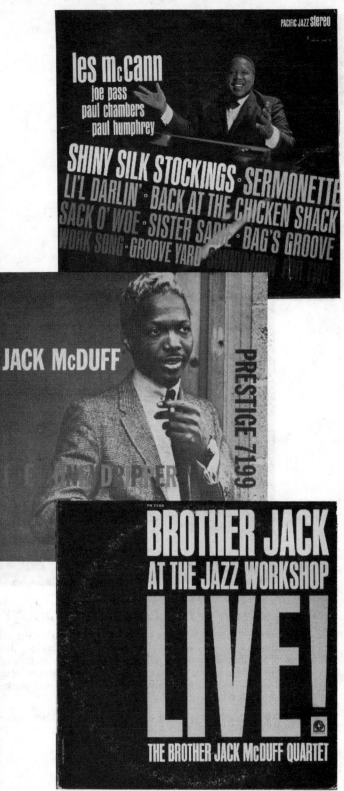

IN SAN FRANCISCO — Pacific Jazz 16 (1960) **$25**.

PRETTY LADY — Pacific Jazz 25 (1961) **$25**.

SINGS/with Gerald Wilson — Pacific Jazz 31 (1961) **$35**.

IN NEW YORK/with Stanley Turrentine — Pacific Jazz 45 (1962) **$45**.

SOMETHING SPECIAL/with Richard Holmes — Pacific Jazz 51 (1962) **$25**.

ON TIME — Pacific Jazz 56 (1962) **$25**.

PLAYS THE SHAMPOO AT THE VILLAGE GATE — Pacific Jazz 63 (1962) **$30**.

THE GOSPEL TRUTH — Pacific Jazz 69 (1963) **$25**.

SOUL HITS/with Joe Pass — Pacific Jazz 78 (1963) **$25**.

JAZZ WALTZ/with The Jazz Crusaders — Pacific Jazz 81 (1964) **$35**.

McCANNA — Pacific Jazz 84 (1964) **$20**.

McCANN/WILSON/with Gerald Wilson Orchestra — Pacific Jazz 91 (1965) **$20**.

BUT NOT REALLY — Limelight 82016/86016 (1965) fold out cover **$20**.

POO BOO — Limelight 82025/86025 (1965) fold out cover **$20**.

FREDDIE McCOY
vibes - born 1932 New York City, NY

LONELY AVENUE/with Tate Houston — Prestige 7395 (1965) blue label with logo on right side **$20**.

JACK McDUFF
organ, composer - born 1926 Champaign, IL

BROTHER JACK McDUFF/with Bill Jennings — Prestige 7174 (1960) yellow label **$80**.

TOUGH 'DUFF/with Jimmy Forrest — Prestige 7185 (1960) yellow label **$75**.

THE HONEYDRIPPER/with Jimmy Forrest — Prestige 7199 (1961) yellow label **$75**.

GOODNIGHT, IT'S TIME TO GO/with Harold Vick — Prestige 7220 (1961) yellow label **$65**.

MEETS THE BOSS/with Gene Ammons — Prestige 7228 (1961) yellow label **$65**.

SCREAMIN'/with Leo Wright — Prestige 7259 (1962) yellow label **$60**.

SOMETHIN' SLICK/with Joe Dukes — Prestige 7265 (1962) yellow label **$50**.

LIVE! — Prestige 7274 (1963) yellow label **$45**.

AT THE JAZZ WORKSHOP, LIVE! — Prestige 7286 (1963) yellow label **$45**.

THE DYNAMIC/with Benny Golson Band — Prestige 7323 (1964) yellow label **$45**.

PRELUDE/with Red Holloway — Prestige 7333 (1964) blue label with logo on right side **$40**.

RECORDED LIVE! — Prestige 7362 (1965) blue label with logo on right side **$35**.

SILK AND SOUL/with Red Holloway — Prestige 7404 (1965) blue label with logo on right side **$35**.

LOU McGARITY
trombone - born 1917 Athens, GA died 1971

SOME LIKE IT HOT/with Dick Cary — Jubilee 1108 (1959) **$60**.

BLUE LOU/with Bob Wilber — Argo 654 (1959) **$40**.

HOWARD McGHEE
trumpet - born 1918 Tulsa, OK

Highly respected trumpet player who worked with Lionel Hampton, Count Basie and JATP among other name groups in the 40's. McGhee has many recordings during this time but was relatively obscure during the late 50's, returning to much activity in the 60's with his own groups and many concerts and festivals.

NIGHT MUSIC/with Jimmy Bunn — Dial 217 (1950) 10" **$175**.

HOWARD McGHEE/with James Moody — Dial 209 (1950) 10" **$175**.

N EVENING WITH/with Charlie Ventura — Verve 8143 (1957) with Verve Records, Inc. on bottom of label **$65**; *reissued* Verve 8143 (1961) with MGM on bottom of label **$45**.

MELANCHOLY BABY — Coral 57276 (1958) maroon label **$45**.

ASY LIVING/with Zoot Sims — Regent 6040 (1956) green label **$45**.

ETOUR TO THE MOON/with Jimmy Raney — Jubilee 1078 (1958) **$45**.

LES McCANN
piano, vocals, composer - born 1935 Lexington, KY

HE TRUTH — Pacific Jazz 2 (1960) **$25**.

PLAYS THE SHOUT — Pacific Jazz 7 (1960) **$25**.

JAZZ GOES TO THE BATTLEFRONT — Hi Lo 6001 (1952) 10" **$125.**

JAZZ GOES TO THE BATTLEFRONT - Vol 2 — Hi Lo 6002 (1952) 10" **$125.**

HOWARD McGHEE/with Teddy Edwards — Aladdin EP 514 (1953) **$50.**

AND HIS ALL STARS — Blue Note 5012 (1953) 10" **$150.**

AND HIS ALL STARS - Vol 2/with Gigi Gryce — Blue Note 5024 (1953) 10" **$150.**

RETURN OF HOWARD McGHEE/with Sahib Shihab — Bethlehem 42 (1956) maroon label **$60.**

LIFE IS JUST A BOWL OF CHERRIES/with Herbie Mann — Bethlehem 61 (1956) maroon label **$60.**

DUSTY BLUE/with Pepper Adams — Bethlehem 6055 (1961) **$35.**

MUSIC FROM THE CONNECTION/with Tina Brooks — Felsted 7512 (1960) **$60.**

HOWARD McGHEE - MILT JACKSON — Savoy 12026 (1956) maroon label **$60.**

JAZZ SOUTH PACIFIC — Savoy 12205 (1964) maroon label **$30.**

TOGETHER AGAIN/with Teddy Edwards — Contemporary 3588/7588 (1961) yellow label **$35.**

MAGGIE'S BACK IN TOWN/with Shelly Manne — Contemporary 3596/7596 (1961) yellow label **$35.**

HOUSE WARMIN'! — Argo 4020 (1962) **$40.**

NOBODY KNOWS YOU WHEN YOU'RE DOWN AND OUT — United Artists 14028/15028 (1962) gray label with silhouette of sax player **$40.**

JIMMY McGRIFF
organ - born 1936 Philadelphia, PA

AT THE ORGAN/with Rudolph Johnson — Sue 1020 (1964) **$40.**

BLUES FOR MISTER JIMMY — Sue 1039 (1965) **$40.**

KEN McINTYRE
alto sax, flute - born 1930 Boston, MA

LOOKING AHEAD/with Eric Dolphy — New Jazz 8247 (1960) **$50.**

STONE BLUE/with John Mancebo Lewis — New Jazz 8259 (1960) **$45.**

YEAR OF THE IRON SHEEP — United Artists 14015/15015 (1962) gray label with silhouette of sax player **$30.**

WAY WAY OUT — United Artists 3336/6336 (1963) black label with colored circles on top **$30.**

HAL McKUSICK
alto sax, clarinet - born 1924 Medford, MS

McKusick experienced extensive work and recordings with many name bands through the 40's and went into working with television and radio through the 50's except for occasional gigs with various groups.

PLAYS - BETTY ST. CLAIR SINGS/with Jimmy Raney — Jubilee 15 (1955) 10" **$100.**

QUARTET - EAST COAST JAZZ 8/with Barry Galbraith — Bethlehem 16 (1955) maroon label **$95.**

IN THE TWENTIETH CENTURY DRAWING ROOM/with Strings — RCA Victor 1164 (1955) dog on top **$50.**

THE JAZZ WORKSHOP/with Jimmy Raney, Art Farmer and Jimmy Cleveland — RCA Victor 1366 (1957) dog on top **$90.**

JAZZ AT THE ACADEMY/with Barry Galbraith — Coral 57116 (1956) maroon label **$80.**

QUINTET/with Art Farmer and Eddie Costa — Coral 57131 (1957) maroon label **$80.**

TRIPLE EXPOSURE/with Billy Byers — Prestige 7135 (1957) yellow label **$70.**

CROSS SECTION - SAXES/with Frank Socolow, Dick Hafer and Jay Cameron — Decca 9209/79209 (1958) maroon label with silver lettering **$60.**

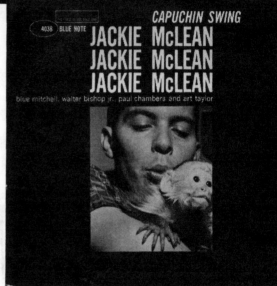

JACKIE McLEAN
alto sax, composer - born 1932 New York City, NY

Coming to prominence with groups like those of Charlie Mingus, Sonny Rollins and as an original member of Art Blakey's Jazz Messengers, McLean is known as a fine bop musician who, through his interest in freer forms, is a good example of the transitions of the early 60's. During the 60's he toured Europe and Japan and worked and recorded in New York City.

THE NEW TRADITION/with Donald Byrd — Ad-Lib 6601 (1955) **$100;** *reissued* Jubilee 1064.

QUINTET — Jubilee 1064 (1957) **$60;** *reissued* Josie 3503.

FAT JAZZ/with Ray Draper — Jubilee 1093 (1957) **$60.**

SEXTET — Josie 3503 (1964) **$25.**

LIGHTS OUT/with Elmo Hope — Prestige 7035 (1956) **$90;** *reissued* New Jazz 8263 (1962) **$40.**

4, 5 AND 6/with Mal Waldron — Prestige 7048 (1956) yellow label **$85;** *reissued* New Jazz 8279 (1962) **$40.**

JACKIE'S PALS/with Bill Hardman — Prestige 7068 (1956) yellow label **$85;** *reissued* New Jazz 8290.

AND COMPANY/with Ray Draper — Prestige 7087 (1957) yellow label **$75;** *reissued* Status 8323 (1965) **$25.**

ALTO MADNESS/with John Jenkins — Prestige 7114 (1957) yellow label **$75;** *reissued* Status 8312 (1965) **$25.**

McLEAN'S SCENE/with Bill Hardman — Prestige-New Jazz 8212 (1958) **$50.**

MAKIN' THE CHANGES/with Mal Waldron — Prestige-New Jazz 8231 (1960) $40.

A LONG DRINK OF THE BLUES/with Mal Waldron — Prestige-New Jazz 8253 (1961) $40.

STEEPLECHASE — New Jazz 8290 (1962) $35; *reissue* of Prestige 7068.

NEW SOIL/with Donald Byrd — Blue Note 4013 (1959) with NY address on label $65; with NY on label $50; with A Division of Liberty on label $20.

SWING, SWANG, SWINGIN'/with Walter Bishop — Blue Note 4024 (1959) with NY address on label $65; with NY on label $50; with A Division of Liberty on label $20.

CAPUCHIN SWING/with Blue Mitchell — Blue Note 4038 (1960) with NY address on label $55; with NY on label $45; with A Division of Liberty on label $20.

JACKIE'S BAG/with Sonny Clark — Blue Note 4051 (1960) with NY address on label $55; with NY on label $45; with A Division of Liberty on label $20.

BLUESNIK/with Freddie Hubbard — Blue Note 4067/84067 (1961) with NY address on label $55; with NY on label $45; with A Division of Liberty on label $20.

A FICKLE SONANCE/with Tommy Turrentine — Blue Note 4089/84089 (1961) with NY address on label $50; with NY on label $40; with A Division of Liberty on label $20.

LET FREEDOM RING/with Walter Davis — Blue Note 4106/84106 (1962) with NY on label $45; with A Division of Liberty on label $20.

ONE STEP BEYOND — Blue Note 4137/84137 (1962) with NY on label $45; with A Division of Liberty on label $20.

DESTINATION OUT — Blue Note 4185/84185 (1964) with NY on label $35; with A Division of Liberty on label $20.

IT'S TIME — Blue Note 4179/84179 (1964) with NY on label $35; with A Division of Liberty on label $20.

ACTION — Blue Note 4218/84218 (1965) with NY on label $35; with A Division of Liberty on label $20.

TED McNABB
leader

AND COMPANY/with Al Cohn and Zoot Zims — Epic 3663/558 (1960) yellow label $50.

*MARIAN McPARTLAND
piano, composer - born 1920 Windsor, England

MARIAN McPARTLAND PIANO — Savoy 15021 (1950) 10" $45.

MARIAN McPARTLAND MOODS — Savoy 15022 (1950) 10" $45.

MARIAN McPARTLAND — Savoy 15027 (1951) 10" $40.

JAZZ AT THE HICKORY HOUSE — Savoy 15032 (1951) 10" $40.

AT STORYVILLE/HICKORY HOUSE — Savoy 12004 (1955) maroon label $25.

LULLABY OF BIRDLAND — Savoy 12005 (1955) maroon label $25.

GREAT BRITAINS — Savoy 12016 (1955) maroon label $25.

AT THE HICKORY HOUSE — Capitol 574 (1955) green label $20.

AFTER DARK — Capitol 699 (1956) green label $20.

TRIO/with Joe Morello — Capitol 785 (1956) green label $20.

BOSSA NOVA PLUS SOUL — Time 52073/2073 (1963) $15.

---

*The only LP's within the scope of this book.

CHARLES McPHERSON
alto sax - born 1929 Joplin, MO

BE-BOP REVISITED — Prestige 7359 (1965) blue label with logo on right side $35.

CON ALMA/with Clifford Jordan — Prestige 7427 (1965) blue label with logo on right side $35.

*CARMEN McRAE
vocals - born 1922 New York City, NY

CARMEN McRAE/with Tony Scott — Bethlehem 1023 (1954) 10" $95.

BY SPECIAL REQUEST/with Mundell Lowe — Decca 8173 (1955) black label with silver lettering $80; EP 2279, EP 2280 (1955) $40; *reissued* Decca 8173 (1964) black label with rainbow strip in middle $20.

TORCHY/with Jack Pleis Orchestra — Decca 8267 (1955) black label with silver lettering $60; *reissued* Decca 8267 (1964) black label with rainbow strip in middle $20.

BLUE MOON/with Tadd Dameron Orchestra — Decca 8347 (1956) black label with silver lettering **$80.**

AFTER GLOW/with Ray Bryant Trio — Decca 8583 (1957) black label with silver lettering **$60**; *reissued* Decca 8583 (1964) black label with rainbow strip in middle **$30.**

MAD ABOUT THE MAN/with Charlie Shavers — Decca 8662 (1957) black label with silver lettering **$75.**

CARMEN FOR COOL ONES/with Buddy Collette — Decca 8738 (1958) black label with silver lettering **$65**; *reissued* Decca 8738 (1964) black label with rainbow strip in middle **$30.**

BIRDS OF A FEATHER/with Ben Webster and Al Cohn — Decca 8815 (1958) black label with silver lettering **$75.**

BOOK OF BALLADS/with Don Abney — Kapp 1117/3001 (1958) **$40.**

SOMETHING TO SWING ABOUT/with Zoot Sims and Jimmy Cleveland — Kapp 1169/3053 (1959) **$45.**

LIVE AT SUGAR HILL — Time 52014/2104 (1963) **$30.**

TONIGHT ONLY/with Dave Brubeck — Columbia 1609/8409 (1961) red label with 3 black logos on each side **$40.**

LOVER MAN/with Eddie Davis and Nat Adderley — Columbia 1730/8530 (1961) red label with 3 black logos on each side **$40.**

TAKE FIVE/with Dave Brubeck — Columbia 2316/9116 (1965) red label with 1 white logo on each side **$30.**

SECOND TO NONE/with Peter Matz — Mainstream 56028/6028 (1965) **$25.**

HAVEN'T WE MET?/with Don Sebesky — Mainstream 56044/6044 (1965) **$25.**

BITTERSWEET — Focus 334 (1965) **$25.**

The only LP's within the scope of this book.

GREIG McRITCHIE
arranger

EASY JAZZ ON A FISH BEAT BASS/with Herbie Harper, Buddy Collette, Russ Freeman and Shelly Manne — Zephyr 12005 (1959) **$65.**

*JAY McSHANN
leader, piano - born 1909 Muskogee, OK

JAY McSHANN/with Charlie Parker — Decca 5503 (1954) 10" **$350.**

The only LP's within the scope of this book.

LOU MECCA
guitar

QUARTET — Blue Note 5067 (1955) 10" **$75.**

JOHN MEHEGAN
piano, composer - born 1920 Hartford, CT

REFLECTIONS/with Kenny Clarke — Savoy 12028 (1955) maroon label **$15.**

A PAIR OF PIANOS/with Eddie Costa — Savoy 12049 (1956) maroon label **$15.**

HOW I PLAY JAZZ PIANO/(Solo) — Savoy 12076 (1957) maroon label **$15.**

CASUAL AFFAIR/with Kenny Dorham — TJ 1 (1959) **$50.**

ACT OF JAZZ/with Dave Bailey — Epic 16007/17007 (1960) yellow label **$15.**

GIL MELLE
saxophones - born 1931 Riverside, CA

Melle's career consists of early West Coast experience with name bands and East Coast appearances, concerts and club dates during the 50's. He has a few recordings but ventured into studio movie and television work in the 60's.

QUINTET-SEXTET/with Eddie Bert and Red Mitchell — Blue Note 5020 (1952) 10" **$155**; EP 203 (1952) **$60.**

QUINTET/with Urbie Green — Blue Note 5033 (1953) 10" **$125.**

QUARTET/with Louis Mecca — Blue Note 5054 (1954) **$100.**

FIVE IMPRESSIONS OF COLOR/with Red Mitchell — Blue Note 5063 (1955) 10" **$95.**

PATTERNS IN JAZZ/with Eddie Bert — Blue Note 1517 (1956) with NY address on label **$60.**

PRIMITIVE MODERN/with Joe Cinderella — Prestige 7040 (1956) yellow label **$50.**

GIL'S GUESTS/with Art Farmer, Hal McKusick and Kenny Dorham — Prestige 7063 (1956) yellow label **$60.**

QUADRAMA/with Joe Cinderella — Prestige 7097 (1957) yellow label **$50.**

THE MELLO-LARKS
vocals
Adele Castle, Tommy Hamm, Joe Eich, Bob Wollter

JUST FOR A LARK — RCA Camden 530 (1959) **$45.**

SERGIO MENDEZ
piano - born 1941 Niteroi, Brazil

HE SWINGER FROM RIO — Atlantic 1434 (1965) with logo on right side **$15.**

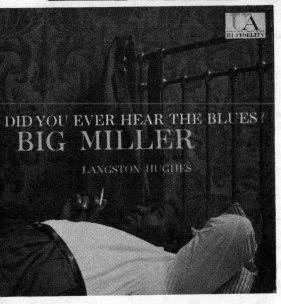

HELEN MERRILL
vocals - born 1929 New York City, NY

During the late 40's and early 50's, Merrill was primarily a night club singer in New York City and spent a short time with Earl Hines in 1952. She was very popular in Europe and Japan where she lived while touring and appearing. Merrill is a good jazz vocalist, best on the slower tunes.

HELEN MERRILL/with Quincy Jones and Clifford Brown — EmArcy 36006 (1955) drummer logo **$70.**

WITH STRINGS/with Richard Heyman and Hank Jones — EmArcy 36057 (1956) drummer logo **$40.**

DREAM OF YOU/with Gil Evans and Art Farmer — EmArcy 36078 (1956) drummer logo **$70.**

MERRILL AT MIDNIGHT/with Hal Mooney and Marian McPartland — EmArcy 36107 (1956) drummer logo **$60.**

THE NEARNESS OF YOU/with Bobby Jaspar and Dick Marx — EmArcy 36134 (1957) drummer logo **$60.**

YOU'VE GOT A DATE WITH THE BLUES/with Kenny Dorham and Frank Wess — Metrojazz 1010 (1959) **$50.**

THE ARTISTRY OF — Mainstream 56014/6014 (1965) **$25.**

METROPOLITAN JAZZ OCTET
LEGEND OF BIX — Argo 659 (1959) **$35.**

THE MIL-COMBO
Connie Milano - bass, Ziggy Millonzi - piano
Don Mamblow - guitar

THE MIL-COMBO — Capitol T579 (1955) green label **$50.**

BARRY MILES
drums, vibes, piano - born 1947 Newark, NJ
MILES OF GENIUS/with Johnny Glasel — Parker 804 (1960) **$35.**

LIZZIE MILES
vocals - born 1895 New Orleans, LA died 1963

MOANS AND BLUES — Cook 1182 (1956) **$60.**

HOT SONGS — Cook 1183 (1956) **$60.**

TORCHY LULLABIES — Cook 1184 (1956) **$60.**

CLAMBAKE ON BOURBON ST. — Cook 11815 (1957) **$60.**

BIG MILLER
vocals - born 1923 Sioux City, IA

A very effective blues/jazz vocalist, Miller began with his own group in the late 40's and later worked with Jay McShann in addition to West Coast club and concert gigs. Through his career he has been backed by some very prominent musicians including Al Cohn, Zoot Sims, Phil Woods and Ben Webster. Among his own few recordings a big hit for Miller and a very fine piece of work was Did You Ever Hear the Blues in 1959.

DID YOU EVER HEAR THE BLUES/with Al Cohn, Zoot Sims and Phil Woods — United Artists 3047 (1959) red label **$60.**

REVELATION AND THE BLUES — Columbia 1611/8411 (1961) red label with 3 black logos on each side **$35.**

SINGS, TWISTS, SHOUTS AND PREACHES/with Bill Perkins and Herbie Harper — Columbia 1808/8808 (1962) red label with 3 black logos on each side **$35.**

DON MILLER
guitar - born 1938 Cincinnati, OH

THE DON MILLER QUARTET — King 712 (1960) **$35.**

JACK MILLMAN
trumpet, fluegelhorn - born 1930 Detroit, MI

BLOWING UP A STORM — Era 20005 (1956) **$60.**

JAZZ STUDIO 4 — Decca 8156 (1956) black label with silver lettering **$60.**

SHADES OF THINGS TO COME — Liberty 6007 (1956) green or blue label **$55.**

CHARLES MINGUS
*bass, composer, leader - born 1922 Nogales, AZ
died 1979*

Mingus is remembered as a bassist of impressive ability and conception since his work, mostly on the West Coast in the early 40's, with many name bands. He established himself in the early 50's in New York City with continued groupings and eventually formed one of his own featuring sidemen of exceptional talent performing his own compositions. Mingus' style throughout his career was to combine nearly the entire history of jazz styles with experimentations of the avante-garde and to do so in a manner that reflected his own personal vision. The number of significant musicians to work with Mingus is truly impressive.

Mingus experienced a period of inactivity during the late 60's but, after publication of his autobiography, Beneath The Underdog, in 1971, was again active as leader of various groups until shortly before his death in 1979.

OCTET/with Ernie Royal — Debut EP 450 (1953) **$60.**

STRINGS AND KEYS/with Spaulding Givens — Debut 1 (1953) 10" **$250.**

MINGUS AT THE BOHEMIA/with Eddie Bert and George Barrow — Debut 123 (1955) **$100.**

JAZZ COLLABORATIONS/with Thad Jones — Debut 17 (1955) 10" **$200.**

CHARLIE MINGUS/with George Barrow — Savoy 15050 (1955) 10" **$125;** *reissued* Savoy 12059 (1956) maroon label **$45.**

JAZZICAL MOODS/with Teo Macero — Period 1107 (1954) 10" **$150;** *reissued* Bethlehem 65.

THE JAZZ EXPERIMENTS OF — Bethlehem 65 (1956) maroon label **$60;** *reissued* Jazztone 1271 (1958) **$40;** *reissues* of Period 1107.

EAST COASTING/with Curtis Porter — Bethlehem 6019 (1957) maroon label **$55.**

A MODERN JAZZ SYMPOSIUM OF MUSIC AND POETRY/with Bill Hardman — Bethlehem 6026 (1957) maroon label **$55.**

MINGUS THREE/with Hampton Hawes and Danny Richmond — Jubilee 1054 (1957) **$55;** *reissued* Josie 3508 (1963) **$25.**

PITHECANTHROPUS ERECTUS/with J.R. Monterose — Atlantic 1237 (1956) black label **$50;** *reissued* Atlantic 1237 (1960) with logo on right side **$30.**

CROWN/with Curtis Porter — Atlantic 1260 (1957) black label **$45;** EP 581 (1957) **$25;** *reissued* Atlantic 1260 (1960) with logo on right side **$30.**

BLUES AND ROOTS/with Pepper Adams — Atlantic 1305 (1959) black label **$45;** *reissued* Atlantic 1305 (1961) with logo on right side **$30.**

OH YEAH/with Roland Kirk — Atlantic 1377 (1961) with logo on right side **$30.**

TONIGHT THE MOON — Atlantic 1416 (1964) with logo on right side **$30.**

MINGUS AH UM/with Booker Ervin — Columbia 1370/8171 (1959) red label with 3 black logos on each side **$40.**

MINGUS DYNASTY/with Benny Golson — Columbia 1440/8236 (1959) red label with 3 black logos on each side **$40.**

MINGUS PRESENTS MINGUS/with Charlie McPherson — Candid 8005/9005 (1960) **$60.**

MINGUS/with Charlie McPherson — Candid 8021/9021 (1960) **$60.**

PRE-BIRD/with Slide Hampton and Clark Terry — Mercury 20627/60627 (1960) black label **$40.**

JAZZ PORTRAITS/with Booker Ervin — United Artists 4036/5036 (1959) red label **$65.**

WONDERLAND/with Booker Ervin — United Artists 14005/15005 (1962) gra label with silhouette of sax player **$50.**

MONEY JUNGLE/with Duke Ellington and Max Roach — United Artists 14017 15017 (1962) gray label with silhouette of sax player **$50.**

TOWN HALL CONCERT — United Artists 14024/15024 (1963) gray label wit silhouette of sax player **$50.**

TIJUANA MOODS/with Curtis Porter — RCA Victor 2533 (1962) dog on top **$45**

CHAZZ!/with Mal Waldron — Fantasy 6002/86002 (1962) **$40.**

QUINTET PLUS MAX ROACH — Fantasy 6009/86009 (1963) **$40.**

BLACK SAINT AND SINNER LADY — Impulse 35 (1963) orange label **$35.**

MINGUS, MINGUS, MINGUS — Impulse 54 (1963) orange label **$35.**

PLAYS PIANO — Impulse 60 (1964) orange label **$35.**

REVISITED/with Eric Dolphy — Limelight 82015/86015 (1965) fold out cove **$20.**

BILLY MITCHELL
tenor sax - born 1926 Kansas City, MO

Mitchell played with Detroit musicians in the late 40's and was the with Woody Herman and Dizzy Gillespie through the 50's. He went o to lead his own group with Al Gray which featured, at different times artists like Tommy Flanagan, Thad and Elvin Jones. He returne again to the Basie band in the mid-60's.

THIS IS/with Bobby Hutcherson — Smash 27027/67027 (1962) **$35.**

A LITTLE JUICY/with Thad Jones — Smash 27042/67042 (1962) **$35.**

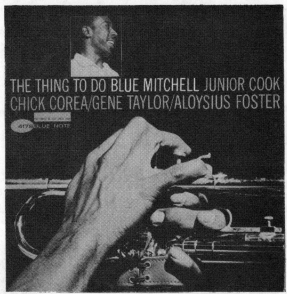

BLUE MITCHELL
trumpet - born 1930 Miami, FL died 1979

BIG SIX/with Johnny Griffin — Riverside 12-273 (1958) blue label with Bill Grauer Pro. **$55.**

OUT OF THE BLUE/with Benny Golson — Riverside 12-293/1131 (1958) blue label mono; black label stereo with Bill Grauer Pro. **$55.**

BLUE SOUL/with Jimmy Heath — Riverside 12-309/1155 (1959) blue label mono; black label stereo with Bill Grauer Pro. **$45.**

BLUE'S MOODS/with Wynton Kelly — Riverside 336/9336 (1960) blue label mono; black label stereo with Bill Grauer Pro. **$40.**

SMOOTH AS THE WIND/with Clark Terry — Riverside 367/9367 (1960) blue label mono; black label stereo with Bill Grauer Pro. **$40.**

A SURE THING/with Pepper Adams — Riverside 414/9414 (1961) blue label mono; black label stereo with Bill Grauer Pro. **$45.**

THE CUP BEARERS/with Junior Cook — Riverside 439/9439 (1963) blue label mono; black label stereo with Bill Grauer Pro. **$40.**

THE THING TO DO/with Junior Cook — Blue Note 4178/84178 (1964) with NY on label **$35**; with A Division of Liberty on label **$20.**

DOWN WITH IT/with Junior Cook — Blue Note 4214/84214 (1965) with NY on label **$35**; with A Division of Liberty on label **$20.**

MITCHELL-RUFF DUO
Dwike Mitchell - piano - born 1930 Jacksonville, FL
Willie Ruff - bass, french horn - born 1931 Sheffield, AL

MITCHELL-RUFF DUO — Epic 3221 (1956) yellow label **$30.**

CAMPUS CONCERT — Epic 3318 (1956) yellow label **$30.**

APPEARING NIGHTLY — Roulette 52002 (1958) white label with multicolored pinwheel **$30.**

PLUS STRINGS & BRASS/with Elvin Jones — Roulette 52013 (1958) white label with multicolored pinwheel **$40.**

JAZZ FOR JUNIORS — Roulette 52025 (1959) white label or light and dark orange roulette wheel label **$20.**

JAZZ MISSION TO MOSCOW — Roulette 52034 (1959) white label or light and dark orange roulette wheel label **$20.**

THE SOUND OF MUSIC — Roulette 52037 (1960) light and dark orange roulette wheel label **$20.**

THE CATBIRD SEAT — Atlantic 1374 (1961) with logo on right side **$15.**

RED MITCHELL
bass - born 1927 New York City, NY

Working to a great degree in the Los Angeles area with many major bands, Mitchell was recorded quite frequently with a number of great

artists which includes Gerry Mulligan, Shelly Manne, Andre Previn and with Hampton Hawes between the 50's and 60's. In addition to this, he has played his part in the more commercial studio type work.

HAPPY MINORS/with Zoot Sims and Bob Brookmeyer — Bethlehem 1033 (1955) 10" **$350.**

JAZZ MAINSTREAM/with Oscar Pettiford — Bethlehem 2 (1955) maroon label one side each **$70.**

RED MITCHELL/with Conte Candoli — Bethlehem 38 (1955) maroon label **$45.**

PRESENTING/with James Clay — Contemporary 3538 (1957) yellow label **$45.**

REJOICE/with Jim Hall — Pacific Jazz 22 (1960) **$35.**

THE MITCHELL-LAND QUINTET - HEAR YE!/with Harold Land — Atlantic 1376 (1961) with logo on right side **$35.**

WHITEY MITCHELL
bass - born 1932 Hackensack, NJ

SEXTETTE/with Steve Lacy and Joe Puma — ABC Paramount 126 (1956) **$65.**

THE MITCHELLS
Red Mitchell, Blue Mitchell, Whitey Mitchell

GET THOSE ELEPHANTS OUT'A HERE/with Pepper Adams, Frank Rehak and Andre Previn — Metrojazz 1012 (1958) **$40.**

MJT PLUS 3
Walter Perkins - drums - born 1932 Chicago, IL
Bob Cranshaw - bass - born 1932 Evanston, IL

DADDY-O PRESENTS/with Paul Serrano and Nicky Hill — Argo 621 (1957) **$45.**

WALTER PERKINS MJT PLUS 3/with Frank Strozier — Vee Jay 1013 (1959) maroon label **$40**; black label **$30.**

MAKE EVERYBODY HAPPY/with Frank Strozier — Vee Jay 3008 (1960) black label **$30.**

MJT PLUS 3/with Frank Stozier — Vee Jay 3014 (1960) black label **$30.**

HANK MOBLEY
tenor sax - born 1930 Eastman, GA

Working his way through one great group after another during the 50's, Mobley demonstrated his continually improving style. In 1955 he broke out on his own to form a group with Horace Silver calling themselves the Hank Mobley Quartet. Mobley also recorded extensively with Lee Morgan and, in the early 60's, joined Miles Davis. With a style somewhere between Sonny Rollins and John Coltrane, Mobley was considered to be one of the better saxmen of his time and all of his earlier original recordings are collectable.

HANK MOBLEY QUARTET/with Horace Silver — Blue Note 5066 (1955) 10" **$150.**

HANK MOBLEY/with Lee Morgan — Blue Note 1540 (1956) with NY address on label **$90**; with NY on label **$45**; with A Division of Liberty on label **$20.**

AND HIS ALL STARS/with Milt Jackson — Blue Note 1544 (1957) with NY address on label **$80**; with NY on label **$45**; with A Division of Liberty on label **$20**.

QUINTET/with Art Farmer — Blue Note 1550 (1957) with NY address on label **$80**; with NY on label **$45**; with A Division of Liberty on label **$20**.

HANK/with John Jenkins — Blue Note 1560 (1957) with NY address on label **$75**; with NY on label **$45**; with A Division of Liberty on label **$20**.

HANK MOBLEY/with Sonny Clark — Blue Note 1568 (1957) with NY address on label **$75**; with NY on label **$45**; with A Division of Liberty on label **$20**.

PECKIN' TIME/with Lee Morgan — Blue Note 1574 (1958) with NY address on label **$80**; with NY on label **$45**; with A Division of Liberty on label **$20**.

SOUL STATION/with Paul Chambers — Blue Note 4031 (1960) with NY address on label **$60**; with NY on label **$45**; with A Division of Liberty on label **$20**.

ROLL CALL/with Freddie Hubbard — Blue Note 4058/84058 (1960) with NY address on label **$60**; with NY on label **$45**; with A Division of Liberty on label **$20**.

WORKOUT/with Grant Green — Blue Note 4080/84080 (1961) with NY address on label **$60**; with NY on label **$45**; with A Division of Liberty on label **$20**.

NO ROOM FOR SQUARES/with Lee Morgan — Blue Note 4149/84149 (1963) with NY on label **$45**; with A Division of Liberty on label **$20**.

THE TURNAROUND/with Freddie Hubbard — Blue Note 4186/84186 (1964) with NY on label **$45**; with A Division of Liberty on label **$20**.

DIPPIN'/with Lee Morgan — Blue Note 4209/84209 (1965) with NY on label **$35**; with A Division of Liberty on label **$20**.

MOBLEY'S MESSAGE/with Jackie McLean — Prestige 7061 (1956) yellow label **$75**.

MOBLEY'S SECOND MESSAGE/with Kenny Dorham — Prestige 7082 (1956) yellow label **$75**.

THE JAZZ MESSAGE/with Donald Byrd — Savoy 12064 (1956) maroon label **$60**.

MODERN JAZZ DISCIPLES
Curits Peagler, Bill Brown, Lee Tucker

MODERN JAZZ DISCIPLES/with Mike Kelly and Ron McCurdy — New Jazz 8222 (1959) **$40**.

RIGHT DOWN FRONT/with William Walley and Wilbur Jackson — New Jazz 8240 (1960) **$40**.

MODERN JAZZ QUARTET
John Lewis - piano, Milt Jackson - vibes
Percy Heath - bass, Kenny Clarke - drums

MJQ was first organized for a recording session in 1952 and was then permanently banded in 1954 with the above listed personnel. In 1955 Connie Kay replaced Kenny Clarke on drums. During their time, MJQ made innumerable recordings, performed concert and festival appearances and conducted annual tours of major U.S. cities as well as tours of Europe, Africa and Japan. Their style appealed not only to jazz fans, and they were also very popular with many who would otherwise not be interested in jazz. In addition to the MJQ recordings, its members also took advantage of opportunities to pursue their own recording and performing careers.

MODERN JAZZ QUARTET — Prestige 160 (1953) **$60**; EP 1303, EP 1325 (1953) **$20**; *reissued* Prestige 7059 (1956) yellow label **$40**; *reissued* Prestige 7059 (1964) blue label with logo on right side **$20**.

MODERN JAZZ QUARTET — Prestige 170 (1954) **$60**; EP 1370 (1954) **$20**; *reissued* Prestige 7057.

CONCORDE — Prestige 7005 (1955) yellow label **$45**; *reissued* Prestige 7005 (1964) blue label with logo on right side **$30**.

DJANGO — Prestige 7057 (1956) yellow label **$45**; *reissued* Prestige 7057 (1964) blue label with logo on right side **$25**.

PLAYS FOR LOVERS — Prestige 7421 (1965) blue label with logo on right side **$25**.

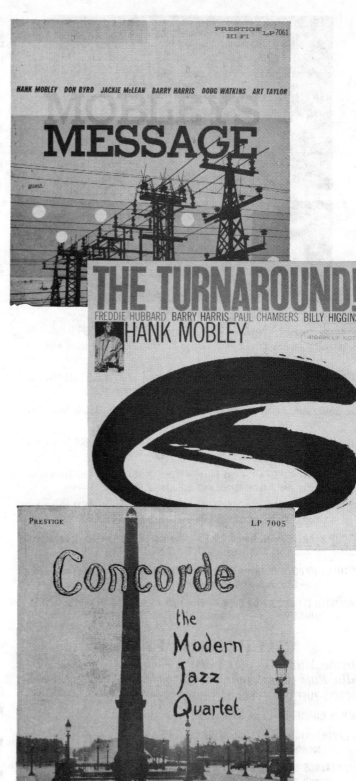

FONTESSA — Atlantic 1231 (1956) black label **$40**; EP 583 (1956) **$20**; *reissued* Atlantic 1231 (1962) with logo on right side **$20**.

AT MUSIC INN/with Jimmy Giuffre — Atlantic 1247 (1956) black label **$60**; *reissued* Atlantic 1247 (1960) with logo on right side **$35**.

THE MODERN JAZZ QUARTET — Atlantic 1265 (1957) black label **$40**; EP 603 (1957) **$10**; *reissued* Atlantic 1265 (1961) with logo on right side **$20**.

ONE NEVER KNOWS (Film Score) — Atlantic 1284 (1957) black label **$40**; *reissued* Atlantic 1284 (1961) with logo on right side **$25**.

AT MUSIC INN - Vol 2/with Sonny Rollins — Atlantic 1299 (1958) black label **$50**; *reissued* Atlantic 1299 (1962) with logo on right side **$35**.

PYRAMID — Atlantic 1325 (1959) black label **$40**; *reissued* Atlantic 1325 (1964) with logo on right side **$25**.

ATLANTIC 1231 FONTESSA
THE MODERN JAZZ QUARTET

HIRD STREAM MUSIC — Atlantic 1345 (1960) with logo on right side **$25.**

HE EUROPEAN CONCERT — Atlantic 2-603 (1960) with logo on right side **$40.**

ND ORCHESTRA (Symphony) — Atlantic 1359 (1960) with logo on right side **$20.**

ONELY WOMAN — Atlantic 1381 (1962) with logo on right side **$25.**

UROPEAN CONCERT - Vol 1 — Atlantic 1385 (1962) with logo on right side **$15.**

UROPEAN CONCERT - Vol 2 — Atlantic 1386 (1962) with logo on right side **$15.**

HE COMEDY — Atlantic 1390 (1962) with logo on right side **$20.**

HE SHERIFF — Atlantic 1414 (1964) with logo on right side **$20.**

OLLABORATION/with Laurindo Almeida — Atlantic 1429 (1964) with logo on right side **$20.** (A)

DDS AGAINST TOMORROW (Soundtrack) — United Artists 4063/5063 (1959) red label **$50.**

ATTERNS — United Artists 4072/5072 (1960) red label **$40.**

ND OSCAR PETERSON TRIO/AT THE OPERA HOUSE — Verve 8269 (1958) with Verve Records, Inc. on bottom of label, one side each **$40.**

THE MODERN JAZZ SEXTET
Dizzy Gillespie, Sonny Stitt, John Lewis, Percy Heath, Skeeter Best, Charlie Persip

HE MODERN JAZZ SEXTET — Norgran 1070 (1956) **$95;** *reissued* Verve 8166 (1957) with Verve Records, Inc. on bottom of label **$65;** with MGM on bottom of label **$35;** *reissued* American Recording Society 429 (1957) **$75.**

MODERN JAZZ SOCIETY
J.J. Johnson, Stan Getz, Tony Scott, Lucky Thompson, Jim Poole, Gunther Schuller, Percy Heath, Connie Kay, Aaron Sachs, Manny Ziegler

MODERN JAZZ SOCIETY — Norgran 1040 (1955) **$95;** EP 140 (1955) **$50;** *reissued* Verve 8131 (1957) with Verve Records, Inc. on bottom of label **$65;** with MGM on bottom of label **$35;** *reissued* American Recording Society 432 (1957) **$75.**

THE MODEST JAZZ TRIO
Jim Hall, Red Mitchell, Red Kelly

GOOD FRIDAY BLUES — Pacific Jazz 10 (1960) **$35.**

GRACHAN MONCUR III
trombone - born 1937 New York City, NY

EVOLUTION/with Lee Morgan — Blue Note 4153/84153 (1963) with NY on label **$35;** with A Division of Liberty on label **$20.**

SOME OTHER STUFF/with Wayne Shorter — Blue Note 4177/84177 (1963) with NY on label **$35;** with A Division of Liberty on label **$20.**

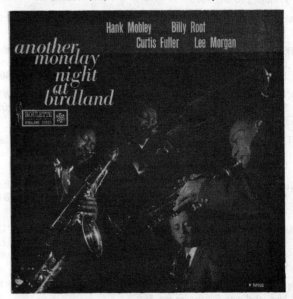

MONDAY NIGHT AT BIRDLAND

VOL 1/with Hank Mobley, Billy Root, Curtis Fuller and Lee Morgan — Roulette 52015 (1958) white label with multicolored pinwheel **$50.**

ANOTHER VOL 2/with Hank Mobly, Billy Root, Curtis Fuller and Lee Morgan — Roulette 52022 (1958) white label with multicolored pinwheel **$50.**

THELONIOUS MONK
piano, composer - born 1920 Rocky Mount, NC died 1982

Thelonious Shere Monk grew up in New York City and was one of the original innovators of the new style of music then being created. He worked with every other major player of that time and locale. Although Monk worked as a sideman occasionally, he preferred to front his own group but, unlike many others who received much public acclaim for their contributions to be-bop, he was largely overlooked until the mid-50's. Since that time he has been recognized by most, if not all, as the important influence he truly is. His writing is integral to his playing; both are unique and, as a result, most listeners tend to respond immediately, positively or negatively and seldom change their minds. No matter what his detractors may profess, Monk's position in the area of jazz history is through his great contributions and forever secure.

THELONIOUS MONK/with Danny Quebec West — Blue Note 5002 (1952) 10" **$250;** *reissued* Blue Note 1510 (1956).

THELONIOUS MONK/with Sahib Shihab — Blue Note 5009 (1952) 10" **$250;** *reissued* Blue Note 1511 (1956).

GENIUS OF MODERN MUSIC - Vol 1/with Danny Quebec West — Blue Note 1510 (1956) with NY address on label $60; with NY on label $40; with A Division of Liberty on label $20.

GENIUS OF MODERN MUSIC - Vol 2/with Sahib Shihab — Blue Note 1511 (1956) with NY address on label $60; with NY on label $40; with A Division of Liberty on label $20.

TRIO/with Art Blakey — Prestige 142 (1952) 10" $100; EP 1329 (1952) $40; *reissued* Prestige 7027 (1956) yellow label $60.

THELONIOUS MONK WITH SONNY ROLLINS — Prestige 166 (1952) 10" $200; EP 1352 (1952) $80; *reissued* Prestige 7075 (1957) yellow label $80.

THELONIOUS MONK/with Frank Foster — Prestige 180 (1954) 10" $150; *reissued* Prestige 7053 (1956).

TRIO/with Art Blakey — Prestige 189 (1954) 10" $100; *reissued* Prestige 7027 (1956) yellow label $60.

FEATURING/with Frank Foster — Prestige 7053 (1956) yellow label $75; *reissue* of Prestige 180.

MONK'S MOODS/with Art Blakey — Prestige 7159 (1958) yellow label $50; *reissue* of Prestige 189 and 7027.

WORK!/with Sonny Rollins — Prestige 7169 (1959) yellow label $60; *reissue of Prestige 166 and 7075.*

WE SEE/with Frank Foster — Prestige 7245 (1962) yellow label $40; *reissue* of Prestige 180 and 7053.

PLAYS DUKE ELLINGTON/with Oscar Pettiford — Riverside 12-201 (1955) white label with Bill Grauer Pro. and photo LP cover $50; *reissued* Riverside 12-201 (1958) blue label with Bill Grauer Pro. and artistic LP cover $40.

THE UNIQUE/with Oscar Pettiford — Riverside 12-209 (1956) white label with Bill Grauer Pro. and photo LP cover $50; *reissued* Riverside 12-209 (1958) blue label with Bill Grauer Pro. and artistic LP cover $40.

BRILLIANT CORNERS/with Sonny Rollins — Riverside 12-226 (1957) white label with Bill Grauer Pro. $80; *reissued* Riverside 12-226/1174 (1958) blue label, mono; black label stereo with Bill Grauer Pro. $45.

THELONIOUS HIMSELF (Solo) — Riverside 12-235 (1957) white label with Bill Grauer Pro. $60; *reissued* Riverside 12-235 (1958) blue label with Bill Grauer Pro. $45.

MONK'S MUSIC/with John Coltrane and Coleman Hawkins — Riverside 12-242 (1957) white label with Bill Grauer Pro. $75; *reissued* Riverside 12-242/1102 (1958) blue label mono; black label 1102 stereo with Bill Grauer Pro. $45.

MULLIGAN MEETS MONK/with Gerry Mulligan — Riverside 12-247/1106 (1957) blue label with Bill Grauer Pro. $60.

THELONIOUS IN ACTION/with Johnny Griffin — Riverside 12-262/1190 (1958) blue label with Bill Grauer Pro. $50.

MISTERIOSO/with Johnny Griffin — Riverside 12-279/1133 (1958) blue label with Bill Grauer Pro. $50.

AT TOWN HALL/with Phil Woods and Pepper Adams — Riverside 12-300/1138 (1959) blue label with Bill Grauer Pro. $35.

5 BY MONK BY 5/with Charlie Rouse — Riverside 12-305/1150 (1959) blue label with Bill Grauer Pro. $45.

ALONE IN SAN FRANCISCO (Solo) — Riverside 12-312/1158 (1959) blue label with Bill Grauer Pro. $30.

QUARTET PLUS TWO AT THE BLACKHAWK/with Charlie Rouse and Harold Land — Riverside 12-323/1171 (1960) blue label with Bill Grauer Pro. $45.

GREATEST HITS — Riverside 421/9421 (1962) blue label with Bill Grauer Pro. $30.

2 HOURS — Riverside 460/9460 (1963) 2 LPs blue label with Bill Grauer Pro. $40.

MONK'S DREAM/with Charlie Rouse — Columbia 1965/8765 (1963) red label with 1 white logo on each side $25.

CRISS-CROSS/with Charlie Rouse — Columbia 2038/8838 (1963) red label with 1 white logo on each side $25.

MONK'S BIG BAND — Columbia 2164/8964 (1964) red label with 1 white logo on each side $20.

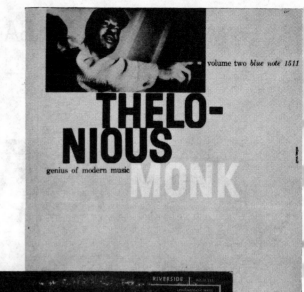

MILES AND MONK AT NEWPORT/with Miles Davis — Columbia 2178/8978 (1964) red label with 1 white logo on each side $20.

IT'S MONK TIME — Columbia 2184/8984 (1965) red label with 1 white logo on each side $20.

MONK — Columbia 2291/9091 (1965) red label with 1 white logo on each side $20.

SOLO — Columbia 2349/9149 (1965) red label with 1 white logo on each side $20.

J.R. MONTEROSE
tenor sax - born 1927 Detroit, MI

J.R. MONTEROSE/with Ira Sullivan and Horace Silver — Blue Note 1536 (1956) with NY address on label $65; with NY on label $50; with A Division of Liberty on label $20.

THE MESSAGE/with Tommy Flanagan — Jaro 5004 (1959) $50.

MONTGOMERY BROTHERS
Monk Montgomery - bass - born 1921 Indianapolis, IN died 1982
Wes Montgomery - guitar - born 1925 Indianapolis, IN died 1968
Buddy Montgomery - piano, vibes, composer born 1930 Indianapolis, IN

The Montgomery Brothers were all self-taught musicians who gained much experience locally. Monk and Buddy were part of a group called the Mastersounds in the late 50's which worked mostly on the West Coast. They produced many recordings but only one included their brother Wes. When Wes was finally confident enough to venture out on his own, he became a very large success. The three brothers made several recordings as the Montgomery Brothers and, since, Wes has gone on to even greater successes while Monk and Buddy continued to be musicians of high caliber with occasional recordings.

AND 5 OTHERS/with Freddie Hubbard — World Pacific 1240 (1958) $50; reissued Pacific Jazz 17 (1960) $35.

MONTGOMERYLAND/with Harold Land — Pacific Jazz 5 (1960) $40.

GROOVE YARD — Riverside 362/9362 (1961) blue label mono; black label stereo with Bill Grauer Pro. $40.

MONTGOMERY BROTHERS — Fantasy 3308/8052 (1960) $40.

IN CANDIDA — Fantasy 3323/8066 (1961) $40.

GEORGE SHEARING AND THE MONTGOMERY BROTHERS — Jazzland 55/955 (1961) original cover with all of them together $35; cover with picture of a girl $25.

MARIAN MONTGOMERY
vocals - born 1934 Natchez, MS

SWINGS FOR WINNERS AND LOSERS/with Joe Newman and Kenny Burrell — Capitol 1884 (1963) tan and black label $45.

LET THERE BE LOVE, LET THERE BE SWING, LET THERE BE MARIAN MONTGOMERY/with Vic Feldman and Leroy Vinnegar — Capitol 1982 (1963) tan and black label $40.

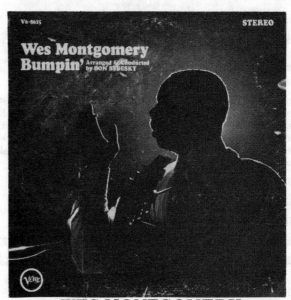

WES MONTGOMERY
guitar - born 1925 Indianapolis, IN died 1968

A self-taught musician with a very individual sound and style, Montgomery became famous around his hometown of Indianapolis where he and his brothers worked during the late 40's and early 50's. Possessor of considerable talent, Montgomery gained significant exposure through recordings with his brothers, through works on his own and in collaboration with many other jazz greats. He was considered by most critics and fans to be the most significant guitar player in jazz since Charlie Christian and was at, perhaps, the height of his career when he suddenly died of a heart attack in 1968.

WES MONTGOMERY TRIO/with Malvin Rhyne and Paul Parker — Riverside 12-310/1156 (1959) blue label mono; black label stereo with Bill Grauer Pro. $50.

INCREDIBLE JAZZ GUITAR/with Tommy Flanagan — Riverside 12-320/1169 (1960) blue label mono; black label stereo with Bill Grauer Pro. $40.

MOVIN' ALONG/with James Clay — Riverside 342/9342 (1960) blue label mono; black label stereo with Bill Grauer Pro. $45.

SO MUCH GUITAR/with Hank Jones — Riverside 382/9382 (1961) blue label mono; black label stereo with Bill Grauer Pro. $35.

FULL HOUSE/with Johnny Griffin — Riverside 434/9434 (1962) blue label mono; black label stereo with Bill Grauer Pro. $45.

MONTGOMERYLAND/with Harold Land — Pacific Jazz 5 (1960) $40.

MOVIN' WES/with Jerome Richardson and Clark Terry — Verve 8610/68610 (1965) with MGM on bottom of label $30.

BUMPIN'/with Grady Tate and Candido — Verve 8625/68625 (1965) with MGM on bottom of label $35.

JACK MONTROSE
tenor sax, composer - born 1928 Detroit, MI

After concluding his formal education in the Los Angeles area, Montrose worked with many name groups such as Art Pepper, Bob Gordon and Shorty Rogers. He went on to play, write and arrange through the 50's with several recordings under his own name in addition to considerable work as an outstanding sideman.

WITH BOB GORDON — Atlantic 1223 (1955) black label **$90**; EP 563, EP 564 (1955) **$45 ea.**; *reissued* Atlantic 1223 (1960) with logo on right side **$45**.

SEXTET/with Conte Candoli and Bob Gordon — Pacific Jazz 1208 (1955) **$75**; EP 37, EP 38 (1955) **$40 ea.**; *reissued* World Pacific 1208 (1958) **$45**.

ARRANGED BY — Pacific Jazz 1214 (1956) **$60**.

BLUES AND VANILLA - QUINTET/with Joe Maini and Red Norvo — RCA Victor 1451 (1958) dog on top **$60**.

HORNS FULL/with Red Norvo and Barney Kessel — RCA Victor 1572 (1958) dog on top **$60**.

JAMES MOODY
tenor, alto saxes, flute, composer - born 1925 Savannah, GA

A fine player who began on alto with Dizzy Gillespie's band in 1947. In the early 50's he ventured to Sweden to team up with Lars Gullin and Arne Domnerus, producing LP's on the Prestige label. During the 50's, Moody recorded extensively with Eddie Jefferson and, in 1957, produced Moody's big hit Moody's Mood For Love. This LP also displays Moody's abilities on all three instruments.

HIS SAXOPHONE AND HIS BAND — Dial 209 (1949) 10" **$300**.

JAMES MOODY IN FRANCE — Roost 405 (1951) 10" **$250**.

WITH STRINGS/with Andre Hodeir — Blue Note 5005 (1952) 10" **$200**.

AND HIS MODERNISTS/with Cecil Payne — Blue Note 5006 (1952) 10" **$200**.

IN SWEDEN - Vol 1/with Arne Domnerus — Prestige 110 (1952) **$150**; EP 1340 (1952) **$60**.

IN SWEDEN - Vol 2/with Arne Domnerus and Lars Gullin — Prestige 125 (1952) **$150**.

IN SWEDEN - Vol 3/with Arne Domnerus — Prestige 146 (1953) **$125**.

MOODY'S MOOD/with Eddie Jefferson — Prestige 192 (1954) 10" **$100**; EP 1324 (1954) **$45**; *reissued* in part Prestige 7072 and 7179.

AND HIS BAND/with Eddie Jefferson — Prestige 198 (1954) 10" **$100**; *reissued* Prestige 7179; *reissued* in part Prestige 7056.

HI FI PARTY/with Eddie Jefferson — Prestige 7011 (1956) yellow label **$75**.

WAIL MOODY WAIL/with Eddie Jefferson — Prestige 7036 (1956) yellow label **$75**.

MOODY'S MOODS/with Eddie Jefferson — Prestige 7056 (1956) yellow label **$60**; *reissue* in part of Prestige 198.

MOODY — Prestige 7072 (1956) yellow label **$60**; *reissue* in part of Prestige 192.

MOODY'S WORKSHOP — Prestige 7179 (1960) yellow label **$45**; *reissue* of Prestige 198 and in part of Prestige 192.

THE MOODY STORY/with Cecil Payne and Babs Gonzales — EmArcy 26004 (1954) 10" **$200**; EP 1-6009, EP 1-6010 (1952) **$75 ea.**; *reissued* EmArcy 36031 (1955) black label **$80**.

MOODSVILLE/with Babs Gonzales — EmArcy 26040 (1954) 10" **$200**; EP 1-6070 (1953) **$75**.

FLUTE 'N BLUES/with John Coles — Argo 603 (1956) **$50**.

MOODY'S MOOD FOR LOVE/with Eddie Jefferson — Argo 613 (1957) **$50**.

LAST TRAIN FROM OVERBROOK/with Sandy Moss — Argo 637 (1958) **$40**.

JAMES MOODY/with Tom McIntosh — Argo 648 (1959) **$40**.

HEY! IT'S/with Eldee Young — Argo 666 (1959) **$40**.

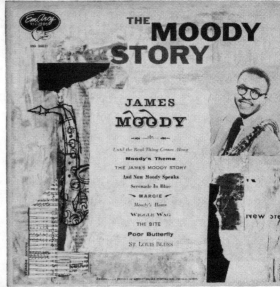

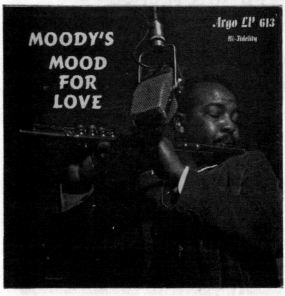

MOODY WITH STRINGS/with Tommy Flanagan — Argo 679 (1961) **$35**.

ANOTHER BAG/with Paul Serrano — Argo 695 (1961) **$35**.

GREAT DAY — Argo 725 (1963) **$25**.

COMIN' ON STRONG — Argo 740 (1964) **$25**.

RUNNING THE GAMUT — Scepter 525 (1965) **$20**.

PHIL MOODY
piano

INTIMATE JAZZ/with Paul Horn — Somerset 10400 (1959) **$15.**

MOONDOG
composer, miscellaneous instruments - born 1916 Marysville, KS

AND HIS FRIENDS — Epic 1002 (1954) 10" **$85.**

CARIBEA — Prestige 7042 (1956) yellow label **$50.**

MORE MOONDOG — Prestige 7069 (1956) yellow label **$50.**

THE STORY OF MOONDOG — Prestige 7099 (1957) yellow label **$50.**

ADA MOORE
vocal

JAZZ WORKSHOP/with John LaPorta and Tal Farlow — Debut 15 (1956) **$50.**

BREW MOORE
tenor sax - born 1924 Indianola, MS died 1973

Capable of excellent work, Moore played with many name bands in New York City during the 40's and was involved with considerable work on the West Coast in the late 50's. He then moved to Europe to live and continue working with a return to the U.S. before his death in Europe in 1972. Moore made several fine recordings at different stages of his career with a few to his credit which are to be considered collectors items.

TENOR SAX/with Gerry Mulligan — Savoy 9028 (1953) 10" **$150.**

QUINTET/with Johnny Marabuto — Fantasy 3-222 (1956) **$60.**

BREW MOORE/with Cal Tjader and Vince Guaraldi — Fantasy 3264 (1958) **$60.**

IN EUROPE/with Lars Gullin — Fantasy 6013/86013 (1962) **$50.**

DEBBY MOORE
vocals, guitar - born 1928 St. Augustine, FL

DEBBY MOORE/with Harry Edison — Top Rank 301 (1959) **$55.**

MARILYN MOORE
vocals - born 1931 Oklahoma City, OK

Moore began working in her home town and moved on to Chicago where she performed with the Woody Herman Band. She was married to tenor player Al Cohn and, after a period of retirement, was backed by Cohn on the only LP to her credit. It was not well received despite her great vocal abilities due to her very close resemblance to Billie Holiday.

MOODY/with Joe Wilder — Bethlehem 73 (1957) maroon label **$85.**

OSCAR MOORE
guitar - born 1916 Austin, TX died 1981

OSCAR MOORE — Tampa 22 (1957) **$35.**

OSCAR MOORE TRIO/with Carl Perkins — Skylark 19 (1954) **$45;** *reissued* Tampa 16 (1957) **$35.**

THE FABULOUS OSCAR MOORE GUITAR — Charlie Parker 830 (1962) **$35.**

SHELLY MOORE
vocals

FOR THE FIRST TIME/with Eddie Harris — Argo 4016 (1962) **$35.**

WILD BILL MOORE
tenor sax

WILD BILL'S BEAT/with Junior Mance — Jazzland 38/938 (1961) **$45.**

BOTTOM GROOVE/with Johnny Smith — Jazzland 54/954 (1961) **$45.**

TERRY MOREL
vocals

SONGS OF A WOMAN IN LOVE/with Ralph Sharon — Bethlehem 47 (1955) maroon label **$80.**

JOE MORELLO
drums - born 1928 Springfield, MA

JOE MORELLO SEXTET/with Art Pepper and Red Norvo — Intro 608 (1956) **$80.**

IT'S ABOUT TIME/with Phil Woods — RCA Victor 2486 (1961) dog on top **$60.**

DICK MORGAN TRIO
piano

AT THE SHOWBOAT/with Keeter Betts — Riverside 12-329/1183 (1960) blue label mono; black label stereo with Bill Grauer Pro. **$30.**

SEE WHAT I MEAN/with Bartell Knox — Riverside 347/9347 (1960) blue label mono; black label stereo with Bill Grauer Pro. **$25.**

SETTIN' IN/with Joe Benjamin — Riverside 383/9383 (1961) blue label mono; black label stereo with Bill Grauer Pro. **$25.**

FRANK MORGAN
alto sax

FRANK MORGAN/with Conte Candoli, Wardell Gray and Carl Perkins — Gene Norman Presents 12 (1955) **$80;** EP 9 (1955) **$40;** *reissued* Whippet 704 (1956) **$60.**

LEE MORGAN
trumpet - born 1938 Philadelphia, PA died 1972

A superb trumpet player who combined elements of earlier styles and developed his own form of expression. Beginning with Dizzy Gillespie in the late 50's, and continuing on with Art Blakey's Jazz Messengers into the 60's, Morgan was an exciting new sound. He alternated fronting his own combo and continued work with Blakey which brought him to the mid-60's and his own big hit The Sidewinder. Morgan continued to work and record regularly until his death in 1972.

INDEED!/with Clarence Sharpe — Blue Note 1538 (1956) with NY address on label **$80;** with NY on label **$45;** with A Division of Liberty on label **$20.**

LEE MORGAN/with Hank Mobley — Blue Note 1541 (1956) with NY address on label **$80;** with NY on label **$45;** with A Division of Liberty on label **$20.**

LEE MORGAN/with Gigi Gryce — Blue Note 1557 (1957) with NY address on label **$75;** with NY on label **$45;** with A Division of Liberty on label **$20.**

CITY LIGHTS/with Curtis Fuller — Blue Note 1575 (1957) with NY address on label **$75**; with NY on label **$45**; with A Division of Liberty on label **$20**.

THE COOKER/with Pepper Adams — Blue Note 1578 (1957) with NY address on label **$65**; with NY on label **$45**; with A Division of Liberty on label **$20**.

CANDY/with Sonny Clark — Blue Note 1590 (1958) with NY address on label **$95**; with NY on label **$45**; with A Division of Liberty on label **$20**.

LEEWAY/with Jackie McLean — Blue Note 4034/84034 (1960) with NY address on label **$60**; with NY on label **$45**; with A Division of Liberty on label **$20**.

THE SIDEWINDER/with Joe Henderson — Blue Note 4157/84157 (1963) with NY on label **$45**; with A Division of Liberty on label **$20**.

SEARCH FOR THE NEW LAND/with Wayne Shorter — Blue Note 4169/84169 (1964) with NY on label **$40**; with A Division of Liberty on label **$20**.

THE RUMPROLLER/with Joe Henderson — Blue Note 4199/84199 (1965) with NY on label **$40**; with A Division of Liberty on label **$20**.

HERE'S/with Clifford Gordon — Vee Jay 3007 (1960) **$45**.

THE YOUNG LIONS/with Frank Strozier and Wayne Shorter — Vee Jay 3013 (1960) **$45**.

EX-PHOOBI-DENT/with Clifford Jordan — Vee Jay 3015 (1960) **$45**.

INTRODUCING/with Hank Mobley — Savoy 12091 (1956) maroon label **$60**.

TAKE TWELVE — Jazzland 80/980 (1962) **$40**.

PAT MORRISSEY
vocals - born Philadelphia, PA
I'M PAT MORRISSEY - I SING — Mercury 20197 (1956) black label **$95**.

SANDY MOSSE
tenor, alto saxes - born 1929 Detroit, MI died 1983
CHICAGO SCENE/with Ira Sullivan — Argo 609 (1956) **$45**.

RELAXIN' WITH/with Junior Mance — Argo 639 (1958) **$45**.

SAM MOST
flute, clarinet, alto sax - born 1930 Atlantic City, NJ
Well known since the late 40's and especially during the 50's for his fine flute work as a sideman and on a few of his own recordings. Most has worked the Las Vegas area from the early 60's and the West Coast in studios or orchestras with occasional jazz appearances.
INTRODUCING A NEW STAR/with Doug Mettone — Prestige EP 1322 (1953) **$45**.

PLUS TWO/with Urbie Green and Louis Bellson — Debut 11 (1953) 10" **$100**.

DOUBLES IN JAZZ/with Marty Flax and Aaron Bell — Vanguard 8522 (1954) maroon and silver label **$60**; *reissued* Jazztone 1256 (1957) **$45** one side of LP is Don Elliott.

I'M NUTS ABOUT THE MOST/with Barry Galbraith — Bethlehem 18 (1955) maroon label **$50**.

MUSICALLY YOURS/with Joe Morello — Bethlehem 6008 (1958) maroon label **$40**.

PLAYS BIRD, MONK & MILES/with Dave Schildkraut — Bethlehem 75 (1957) maroon label **$70**.

WITH STRINGS/with Jimmy Raney — Bethlehem 78 (1957) maroon label **$40**.

KEN MOULE
piano, arranger - born 1925 Essex, England
KEN MOULE ARRANGES FOR/with Ronnie Ross — London 1673 (1957) **$60**.

GERRY MULLIGAN
baritone sax, composer, piano - born 1927
New York City, NY
An exceptionally agile baritone player and early in his career an important composer and arranger, Mulligan first gained recognition with Gene Krupa in the late 40's. He then played a significant part in the Miles Davis Capitol recordings in the early 50's. On the West

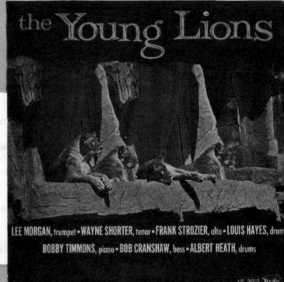

Coast, he created quite a stir by using unusual instrumentation in many groups he led throughout the 50's which was especially evident with his pianoless quartet. Some of his best recordings, however, are those with Chet Baker during this same time. Through the 60's he worked with a 13 piece group for recordings and tours when economically feasible, and with smaller groups in between. Mulligan has acquired many awards and continues to enjoy playing which he communicates in everything he does.

GERRY MULLIGAN BLOWS/with Allen Eager — Prestige 120 (1952) 10" **$250** EP 1317, EP 1318 (1952) **$75** ea.; *reissued* Prestige 7006 (1955).

MULLIGAN TOO — Prestige 141 (1953) 10" **$200**; *reissued* Prestige 7006 (1955)

PLAYS MULLIGAN — Prestige 7006 (1955) yellow label **$75**; *reissue* of Prestige 120 and 141.

HISTORICALLY SPEAKING — Prestige 7251 (1963) yellow label, *reissue* matte **$40**.

QUARTET/with Chet Baker — Pacific Jazz 1 (1953) 10" **$150**; EP 4-1, EP 4-13 (1952) **$50** ea.

GERRY MULLIGAN QUARTET/with Lee Konitz — Pacific Jazz 2 (1953) 10" **$125**; EP 4-2 (1953) **$50**.

MULLIGAN — Pacific Jazz 5 (1953) 10" **$125**; reissued Pacific Jazz 1207.

GERRY MULLIGAN WITH LEE KONITZ — Pacific Jazz 10 (1954) 10" **$125**; EP 4-11, EP 4-21 (1954) **$50** ea.; reissued World Pacific 406/1273 (1958) **$65**; reissued Pacific Jazz 38 (1961) **$45**.

CALIFORNIA CONCERTS/with Zoot Sims — Pacific Jazz 1201 (1955) **$95**; EP 4-28 (1955) **$50**; reissued World Pacific 1201 (1958) **$70**; reissued Pacific Jazz 50 (1962) **$45**.

THE ORIGINAL QUARTET/with Chet Baker — Pacific Jazz 1207 (1955) **$80**; reissued World Pacific 1207 (1958) **$60**.

PARIS CONCERT/with Bob Brookmeyer — Pacific Jazz 1210 (1955) **$80**; EP 4-41, EP 4-42 (1955) **$40** ea.; reissued World Pacific 1210 (1958) **$60**.

"MULLIGAN AT STORYVILLE"/with Bob Brookmeyer — Pacific Jazz 1228 (1957) **$85**; EP 4-63, EP 4-64 (1957) **$40** ea.; reissued World Pacific 1228 (1958) **$60**.

SONGBOOK - Vol 1/with Allen Eager, Zoot Sims, Al Cohn and Lee Konitz — Pacific Jazz 1237 (1957) **$85**; EP 4-67, EP 4-50 (1957) **$40** ea.; reissued World Pacific 1237/1001 (1958) **$60**.

REUNION/with Chet Baker — Pacific Jazz 1241 (1957) **$70**; EP 4-49, EP 4-68 (1957) **$35** ea.; reissued World Pacific 1241/1007 (1958) **$60**; reissued Pacific Jazz 47 (1962) **$35**.

ANNIE ROSS SINGS A SONG WITH MULLIGAN — World Pacific 1253/1020 (1959) **$80**; reissued Kimberly 2018/11018 (1963) **$45**.

THE GENIUS OF — Pacific Jazz 8 (1960) **$45**.

TIMELESS/with Chet Baker — Pacific Jazz 7 (1960) **$45**.

QUARTET — Fantasy 3-6 (1953) 10" **$125**; EP 4008, EP 4028 (1953) **$45** ea.; reissued Fantasy 3-220 red vinyl.

GERRY MULLIGAN QUARTET/PAUL DESMOND QUINTET — Fantasy 3-220 (1956) one side each, red vinyl **$60**; reissue of Fantasy 3-6 (1953).

AND HIS TEN-TETTE/with Bud Shank — Capitol H-439 (1953) 10" **$125**; EP 1-439, EP 2-439 (1953) **$40** ea.; reissued Capitol T691.

MODERN SOUNDS/with Shorty Rogers — Capitol T691 (1956) green label **$70**; reissued Capitol 2025 (1963) tan and black label, one side each; Mulligan side is reissue of Capitol H439 (1953) **$45**.

GERRY MULLIGAN QUARTET/with Chet Baker — Gene Norman Presents Vol. 3 (1952) 10" **$100**; reissued Gene Norman Presents 26.

CHET BAKER - GERRY MULLIGAN - BUDDY DeFRANCO — Gene Norman Presents 26 (1957) gray label, one side is DeFranco **$50**; flipside is Mulligan and reissue of Gene Norman Presents Vol. 3 (1952).

SEXTET/with Zoot Sims and Bob Brookmeyer — EmArcy 36056 (1956) **$65**; EP 1-6146 (1956) **$30**.

MAINSTREAM OF JAZZ/with Zoot Sims and Bob Brookmeyer — EmArcy 36101 (1957) **$65**.

PROFILE/with Bob Brookmeyer — Mercury 20453 (1959) black label **$45**.

JAZZ CONCERTO CROSSO/with Bob Brookmeyer — ABC Paramount 225 (1958) **$75**.

I WANT TO LIVE/with Frank Rosolino and Bud Shank — United Artists 4006/5006 (1958) red label **$75**.

NIGHTWATCH/with Bob Brookmeyer — United Artists 4085/5085 (1959) red label **$60**.

TWO OF A MIND/with Paul Desmond — RCA Victor 2624 (1962) dog on top **$45**.

AT NEWPORT/with Oscar Peterson — Verve 8235 (1957) with Verve Records, Inc. on bottom of label **$60**; reissued Verve 8559/68559 (1963) with MGM on bottom of label **$35**.

THE GERRY MULLIGAN/PAUL DESMOND QUARTET — Verve 8246 (1958) with Verve Records, Inc. on bottom of label **$50**; reissued Verve 8478 (1962) **$35**.

GETZ AND MULLIGAN IN HI FI — Verve 8249/6003 (1958) with Verve Records, Inc. on bottom of label **$60**; reissued Verve 8535 (1963) **$35**.

GERRY MULLIGAN MEETS BEN WEBSTER — Verve 8343/6104 (1959) with Verve Records, Inc. on bottom of label **$50**; reissued Verve 8534/68534 (1964) with MGM on bottom of label **$30**.

GERRY MULLIGAN MEETS JOHNNY HODGES — Verve 8367/68367 (1960) with Verve Records, Inc. on bottom of label **$45**; reissued Verve 8536/68536 (1964) with MGM on bottom of label **$30**.

CONCERT JAZZ BAND — Verve 8388/68388 (1960) with Verve Records, Inc. on bottom of label **$45**; reissued Verve 8388/68388 (1963) with MGM on bottom of label **$30**.

CONCERT JAZZ BAND AT THE VILLAGE VANGUARD — Verve 8396/68396 (1961) with Verve Records, Inc. on bottom of label **$40**; *reissued* Verve 8396/68396 (1963) with MGM on the bottom of the label **$30**.

A CONCERT IN JAZZ — Verve 8415/68415 (1961) with MGM on bottom of label **$40**.

CONCERT JAZZ BAND ON TOUR/with Zoot Sims — Verve 8438/68438 (1962) with MGM on bottom of label **$35**.

QUARTET/with Bob Brookmeyer — Verve 8466/68466 (1962) with MGM on bottom of label **$35**.

BLUES IN TIME/with Paul Desmond — Verve 8478/68478 (1962) with MGM on bottom of label **$35**; *reissue* of Verve 8246.

MULLIGAN MEETS GETZ — Verve 8535/68535 (1963) with MGM on bottom of label **$35**; *reissue* of Verve 8249.

GERRY MULLIGAN '63 — Verve 8515/68515 (1963) with MGM on bottom of label **$30**.

ESSENTIAL — Verve 8567/68567 (1964) with MGM on bottom of label *reissue* matter **$30**.

MULLIGAN MEETS MONK/with Thelonious Monk — Riverside 12-247 (1957) blue label with Bill Grauer Pro. **$65**. *reissued* Riverside 1106 (1958) black label with Bill Grauer Pro. **$50**.

WHAT IS THERE TO SAY/with Art Farmer — Columbia 1307/8116 (1959) red label with 3 black logos on each side **$35**.

JERU/with Tommy Flanagan — Columbia 1932/8732 (1963) red label with 1 white logo on each side **$25**.

SPRING IS SPRUNG — Phillips 200-077/600-077 (1963) **$25**.

NIGHT LIGHTS — Phillips 200-108/600-108 (1964) **$25**.

GREAT/with Bill Robinson — Crown 363/5363 (1963) **$30**.

GERRY MULLIGAN/with Buddy Collette — Crown 411/5411 (1964) **$30**.

IF YOU CAN'T BEAT 'EM, JOIN 'EM — Limelight 82021/86021 (1965) fold out cover **$25**.

FEELIN' GOOD — Limelight 82030/86030 (1965) fold out cover **$25**.

SOMETHING BORROWED, SOMETHING BLUE/with Zoot Sims — Limelight 82040/86040 (1965) **$25**.

MARK MURPHY
vocals - born 1932 Syracuse, NY

A very original performer, Murphy was busy recording, appearing and with club work in the late 50's and worked almost exclusively in Europe into the 60's.

MEET MARK MURPHY — Decca 8390 (1956) black label with silver lettering **$75**.

LET YOURSELF GO — Decca 8632 (1958) black label with silver lettering **$60**.

THIS COULD BE THE START OF SOMETHING/with Bill Holman — Capitol 1177 (1959) black label with logo on left side **$60**.

HIP PARADE — Capitol 1299 (1960) black label with logo on left side **$50**.

PLAYING THE FIELD/with Bill Holman — Capitol 1458 (1960) black label with logo on left side **$50**.

RAH/with Clark Terry and Jimmy Cleveland — Riverside 395/9395 (1961) blue label mono; black label stereo with Bill Grauer Pro. **$45**.

THAT'S HOW I LOVE THE BLUES/with Nick Travis and Clark Terry — Riverside 441/9441 (1962) blue label mono; black label stereo with Bill Grauer Pro. **$45**.

A SWINGIN' SINGIN' AFFAIR — Fontana 27537/67537 (1965) **$25**.

VIDO MUSSO
tenor sax, clarinet - born 1913 Carrini, Sicily died 1982

Musso demonstrated his big tone through the 40's with big bands such as Benny Goodman, Gene Krupa, Harry James and Stan Kenton. He did some work on the West Coast in the 50's and since

1957, lived and worked in Las Vegas performing in bands of his own and backing other name artists.

THE SWINGIN'ST/with Maynard Ferguson — Modern 1207 (1956) **$50**; *reissued* Crown 5007 (1957) with liner notes on back cover **$45**.

TEENAGE DANCE PARTY — Crown 5029 (1957) **$35**.

BOOTS MUSSULLI
alto, baritone saxes - born 1917 Milford, MA

Mussulli was well known in the 40's for his work with big name bands which included repeated jobs with Stan Kenton into the 50's. He became increasingly involved with music education in the Boston area and continued his career with occasional combo work into the 60's.

KENTON PRESENTS/with Shelly Manne — Capitol H6506 (1954) 10" **$100**; EP 6503 (1954) **$45**; *reissued* Capitol T6506 (1955) green label **$65**.

SERGE CHALOFF AND BOOTS MUSSULLI/with Russ Freeman — Storyville 318 (1954) 10" **$175**; EP 412, EP 413 (1954) **$65 ea**.

MORRIS NANTON TRIO
piano - born 1929 Perth Amboy, NJ

FLOWER DRUM SONG/with Osie Johnson — Warner Brothers 1256 (1958) **$25.**

THE ORIGINAL JAZZ PERFORMANCE OF ROBERTA/with Charlie Persip — Warner Brothers 1279 (1958) **$25.**

PREFACE — Prestige 7345 (1965) blue label with logo on right side **$20.**

SOMETHING WE'VE GOT — Prestige 7409 (1965) blue label with logo on right side **$20.**

*TED NASH and DICK NASH
Ted - saxes, flute - born 1922 Somerville, MA
Dick - trombone - born 1928 Somerville, MA

THE BROTHERS NASH/with Jimmy Rowles — Liberty 6011 (1956) green label **$60.**

The only LP's within the scope of this book.

FATS NAVARRO
trumpet - born 1923 Key West, FL died 1950

A great trumpet player who demonstrated his mastery of the styles which preceded him while displaying his own unique and identifiable sound and style. After gaining recognition with Andy Kirk in the 50's, Dizzy Gillespie recommended Navarro as his replacement with the Billy Eckstine Band. During his year and a half with Eckstine he recorded and came to the attention of the jazz public. Navarro worked with combos of his own and those of others, including Tadd Dameron in the late 40's. He gradually began to record and appear less until his death in 1950 from health problems aggravated by narcotics addiction. Nevertheless, his style has remained influential over the decades.

FATS NAVARRO — Prestige EP 1321 (1950) **$50.**

ALL STARS SERIES: NEW SOUNDS OF MODERN MUSIC/with Leo Parker and Tadd Dameron — Savoy 9005 (1953) 10" **$150.**

NEW TRENDS OF JAZZ/with Charlie Rouse and Tadd Dameron — Savoy 9019 (1953) 10" **$150.**

MEMORIAL — Savoy 12011 (1958) maroon label **$35;** *reissue of Savoy matter.*

NOSTALGIA — Savoy 12133 (1958) maroon label **$35;** *reissue of Savoy matter.*

FATS NAVARRO MEMORIAL — Blue Note 5004 (1952) 10" **$250.**

THE FABULOUS - Vol 1 — Blue Note 1531 (1956) with NY address on label **$85;** with NY on label **$45;** with A Division of Liberty on label **$20.**

THE FABULOUS - Vol 2 — Blue Note 1532 (1956) with NY address on label **$85;** with NY on label **$45;** with A Division of Liberty on label **$20.**

CLASSICS OF MODERN JAZZ/with Tadd Dameron Band — Jazzland 50/950 (1962) **$35.**

JIMMY NEELY TRIO
piano

MISIRLOW/with Michael Mulia and Rudy Lawless — Tru-Sound 15002 (1962) **$20.**

OLIVER NELSON
alto, tenor saxes, flute, composer - born 1932
St. Louis, MO died 1975

A very accomplished musician who worked through the 50's with Louis Jordan, Erskine Hawkins and Louis Bellson and, through his composing and arranging abilities, came to work and record with many fine groups under his own name in the 60's. In the late 60's he began to work in studio situations in California, enjoying much success composing for television and movies with occasional work playing and recording in jazz contexts until his death from a heart attack in 1975.

MEET/with Kenny Dorham — New Jazz 8224 (1959) **$60.**

TAKIN' CARE OF BUSINESS/with Lem Winchester — New Jazz 8233 (1960) **$50.**

SCREAMIN' THE BLUES/with Eric Dolphy — New Jazz 8243 (1960) **$50.**

STRAIGHT AHEAD/with Eric Dolphy — New Jazz 8255 (1961) **$50.**

THE BLUES AND THE ABSTRACT TRUTH/with Eric Dolphy and Freddie Hubbard — Impulse 5 (1961) orange label **$35.**

MORE BLUES — Impulse 75 (1964) orange label **$30.**

AFRO/AMERICAN SKETCHES/with Orchestra — Prestige 7225 (1962) yellow label **$45.**

IMPRESSIONS OF PHAEDRA — United Artists 14019/15019 (1962) gray label with silhouette of sax player **$45.**

FULL NELSON — Verve 8508/68508 (1963) with MGM on bottom of label **$25.**

FANTABULOUS — Argo 737 (1964) **$35.**

TRACY NELSON
vocals - born 1945

DEEP ARE THE ROOTS — Prestige 7393 (1965) blue label with logo on right side **$25.**

*PETER NERO TRIO
born 1934 New York City, NY
Peter Nero - piano, Max Wayne - bass,
Dick Stein - drums

JUST FOR YOU — Premier 2011 (1963) **$10.**

The only LP's within the scope of this book.

BERNIE NEROW TRIO
piano

BERNIE NEROW TRIO/with Max Wayne and Dick Stein — Mode 117 (1957) **$30.**

NEW YORK ART QUARTET
John Tchicai, Roswell Rudd, etc.

NEW YORK ART QUARTET — ESP 1004 (1965) **$20.**

NEW YORK JAZZ QUARTET
Herbie Mann, Mat Mathews, Whitey Mitchell,
Joe Puma

NEW YORK JAZZ QUARTET — Elektra 115 (1957) **$45.**

GOES NATIVE — Elektra 118 (1957) **$45;** *reissued* Savoy 12175 (1961) maroon label **$25.**

113

NEW YORK JAZZ SEXTET
Art Farmer, James Moody, Tommy Flanagan, etc.

GROUP THERAPY — Scepter 526 (1964) **$20.**

PHINEAS NEWBORN, JR.
piano - born 1931 Whiteville, TN

HERE IS PHINEAS/with Calvin Newborn — Atlantic 1235 (1956) black label **$45.**

PHINEAS' RAINBOW/with Calvin Newborn — RCA Victor 1421 (1956) dog on top **$40;** EP 1121 (1956) **$20.**

WHILE THE LADY SLEEPS/with Strings — RCA Victor 1474 (1957) dog on top **$30.**

PLAYS JAMAICA/with Sahib Shihab and Jimmy Cleveland — RCA Victor 1589 (1957) dog on top **$50.**

FABULOUS PHINEAS/with Calvin Newborn — RCA Victor 1873 (1958) dog on top **$40.**

PIANO PORTRAITS/with Roy Haynes — Roulette 52031 (1959) light and dark orange roulette wheel label **$35.**

I LOVE A PIANO — Roulette 52043 (1959) light and dark orange roulette wheel label **$25.**

THE WORLD OF PIANO/with Paul Chambers — Contemporary 3600/7600 (1961) yellow label **$20.**

GREAT JAZZ PIANO — Contemporary 3611/7611 (1963) yellow label **$20.**

DAVID "FATHEAD" NEWMAN
alto, tenor saxes, flute - born 1933 Dallas, TX

Newman originally gained notice while with the Ray Charles Band from 1954 to 1964. Initially regarded as a R&B player, he, like Charles, earned the respect of many jazz fans in the late 50's and has continued through his recordings every since. Newman has worked with his own groups and with other name bands including Ray Charles from time to time, Herbie Mann and others. The recordings listed below are his collectables from the time that he was into mainstream jazz and at his best.

FATHEAD: RAY CHARLES PRESENTS DAVID FATHEAD NEWMAN/with Ray Charles and Bennie Crawford — Atlantic 1304 (1959) black label **$45;** *reissued* Atlantic 1304 (1961) with logo on right side **$35.**

STRAIGHT AHEAD/with Wynton Kelly and Paul Chambers — Atlantic 1366 (1960) with logo on right side **$35.**

FATHEAD COMES ON — Atlantic 1399 (1962) with logo on right side **$35.**

SOUNDS OF THE WIDE OPEN SPACES/with James Clay — Riverside 327/1178 (1960) blue label mono; black label stereo with Bill Grauer Pro. **$35.**

JOE NEWMAN
trumpet - born 1922 New Orleans, LA

Newman is probably best known for his work with Count Basie's groups between 1952 and 61. Since that time, he has been deeply involved with jazz education in New York City but has also worked with many great bands for recordings and tours and has appeared in clubs with groups of his own. Newman is a highly respected soloist and individual.

JOE NEWMAN AND HIS BAND/with Frank Wess and Frank Foster — Vanguard 8007 (1954) 10" **$125;** *reissued* American Recording Society 447.

AND THE BOYS IN THE BAND/with Frank Wess and Frank Foster — Storyville 318 (1954) 10" **$125;** EP 428, EP 429 (1954) **$50 ea.**

JOE NEWMAN SEXTET/with Bill Byers and Gene Quill — Storyville 906 (1956) **$85;** *reissued* Jazztone 1217.

I FEEL LIKE A NEWMAN/with Frank Wess — Storyville 905 (1956) **$85.**

NEW SOUNDS IN SWING — Jazztone 1217 (1956) **$60;** *reissued* American Recording Society 451 (1959) **$60;** *reissues* of Storyville 906 (1956).

THE COUNT'S MEN/with Frank Foster — Jazztone 1220 (1956) **$60.**

SWING LIGHTLY/with Ruby Braff — Jazztone 1265 (1957) **$40.**

BASICALLY SWING — American Recording Society 447 (1958) **$60;** *reissue* of Vanguard 8007 (1954).

ALL I WANT TO DO IS SWINGIN'/with Al Cohn and Freddie Green — RCA Victor 1118 (1955) dog on top **$75.**

I'M STILL SWINGING/with Al Cohn and Gene Quill — RCA Victor 1198 (1955) dog on top **$75;** EP 708 (1955) **$40.**

SALUTE TO SATCH/with Orchestra — RCA Victor 1324 (1956) dog on top **$45.**

MIDGETS/with Frank Wess — Vik 1060 (1956) **$75.**

THE HAPPY CATS/with Frank Wess and Frank Rehak — Coral 57121 (1957) maroon label **$60.**

FT SWINGIN' JAZZ/with Shirley Scott — Coral 57208 (1958) maroon label $60.

CKING HORNS/with Zoot Sims — Rama 1003 (1957) $65; reissued Roulette 52009 (1958) white label with multicolored pinwheel $50.

TH WOODWINDS/with Frank Wess and Freddie Green — Roulette 52014 (1958) white label with multicolored pinwheel $35.

UNTIN'/with Al Grey and Frank Wess — World Pacific 1288 (1960) $45.

VE AT FIVE/with Frank Wess and Tommy Flanagan — Swingville 2011 (1960) $45.

OD 'N GROOVY/with Frank Foster and Tommy Flanagan — Swingville 2019 (1961) $45.

E'S HAP'NIN'S/with Tommy Flanagan — Swingville 2027 (1961) $45.

COUNT BASIE'S/with Oliver Nelson — Mercury 20696/60696 (1961) black label $40.

HERBIE NICHOLS

piano, composer - born 1919 New York City, NY

E PROPHETIC - Vol 1/with Art Taylor — Blue Note 5068 (1955) 10" $100.

E PROPHETIC - Vol 2/with Art Taylor — Blue Note 5069 (1955) 10" $100.

IO/with Max Roach — Blue Note 1519 (1956) with NY address on label $80; with NY on label $50.

VE, GLOOM, CASH AND LOVE/with George Duvivier — Bethlehem 81 (1957) maroon label $80.

The Octet

contemporary C2517

Lennie Niehaus
volume 2 •

LENNIE NIEHAUS

alto sax, composer - born 1929 St. Louis, MO

fine player who was well known for his endeavors with Stan enton in the 50's, during which time he recorded on his own and ith other musicians of the West Coast scene. Niehaus exercised his and at composing towards the early 60's and has directed most of is efforts since to writing for television and movies. The handful of Ps that Niehaus produced during his time should certainly be aced amongst some of the best collectables to pursue.

HE QUINTET/with Jack Montrose and Bob Gordon — Contemporary 2513 (1954) 10" $200; EP 4013, EP 4014 (1954) $60 ea.; reissued Contemporary 3518 (1956) yellow label $60; with 4 additional sides.

HE OCTET/with Jack Montrose and Bob Gordon — Contemporary 2517 (1954) 10" $200; EP 4016, EP 4017 (1954) $60 ea.; reissued Contemporary 3540.

HE OCTET NO. 2/with Bill Holman and Jimmy Giuffre — Contemporary 3503 (1955) yellow label $50.

HE QUINTETS AND STRINGS/with Bill Perkins and Bob Gordon — Contemporary 3510 (1955) yellow label $50.

HE SEXTET/with Bill Perkins and Jimmy Giuffre — Contemporary 3524 (1956) yellow label $50.

ZOUNDS! THE OCTET — Contemporary 3540 (1956) yellow label $50; reissue of Contemporary 2517 (1954) with 4 additional sides.

I SWING FOR YOU/with Bill Perkins and Steve Perlow — EmArcy 36118 (1957) with EmArcy in Mercury logo $65; reissued Mercury 20555/60123 (1960) black label $45.

PHIL NIMMONS

alto sax, clarinet - born 1923 Kamloops, British Columbia, Canada

THE CANADIAN SCENE/with Ross Culley and Eddie Karam — Verve 8025 (1956) with Verve Records, Inc. on bottom of label $50; with MGM on bottom of label $30.

NIMMONS 'N NINE/with Ross Culley and Eddie Karam — Verve 8376 (1958) with Verve Records, Inc. on bottom of label $50; with MGM on bottom of label $30.

SAL NISTICO

tenor sax - born 1937 Syracuse, NY

A member of the Mangione Brothers group in the early 60's, Nistico has since worked and recorded with many of the best big bands including Woody Herman, Count Basie and Buddy Rich. Nistico is a hard driving saxophonist who delivers a very powerful and unique style.

HEAVYWEIGHTS/with Nat Adderley — Jazzland 66/966 (1962) $40.

COMIN' ON UP/with Sal Amico — Riverside 457/9457 (1963) blue label mono; black label stereo with Bill Grauer Pro. $40.

KEN NORDINE

jazz narration

WORD JAZZ — Dot 3075 (1957) $35.

SON OF WORD JAZZ — Dot 3096/25096 (1958) $35.

WORD JAZZ - Vol 2 — Dot 3301/25301 (1961) $25.

RED NORVO

vibes, xylophone - born 1908 Beardstown, IL

Being featured in the 30's with Paul Whiteman's Orchestra on radio brought success to Norvo who led bands of his own through the 30's and 40's. Norvo also headed trios in the 50's on the West Coast and since that time has worked most frequently out of Las Vegas, with a few additional recordings. Norvo is acknowledged as the first jazz musician on mallet instruments starting on xylophone and switching to vibes in 1943. His tasteful style has always remained constant whatever the setting.

THE RED NORVO ORCHESTRA — X Label EP 10 (1954) $50.

RED'S ROSE ROOM — X Label 3034 (1954) 10" $80.

TOWN HALL CONCERT — Vol 1/with Orchestra — Commodore 20,023 (1950) 10" $100.

TOWN HALL CONCERT - Vol 2/with Orchestra/Bill Coleman Quartet — Commodore 20,027 (1950) 10" $100.

IMPROVISATION/with Aaron Sachs — EmArcy 26002 (1954) 10" $60.

TRIO/with Charlie Mingus and Tal Farlow — Discovery 3012 (1953) 10" $80.

TRIO/with Charlie Mingus and Tal Farlow — Discovery 3018 (1953) 10" $80; EP 18 (1953) $40.

DANCING ON THE CEILING/with Jimmy Raney and Red Mitchell — Decca 5501 (1953) 10" $75; EP 2115 (1953) $40.

TRIO — Fantasy 3-12 (1953) 10" $75; EP 4026, EP 4027 (1953) $30 ea.; reissued Fantasy 3244 (1956) $35.

TRIO — Fantasy 3-19 (1955) $35.

WITH STRINGS (Trio)/with Tal Farlow and Red Mitchell — Fantasy 3-218 (1956) $35.

KATI BELL NUBIN
vocals

SOUL SOUL SEARCHIN'/with Dizzy Gillespie and Coleman Hawkins — Verve 3004 (1961) with Verve Records, Inc. on bottom of label **$45**; with MGM on bottom of label **$25**.

FABULOUS JAM SESSION/with Dizzy Gillespie and Charlie Parker — Dial 903 (1953) **$75**.

AD LIB/with Buddy Collette — Liberty 3035 (1956) **$60**.

VIB-RATIONS/with Jack Montrose — Liberty 6012 (1956) **$60**.

RED NORVO QUINTET/with Bob Drasnin — Rave 101 (1956) **$75**; *reissued* Tampa 35.

NORVO NATURALLY — Tampa 35 (1957) **$45**.

MUSIC TO LISTEN TO — Contemporary 3534 (1957) yellow label **$40**; *reissued* Contemporary 7009 (1958) black label **$35**.

AND HIS ALL STARS — Epic 3128 (1956) **$70**.

TRIO — Rondo-Lette 28 (1958) **$40**.

WINDJAMMER CITY STYLE/with Jerry Dodgion — Dot 3126 (1958) **$40**.

ART PEPPER - RED NORVO SEXTET COLLECTIONS — Score 4031 (1959) **$50**; *reissue* of Intro 608 (1956); listed under Joe Morello.

MOVE/with Charlie Mingus — Savoy 12088 (1956) maroon label **$35**.

MIDNIGHT ON CLOUD 69/with George Shearing — Savoy 12093 (1957) maroon label **$45**; 4 sides only.

MAINSTREAM JAZZ — Continental 16005 (1962) **$45**.

PRETTY IS THE ONLY WAY TO FLY — Charlie Parker 833 (1962) **$35**.

HI FIVE/with Bob Drasnin — RCA Victor 1420 (1957) dog on top **$60**.

SOME OF MY FAVORITES/with Ben Webster — RCA Victor 1449 (1957) dog on top **$50**; 4 sides only and 4 sides by Matt Dennis.

RED PLAYS THE BLUES/with Harold Land — RCA Victor 1729 (1958) dog on top **$50**; includes 4 sides from RCA Victor 1449.

IN STEREO/with Helen Humes — RCA Victor 1711 (1958) dog on top **$50**.

ANITA O'DAY
vocals - born 1919 Chicago, IL

Ms. O'Day established a reputation as a modern singer with Gene Krupa in the early 40's and worked with Stan Kenton in the mid-40's. Since this time, the husky-voiced O'Day has been a very successful singer and has proven to be an influential artist throughout her career. She is considered to be "a jazz singer's jazz singer" and has helped to set the pace with many fine recordings, appearances and tours which included annual overseas gigs. A very professional attribute of Ms. O'Day's is her continued efforts, even through very stormy personal problems, to develop the style which brought her initial acclaim.

SPECIALS/with Benny Carter — Advance 8 (1951) 10" **$225**; *reissued* Coral 56073.

SINGIN' AND SWINGIN' — Coral 56073 (1953) **$175**; Coral 9-8072 (1953) 7" 4 record box set **$80**; *reissue* of Advance 8 (1951).

COLLATES/with Roy Eldridge and Cecil Payne — Clef 130 (1953) **$150**; EP 134, EP 152, EP 168 (1953) **$60** ea.; *reissued* Norgran 1049.

ANITA O'DAY/with Bud Lavine — Norgran 30 (1954) 10" **$125**; EP 79, EP 80 (1954) **$60** ea.; *reissued* Norgran 1057.

ANITA O'DAY & THE THREE SOUNDS

NGS JAZZ — Norgran 1049 (1955) **$95**; *reissue* of Clef 130 (1953).

N EVENING WITH — Norgran 1057 (1956) **$85**; *reissued* Verve 2050 (1957) with Verve Records, Inc. on bottom of label **$75**; *reissues of Norgran 30 (1954)*.

NITA/with Buddy Bregman Orchestra — Verve 2000 (1956) with Verve Records, Inc. on bottom of label **$80**; *reissue* of Verve 8483.

CK YOURSELF UP/with Buddy Bregman Orchestra — Verve 2043 (1956) with Verve Records, Inc. on bottom of label **$75**; with MGM on bottom of label **$35**.

HE LADY IS A TRAMP — Verve 2049 (1956) **$60**; *reissue* of Norgran 1049 (1955) and Clef 130 (1952).

NITA SINGS THE MOST/with Oscar Peterson — Verve 8259 (1958) with Verve Records, Inc. on bottom of label **$75**; with MGM on bottom of label **$35**.

NGS THE WINNERS/with Russ Garcia Orchestra — Verve 8283/6002 (1958) with Verve Records, Inc. on bottom of label **$75**; *reissued* Verve 8485/68485 (1962) **$35**.

T MISTER KELLY'S/with Joe Masters — Verve 2113/6043 (1958) with Verve Records, Inc. on bottom of label **$60**; with MGM on bottom of label **$35**.

WINGS COLE PORTER/with Billy May Orchestra — Verve 2118/6059 (1959) with Verve Records, Inc. on bottom of label **$50**; with MGM on bottom of label **$35**.

OOL HEAT/with Jimmy Giuffre — Verve 8312/6046 (1959) with Verve Records, Inc. on bottom of label **$70**; with MGM on bottom of label **$35**.

WING RODGERS AND HART/with Billy May Orchestra — Verve 2141 (1959) with Verve Records, Inc. on bottom of label **$50**; with MGM on bottom of label **$35**.

WAITER, MAKE MINE BLUES/with Russ Garcia Orchestra — Verve 2145/62145 (1960) with Verve Records, Inc. on bottom of label **$45**; with MGM on bottom of label **$35**.

RAV'LIN' LIGHT/with Ben Webster — Verve 2157/62157 (1961) with Verve Records, Inc. on bottom of label **$45**; with MGM on bottom of label **$35**.

LL THE SAD YOUNG MEN/with Gary McFarland Orchestra — Verve 8442/68442 (1961) with Verve Records, Inc. on bottom of label **$45**; with MGM on bottom of label **$35**.

IME FOR TWO/with Cal Tjader — Verve 8472/68472 (1962) with MGM on bottom of label **$35**.

HAT IS ANITA — Verve 8483/68483 (1962) with MGM on bottom of label **$30**; *reissue* of Verve 2000.

AND THE THREE SOUNDS — Verve 8514/68514 (1963) with MGM on bottom of label **$30**.

NCOMPARABLE — Verve 8572/68572 (1964) with MGM on bottom of label **$30**.

OR OSCAR — American Recording Society 426 (1957) **$80**.

*CHICO O'FARRILL
composer - born 1921 Havana, Cuba

CHICO O'FARRILL JAZZ/with Flip Phillips, Nick Travis and Roy Eldridge — Clef 132 (1953) 10" **$125**; EP 133 (1953) **$50**; *reissued* Clef 699 (1956) **$75**.

JAZZ NORTH AND SOUTH OF THE BORDER — Verve 8083 (1957) with Verve Records, Inc. on bottom of label **$60**; *reissue* of Clef 132 (1953).

---

*The only LP's within the scope of this book.

RUTH O'LAY
vocals - born 1927 San Francisco, CA

O'LAY — EmArcy 36125 (1958) with EmArcy in Mercury logo **$45**.

EASY LIVING — Mercury 20390/60069 (1959) black label **$45**.

IN PERSON — United Artists 3115/6115 (1960) black label **$40**.

O'LAY! OK — Everest 5218/1218 (1963) **$30**.

*ODETTA
vocals, guitar - born 1930 Birmingham, AL

AND THE BLUES/with Buck Clayton, Vic Dickerson and Ahmed Abdul-Malik — Riverside 417/9417 (1962) blue label mono; black label stereo with Bill Grauer Pro. **$40**.

---

*The only LP's within the scope of this book.

ANTHONY ORTEGA
alto sax, clarinet - born 1928 Los Angeles, CA

ANTHONY ORTEGA/with Einar Iversen — Vintage 2 (1954) 10" **$85**.

JAZZ FOR YOUNG MODERNS/with Art Farmer and Abdul Ahmed-Malik — Bethlehem 79 (1957) maroon label **$45**.

A MAN AND HIS HORN — Herald 0101 (1958) **$60**.

MARY OSBORNE
guitar, vocals - born 1921 Minot, ND

A GIRL AND HER GUITAR — Warwick 2004 (1961) **$50**.

*HAZY OSTERWALD

SWISS JAZZ — Bally 12004 (1956) **$40**.

---

*The only LP's within the scope of this book.

HAROLD OUSLEY
tenor sax - born 1929 Chicago, IL

TENOR SAX/with Julian Priester — Bethlehem 6059 (1961) maroon label **$35**.

JOHNNY PACE
vocals

CHET BAKER INTRODUCES — Riverside 12-292/1130 (1958) blue label mono; black label stereo **$50**.

MIKE PACHECO
bongos

BONGO SKINS/with Carl Perkins and Oscar Moore — Tampa 10 (1957) **$50**.

BONGO SESSION — Tampa 21 (1957) **$50**.

BONGO DATE — Tampa 30 (1957) **$50**.

HOT SKINS/with Shelly Manne — Interlude 513/1013 (1959) **$40**.

*PATTI PAGE
vocals - born Tulsa, OK

IN THE LAND OF HI FI/with Pete Rugolo Orchestra featuring Bob Cooper and Georgie Auld — EmArcy 36074 (1956) with drummer logo, original cover has her with 6 mics and EmArcy logo on left upper corner **$50**; *reissued* EmArcy 36074 (1958) with her on stage with Mercury logo on right upper corner and Custom High Fidelity on bottom **$35**.

---

*The only LP's within the scope of this book.

THE PAGE 7
Page Cavanaugh, Lew McCreary, Dave Wells
Bob Jung, Jack Sperling, John Pisano, Don Bagley

AN EXPLOSION IN POP MUSIC — RCA Victor 2734 (1963) dog on top **$35**.

MARTY PAICH
piano, composer - born 1925 Oakland, CA

Paich worked on the West Coast somewhat with name bands and while in the service in the early 40's. He studied to obtain his Masters degree in music during the late 40's and began working with some of the best bands in the area including Shelly Manne and Shorty Rogers while arranging for groups of all sizes and vocalists such as Peggy Lee. His abilities as a composer and arranger have led him to extensive studio work in years since, doing movies, television and various collaborations.

OCTET/with Conte Candoli and Bob Cooper — Gene Norman Presents 10 (1955) 10" red vinyl **$100**; *reissued* Gene Norman Presents 21 (1956) gray label with 6 additional sides **$70**.

JAZZ CITY WORKSHOP/with Herbie Harper — Bethlehem 44 (1955) maroon label **$70**.

QUARTET/with Art Pepper — Tampa 28 (1957) **$85**; *reissued* Interlude 514/1014 (1959) **$50**.

JAZZ FOR RELAXATION/with Howard Roberts — Tampa 23 (1957) **$50**.

TRIO/with Red Mitchell and Mel Lewis — Mode 105 (1957) **$40**.

JAZZ BAND BALL/with Jack Sheldon — Mode 110 (1957) **$70**; *reissued* Interlude 509.

REVEL WITHOUT PAUSE — Interlude 509/1009 (1959) **$40**; *reissue* of Mode 110.

BIG BAND/with Buddy Childers and Bob Cooper — Cadence 3010 (1958) **$40**.

THE BROADWAY BIT/with Art Pepper and Bill Perkins — Warner Brothers 1296 (1959) **$45**.

I GET A BOOT OUT OF YOU/with Art Pepper and Bill Perkins — Warner Brothers 1349 (1959) **$45**.

PIANO QUARTET/with Pete Jolly, John Towner Williams and Jimmy Rowles — RCA Victor 2164 (1959) dog on top **$40**.

PIANO QUARTET/with Pete Jolly, John Towner Williams and Jimmy Rowles — RCA Victor 2259 (1960) dog on top **$40**.

CHARLIE "BIRD" PARKER
alto sax, composer - born 1920 Kansas City, KS
died 1955

The significance of Parker to the be-bop style of jazz in particular, and jazz styles in general, can hardly be overstated. Coming from the Kansas City mode of jazz in the mid-30's, Parker already displayed signs of possessing new ideas and the ability to execute them in ways that paralleled the many other musicians who contributed to the dramatic new sound that later became known as be-bop. His style of playing was so influential that nearly no one associated with jazz since has remained unaffected. His musical ideas and abilities were of such a level that post-Parker jazz has required a great deal more from those who wish to play it.

In the late 30's, Parker worked most notably with Jay McShann. In 1939 he began to appear on the New York City scene and within the next few years became acquainted and worked with many of the players whose efforts would result in the new style. During the early

40's, he worked with many name bands, often in the company of Dizzy Gillespie with whom, in 1945, he made some combo recordings that paved the way for acceptance of be-bop.

Along with his stature came Parker's volatile personality, personal problems, physical ailments and narcotics addiction which led him to many gigs as a single for much of the remainder of his career. However, he often recorded with all star groups, usually appearing with Lester Young and previously unknown but promising musicians such as Miles Davis in the late 40's. In the 50's he made some important recordings with strings but was usually working with local groups of varying degrees. Not surprisingly, Parker's personal problems took their toll--his health was rapidly diminishing and he died of a combination of causes in 1955. Parker is, and rightly should be, considered a one-of-a-kind jazz giant. His influence is still existent through his tremendous number of fine recordings and he has truly left behind him a new perspective to the word "genius" for the jazz world to ponder.

JAZZ AT MASSEY HALL/with Dizzy Gillespie, Bud Powell, Max Roach and Charlie Mingus — Debut 2 (1953) 10" **$250**; *reissued* Debut 124 (1957) with Parker under the name of Charlie Chan.

JAZZ AT MASSEY HALL/with Dizzy Gillespie, Bud Powell, Max Roach and Charlie Mingus — Debut 4 (1953) 10" **$250**; *reissued* Debut 124 (1957) with Parker under the name of Charlie Chan.

JAZZ AT MASSEY HALL/with Dizzy Gillespie, Bud Powell, Max Roach and Charlie Mingus — Debut 124 (1957) **$100**; *reissued* Debut 124 (1959) **$85**; *reissues* of Debut 2 and 4.

CHARLIE PARKER/with Red Rodney — Debut EP 35, EP 36, EP 37 (1950) **$60 ea.**

CHARLIE PARKER/with Miles Davis — Debut EP 38, EP 39, EP 40 (1950) **$60 ea.**

JAZZ AT MASSEY HALL — Fantasy 6003 (1962) **$40**; *reissue* of Debut 124 with Parker under the name of Charlie Chan.

QUINTET/with Lucky Thompson — Dial 201 (1948) 10" **$350**.

QUINTET/with Lucky Thompson — Dial 202 (1948) 10" **$350**.

QUINTET/with Miles Davis — Dial 203 (1948) 10" **$350**.

SEXTET/with J.J. Johnson — Dial 207 (1948) 10" **$300**.

BIRD BLOWS THE BLUES/with Howard McGhee — Dial 901 (1953) **$100**.

ALTERNATE MASTERS/with Miles Davis — Dial 904 (1953) **$100**.

ALTERNATE MASTERS — Dial 905 (1953) **$100**; *reissue* of Dial matter.

CHARLIE PARKER - Vol 1/with Miles Davis — Savoy 9000 (1953) 10" **$150**.

CHARLIE PARKER - Vol 2/with Dizzy Gillespie — Savoy 9001 (1953) 10" **$150**.

CHARLIE PARKER - Vol 3/with Miles Davis — Savoy 9010 (1953) 10" **$150**.

CHARLIE PARKER - Vol 4/with Dizzy Gillespie — Savoy 9011 (1953) 10" **$150**.

BIRD, DIZ, BUD, MAX — Savoy 9034 (1954) 10" **$100**.

THE IMMORTAL/with Dizzy Gillespie — Savoy 12001 (1955) maroon label **$45**.

MEMORIAL/with Miles Davis — Savoy 12000 (1955) maroon label **$45**.

GENIUS OF — Savoy 12009 (1955) maroon label **$45**; *reissue* of Savoy 9001.

GENIUS OF — Savoy 12014 (1955) maroon label **$45**; *reissue* of Savoy 9000.

GREATEST RECORDING SESSION — Savoy 12079 (1957) maroon label **$45**; *reissue* in part of Savoy 9000 and 9001.

BIRD'S NIGHT — Savoy 12138 (1960) maroon label **$35**; *reissue* of Savoy matter.

AN EVENING AT HOME WITH THE BIRD/with Max Roach — Savoy 12152 (1962) maroon label **$30**.

BIRD RETURNS — Savoy 12179 (1964) maroon label **$30**; *reissue* of Savoy matter.

NEWLY DISCOVERED SIDES BY — Savoy 12186 (1964) maroon label **$30**.

WITH STRINGS — Mercury 35010 (1950) 10" **$200**.

CHARLIE PARKER/with Al Haig — Clef 157 (1952) 10" **$175**; EP 208, EP 209 (1952) **$60 ea.**

WITH STRINGS — Clef 501 (1953) 10" **$125**; EP 512, EP 513 (1953) **$50 ea.**

WITH STRINGS - Vol 2 — Clef 509 (1953) 10" **$125**.

BIRD AND DIZ/with Dizzy Gillespie — Clef 512 (1953) 10" **$175**; EP 255, EP 278, EP 337, EP 511 (1952) **$60 ea.**

SOUTH OF THE BORDER/with Walter Bishop — Clef 513 (1953) 10" **$125**; EP 506, EP 507 (1952) **$60 ea.**

BIG BAND — Clef 609 (1954) **$90**; EP 235, EP 505 (1953) **$60 ea.**

WITH STRINGS — Clef 675 (1955) **$85**; *reissue* of Clef 501 and 509 (1954).

THE MAGNIFICENT/with Red Rodney — Clef 646 (1955) **$85**; EP 336 (1952) **$50**.

CHARLIE PARKER — Clef EP 503 (1953) **$50**.

CHARLIE PARKER — Clef EP 255 (1952) **$50**.

SEPTET — Jazztone 1204 (1956) **$40**; *reissue* of Dial matter.

THE FABULOUS BIRD — Jazztone 1214 (1956) **$40**; *reissue* of Dial matter.

BIRD AT ST. NICK'S/with Red Rodney — Jazz Workshop 500 (1958) **$85**; *reissued* Fantasy 6012 (1964) **$30**.

BIRD ON 52ND STREET/with Miles Davis — Jazz Workshop 501 (1958) **$85**; *reissued* Fantasy 6011 (1964) **$30**.

ONCE THERE WAS BIRD — Charlie Parker 408 (1961) **$35**.

BIRD IS FREE — Charlie Parker 401 (1961) **$45**.

THE HAPPY BIRD — Charlie Parker 404 (1961) **$45**.

CHARLIE PARKER — Charlie Parker 406 (1961) **$35**.

BIRD SYMBOLS — Charlie Parker 407 (1961) **$35**.

ALL STAR SEXTET/with Miles Davis and J.J. Johnson — Roost 2210 (1957) **$50**; *reissue* of Dial matter.

DIZ 'N BIRD IN CONCERT — Roost 2234 (1959) **$50**.

THE WORLD OF — Roost 2257 (1965) **$30**.

LES JAZZ COOL - Vol 1/with Fats Navarro — Jazz Cool 101 (1960) **$45**.

LES JAZZ COOL - Vol 2/with Kenny Dorham — Jazz Cool 102 (1960) **$45**.

LES JAZZ COOL - Vol 3/with Kenny Dorham — Jazz Cool 103 (1960) **$45**.

BIRD LIVES/with Sarah Vaughan — Continental 16004 (1962) **$40**.

A HANDFUL OF MODERN JAZZ/with Miles Davis — Baronet 105 (1962) **$25**; *reissue* of Dial matter.

THE EARLY BIRD — Baronet 107 (1962) **$25**; *reissue* of Dial matter.

THE EARLY BIRD — Blue Ribbon 8011 (1963) **$25**; *reissue* of Dial matter.

A NIGHT AT CARNEGIE HALL/with Dizzy Gillespie — Birdland 425 10" **$75**.

NIGHT & DAY (GENIUS #1) — Verve 8003 (1957) with Verve Records, Inc. on bottom of label **$60**; with MGM on bottom of label **$35**; *reissue* of Clef 609.

APRIL IN PARIS (GENIUS #2) — Verve 8004 (1957) with Verve Records, Inc. on bottom of label **$60**; with MGM on bottom of label **$35**. Ⓐ

NOW'S THE TIME (GENIUS #3) — Verve 8005 (1957) with Verve Records, Inc. on bottom of label **$60**; with MGM on bottom of label **$35**; *reissue* of Clef 157.

BIRD & DIZ (GENIUS #4) — Verve 8006 (1957) with Verve Records, Inc. on bottom of label **$60**; with MGM on bottom of label **$35**; *reissues* of Clef 512. Ⓐ

PLAYS COLE PORTER (GENIUS #5) — Verve 8007 (1957) with Verve Records, Inc. on bottom of label **$60**; with MGM on bottom of label **$35**.

FIESTA (GENIUS #6) — Verve 8008 (1957) with Verve Records, Inc. on bottom of label **$60**; with MGM on bottom of label **$35**.

JAZZ PERENNIAL (GENIUS #7) — Verve 8009 (1957) with Verve Records, Inc. on bottom of label **$60**; with MGM on bottom of label **$35**.

SWEDISH SCHNAPPS (GENIUS #8) — Verve 8010 (1957) with Verve Records, Inc. on bottom of label **$60**; with MGM on bottom of label **$35**.

STORY - Vol 1 — Verve 8000 (1957) with Verve Records, Inc. on bottom of label **$50**; with MGM on bottom of label **$35**.

STORY - Vol 2 — Verve 8001 (1957) with Verve Records, Inc. on bottom of label **$50**; with MGM on bottom of label **$35**.

STORY - Vol 3 — Verve 8002 (1957) with Verve Records, Inc. on bottom of label **$50**; with MGM on bottom of label **$35**.

THE CHARLIE PARKER STORY — Verve 8100-3 (1958) 3 record box set with Verve Records, Inc. on bottom of label **$75**; *reissues* of Verve 8000, 8001 and 8002; with MGM on bottom of label **$45**; *reissue* of original Story Vols. 1, 2 and 3.

ESSENTIAL — Verve 8409 (1961) with MGM on bottom of label **$35**.

JACY PARKER
piano, vocals

SPOTLIGHT ON/with Ernie Royal — Verve 8424/68424 (1962) with MGM on bottom of label **$30**.

LEO PARKER
baritone sax - born 1925 Washington, DC died 1962

In the mid-40's Parker recorded with Fats Navarro and Dexter Gordon among others and is known for his "Mad Lad" recordings with Charles Thompson. Since this time, he has leaned more towards the R&B side of music and has worked considerably less in the jazz field.

ALL STAR SERIES/with Dexter Gordon and J.J. Johnson — Savoy 9009 (1953) 10" **$150**.

NEW TRENDS OF JAZZ/with Gene Ammons and Howard McGhee — Savoy 9018 (1953) 10" **$150**.

LET ME TELL YOU ABOUT IT/with Dave Burns and Bill Swindell — Blue Note 4087 (1961) with NY address on label **$75**; with NY on label **$50**; with A Division of Liberty on label **$20**.

ROLLIN' WITH LEO/with Bill Swindell and Dave Burns — Blue Note 4095 (1961) with NY address on label **$75**; with NY on label **$50**; with A Division of Liberty on label **$20**.

HORACE PARLAN
piano - born 1931 Pittsburgh, PA

Parlan gained experience in his hometown of Pittsburgh in the early 50's. He then moved on to New York City and worked with Charlie Mingus followed by stints with other great players such as Dexter Gordon and Stanley Turrentine.

MOVIN' & GROOVIN'/with Al Harewood and Sam Jones — Blue Note 4028 (1960) with NY address on label **$50**; with NY on label **$40**; with A Division of Liberty on label **$20**.

US THREE/with Al Harewood and George Tucker — Blue Note 4037 (1960) with NY address on label **$50**; with NY on label **$40**; with A Division of Liberty on label **$20**.

SPEAKIN' MY PIECE/with Tommy and Stanley Turrentine — Blue Note 4043 (1960) with NY address on label **$65**; with NY on label **$45**; with A Division of Liberty on label **$20**.

HEADIN' SOUTH/with Ray Barretto — Blue Note 4062 (1960) with NY address on label **$45**; with NY on label **$35**; with A Division of Liberty on label **$20**.

ON THE SPUR OF THE MOMENT/with Tommy and Stanley Turrentine — Blue Note 4074 (1961) with NY address on label **$65**; with NY on label **$45**; with A Division of Liberty on label **$20**.

UP & DOWN/with Booker Ervin and Grant Green — Blue Note 4082 (1961) with NY address on label **$65**; with NY on label **$45**; with A Division of Liberty on label **$20**.

JOE PASS
guitar - born 1929 New Brunswick, PA

CATCH ME!/with Clare Fischer — Pacific Jazz 73 (1963) **$35**.

FOR DJANGO — Pacific Jazz 85 (1965) **$35**.

12 STRING GUITAR — World Pacific 1821 (1964) **$25**.

JOHNNY PATE
bass - born 1923 Chicago Heights, IL

AT THE BLUE NOTE — Stepheny 4002 (1957) **$45**.

JAZZ GOES IVY LEAGUE — King 561 (1958) without crown on label **$35**.

SWINGIN' FLUTE — King 584 (1958) without crown on label **$35**.

A DATE WITH — King 611 (1959) without crown on label **$35**.

DON PATTERSON
organ - born 1936 Columbus, OH

THE EXCITING NEW ORGAN OF/with Booker Ervin — Prestige 7331 (1964) blue label with logo on right side **$45**.

HIP CAKE WALK/with Booker Ervin — Prestige 7349 (1965) blue label with logo on right side **$40**.

PATTERSON'S PEOPLE/with Sonny Stitt — Prestige 7381 (1965) blue label with logo on right side **$40**.

SATISFACTION/with Billy James — Prestige 7430 (1965) blue label with logo on right side **$35**.

JAZZ & ROMANTIC PLACES

DAVE PELL OCTET: ATLANTIC 1216

JOHN "BIG" PATTON
organ - born 1936 Kansas City, MO

LONG CAME JOHN/with Harold Vick — Blue Note 4130/84130 (1963) with NY on label **$45**; with A Division of Liberty on label **$20**.

LUE JOHN/with Tommy Turrentine — Blue Note 4143/84143 (1963) with NY on label **$45**; with A Division of Liberty on label **$20**.

HE WAY I FEEL/with Grant Green — Blue Note 4174/84174 (1964) with NY on label **$35**; with A Division of Liberty on label **$20**.

H BABY!/with Blue Mitchell — Blue Note 4192/84192 (1965) with NY on label **$40**; with A Division of Liberty on label **$20**.

OT A GOOD THING GOIN'/with Grant Green — Blue Note 4229/84229 (1965) with NY on label **$35**; with A Division of Liberty on label **$20**.

CECIL PAYNE
baritone, alto saxes - born 1922 Brooklyn, NY

he first baritone sax player to move into the bop style, Payne worked ith Dizzy Gillespie, Tadd Dameron, James Moody and Illinois acquet from the 40's into the 50's during which time he appeared on ountless recordings. He then worked with Randy Weston on-and-off rom the late 50's which included tours of Europe.

ECIL PAYNE QUINTET AND QUARTET/with Kenny Dorham — Signal 1203 (1955) **$70**; *reissued* Savoy 12147.

IGHT AT THE FIVE SPOT/with Phil Woods — Signal 1204 (1955) **$70**.

ERFORMING CHARLIE PARKER MUSIC/with Clark Terry — Charlie Parker 801 (1962) **$40**.

HE CONNECTION/with Bennie Green — Charlie Parker 806 (1962) **$40**.

ATTERNS OF JAZZ — Savoy 12147 (1960) maroon label **$35**; *reissue* of Signal 1203.

*FREDA PAYNE
vocals

FTER THE LIGHTS GO DOWN LOW — Impulse 53 (1964) orange label **$35**.

*The only LP's within the scope of this book.

DUKE PEARSON
piano - born 1932 Atlanta, GA

ROFILE/with Gene Taylor and Lex Humphries — Blue Note 4022 (1959) with NY address on label **$45**; with NY on label **$35**; with A Division of Liberty on label **$20**.

TENDER FEELIN'S/with Gene Taylor and Lex Humphries — Blue Note 4035 (1959) with NY address on label **$45**; with NY on label **$35**; with A Division of Liberty on label **$20**.

WAHOO! — Blue Note 4191/84191 (1964) with NY on label **$45**; with A Division of Liberty on label **$20**.

HUSH!/with Donald Byrd and Johnny Coles — Jazzline 33-02 (1962) **$60**.

BERNARD PEIFFER
piano, composer - born 1922 Epinal, France died 1976

BERNARD PEIFFER — Norgran 11 (1954) 10" **$75**.

LE MOST/with Bobby Jaspar — EmArcy 26036 (1954) 10" **$75**.

BERNIE'S TUNES/with Joe Puma — EmArcy 36080 (1956) with drummer logo **$45**.

THE ASTOUNDING — Decca 8626 (1958) black label with silver lettering **$30**.

PIANO A LA MOOD — Decca 9203 (1958) black label with silver lettering **$30**.

JAZZ FROM SAINT GERMAIN DES PRES/with Don Byas — Verve 8119 (1957) with Verve Records, Inc. on bottom of label **$45**; one side of LP each.

MODERN JAZZ FOR PEOPLE WHO LIKE ORIGINAL MUSIC — Laurie 1006 (1960) **$20**.

PLAYS COLE PORTER'S CAN CAN — Laurie 1008 (1960) **$20**.

*DAVE PELL
saxophones, clarinet - born 1925 Brooklyn, NY

Pell gained big band experience in the east in the early 40's and through activity on the West Coast from 1945 with several club appearances and recordings which featured other West Coast musicians of that era. After recording for many labels, he moved into arranging and recording work himself, producing and publishing since the 50's.

PLAYS IRVING BERLIN/with Ronny Lang — Trend 1003 (1953) 10" **$100**; EP 505, EP 506 (1953) **$40 ea.** *reissued* Kapp 1036 (1958) **$50**.

WITH LUCY ANN POLK — Trend 1008 (1953) 10" **$100**.

PLAYS RODGERS AND HART/with Bob Gordon — Trend 1501 (1954) **$80**; *reissued* Kapp 1025 (1958) **$50**.

PLAYS BURKE AND VAN HEUSEN/with Ronny Lang — Kapp 1034 (1958) **$50**.

JAZZ AND ROMANTIC PLACES/with Bob Gordon — Atlantic 1216 (1955) black label **$75**; EP 548, EP 549, EP 550 (1955) **$25 ea.**

LOVE STORY/with Don Fagerquist — Atlantic 1249 (1956) black label **$60**.

JAZZ GOES DANCING/with Ray Sims — RCA Victor 1320 (1956) dog on top **$40**.

SWINGIN' IN THE OL' CORRAL/with Marty Berman — RCA Victor 1394 dog on top **$50**; EP 1-1394, EP 2-1394, EP 3-1394 (1956) **$25 ea.**

PELL OF A TIME/with Pepper Adams and Jack Sheldon — RCA Victor 1524 (1957) dog on top **$60**.

CAMPUS HOP/with Jack Sheldon and Bob Enevoldsen — RCA Victor 1662 (1957) dog on top **$60**.

I HAD THE CRAZIEST DREAM/with Bob Gordon — Capitol 925 (1958) black label with logo on left side **$50**.

THE BIG SMALL BANDS/with Art Pepper and Jack Sheldon — Capitol 1309 (1959) black label with logo on left side **$40**.

OLD SOUTH WAILS/with Jack Sheldon — Capitol 1512 (1961) black label with logo on left side **$40**.

I REMEMBER, JOHN KIRBY/with Benny Carter — Capitol 1687 (1962) black label with logo on top **$35**.

SWINGIN' SCHOOL SONGS/with Bob Enevoldsen and Marty Paich — Coral 57248/757248 (1958) maroon label **$40**.

PLAYS DUKE ELLINGTON BIG BAND SOUNDS — Tops 3007 (1961) **$20**.

*The only LP's within the scope of this book.

ART PEPPER

alto sax - born 1925 Gardena, CA died 1982

A West Coast musician by birth, Pepper early on showed a new voice on alto which reflected the styles of Charlie Parker and Lee Konitz; all the while displaying his own distinct sound and approach. Beginning in his teens he played in every jam session possible and with many big name stars, gaining national exposure through gigs with Stan Kenton in the early 40's. Pepper went into the service and returned to Kenton's band when discharged and continued to work and record until the early 50's.

Pepper's popularity was such that, through most of the 50's and 60's, in spite of a serious narcotics problem, he worked with many name groups and made recordings that are now considered to be classics. In 1968 while working with Buddy Rich's Band, his health deteriorated to the point of hospitalization followed by several years in a drug program which eventually lead to his reemergence in the mid-70's. In the late 70's, Pepper worked and recorded quite often, wrote his autobiography with his wife Laurie, and assisted with a film about his life called Notes From A Jazz Survivor. Art Pepper worked until suffering a stroke, which he died of a week later in June of 1982.

QUARTET/with Hampton Hawes — Discovery 3019 (1952) 10" **$150**; EP 19 (1952) **$60**.

QUINTET/with Jack Montrose — Discovery 3023 (1953) 10" **$150**; *reissued* Savoy 12089.

THE RETURN OF/with Jack Sheldon — Jazz West 10 (1956) **$85**; *reissued* Score 4032 (1958) **$60**.

QUARTET/with Russ Freeman — Tampa 20/1001 (1957) **$85**; *reissued* Interlude 512/1012 (1959) **$50**.

MODERN ART/with Russ Freeman — Intro 606 (1956) **$85**.

ART PEPPER/RED NORVO SEXTET — Score 4031 (1959) **$50**; *reissue* of Intro 608 listed under Joe Morello.

PLAYBOYS/with Chet Baker — Pacific Jazz 1234 (1956) **$85**; *reissued* World Pacific 1234 (1958) **$60**.

PICTURE OF HEALTH/with Chet Baker — Pacific Jazz 18 (1962) **$40**; *reissue* of Pacific Jazz 1234.

THE ARTISTRY OF PEPPER/with Bud Shank — Pacific Jazz 60 (1963) **$40**.

MEETS RHYTHM SECTION/with Red Garland — Contemporary 3532 (1957) **$60**; *reissued* Contemporary 7018 (1958) **$50**.

PLUS ELEVEN/with Jack Sheldon and Bill Perkins — Contemporary 3568/7568 (1959) yellow label mono; black label stereo **$40**.

GETTIN' TOGETHER/with Conte Candoli — Contemporary 3573/7573 (1960) yellow label mono; black label stereo **$45**.

SMACK UP/with Jack Sheldon — Contemporary 3602/7602 (1961) yellow label mono; black label stereo **$45**.

INTENSITY — Contemporary 3607/7607 (1961) yellow label mono; black label stereo **$45**.

SURF RIDE/with Jack Montrose — Savoy 12089 (1957) maroon label **$60**; *reissue* of Discovery matter.

TWO ALTOS/with Sonny Redd — Regent 6069 (1959) green label **$60**.

PEPPER - MANNE — Charlie Parker 836 (1963) one side each **$35**.

BILL PERKINS

tenor, baritone saxes, flute
born 1924 San Francisco, CA

Perkins studied music and engineering during the early 40's and began playing with Woody Herman and Stan Kenton in the early 50's. He also recorded under his own name during this time and, in 1956, produced his very best in 2° East - 3° West with John Lewis. Perkins is a superb tenorman who, somehow, missed out on his due credit. He studied record engineering and began working in studios in the 60's.

GRAND ENCOUNTER 2° East - 3° West/with John Lewis — Pacific Jazz 1217 (1956) **$85**; *reissued* World Pacific 1217 (1958) **$65**; *reissued* Pacific Jazz 44 (1962) **$45**.

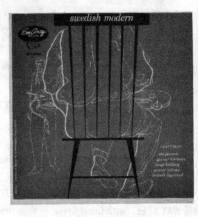

ON STAGE/with Bud Shank — Pacific Jazz 1221 (1956) **$85**; EP 4-48 (1956) **$45**; *reissued* World Pacific 1221 (1958) **$60**.

JUST FRIENDS/with Art Pepper and Richie Kamuca — Pacific Jazz 401 (1956) **$85**; *reissued* World Pacific 401 (1958) **$60**.

TENORS HEAD ON/with Richie Kamuca — Liberty 3051 (1957) **$50**.

THE BROTHERS/with Al Cohn and Richie Kamuca — RCA Victor 1162 (1956) dog on top **$60**.

BOSSA NOVA — Liberty 3293/7293 (1963) **$40**.

CARL PERKINS

piano - born 1928 Indianapolis, IN died 1958

A talented and self-taught musician, Perkins worked with many name bands in the late 40's moving to California to live and play through the 50's. He worked considerably but was seldom recorded. Nonetheless, he was a respected artist and a great sideman for many other artists.

INTRODUCING/with Leroy Vinnegar and Lawrence Marable — Dootone 211 (1956) **$95**; EP 213 (1956) **$60**.

CHARLIE PERSIP

drums - born 1929 Morristown, NJ

AND THE JAZZ STATESMEN/with Roland Alexander and Freddie Hubbard — Bethlehem 6046 (1960) maroon label **$40**.

AKE PERSSON

trombone - born 1932 Hässleholm, Sweden died 1975

NEW SOUNDS OF SWEDEN/with Arne Domnerus — Prestige 173 (1953) 10" **$150**.

SWEDISH MODERN/with Gunnar Bjorksten — EmArcy 26039 (1954) 10" **$150**; EP 1-6068, EP 1-6069 (1954) **$60** ea.

PLAYS PRETTY — Mercury/Clef 119 (1952) 10" **$150**; *reissued* Verve 2004.

COLLATES # 2 — Mercury/Clef 127 (1953) 10" **$100**; EP 171 (1952) **$50**; *reissued* Clef 696.

SINGS — Mercury/Clef 145 (1953) 10" **$100**; EP 191, EP 192 (1953) **$50 ea.**; *reissued* Verve 2012.

PLAYS PRETTY #2 — Mercury/Clef 155 (1953) 10" **$100**; EP 231, EP 232 (1953) **$50 ea.**

QUARTET #2 — Mercury/Clef 168 (1953) 10" **$100**.

PLAYS COLE PORTER — Mercury/Clef 603 (1953) **$95**; EP 103, EP 104, EP 105 (1953) **$35 ea.**

PLAYS IRVING BERLIN — Mercury/Clef 604 (1953) **$95**; EP 106, EP 107, EP 108 (1953) **$35 ea.**

PLAYS GEORGE GERSHWIN — Mercury/Clef 605 (1953) **$95**; EP 100, EP 101, EP 102 (1953) **$35 ea.**

PLAYS DUKE ELLINGTON — Mercury/Clef 606 (1953) **$90**; EP 109, EP 110, EP 111 (1953) **$30 ea.**

PLAYS JEROME KERN — Clef 623 (1954) **$90**; EP 211, EP 212, EP 213 (1954) **$30 ea.**

PLAYS RICHARD RODGERS — Clef 624 (1954) **$90**; EP 114, EP 115, EP 116 (1953) **$30 ea.**

PLAYS VINCENT YOUMANS — Clef 625 (1954) **$85**; EP 217, EP 218, EP 219 (1954) **$25 ea.**

PLAYS HARRY WARREN — Clef 648 (1955) **$85**; EP 240, EP 241, EP 242 (1955) **$25 ea.**

PLAYS HAROLD ARLEN — Clef 649 (1955) **$85**; EP 243, EP 244, EP 245 (1955) **$25 ea.**

PLAYS JIMMY McHUGH — Clef 650 (1955) **$85**; EP 246, EP 247, EP 248 (1955) **$25 ea.**

QUARTET — Clef 688 (1956) **$75**; *reissue* of Clef 116.

RECITAL — Clef 694 (1956) **$65**; *reissued* Verve 2044 (1957) **$55**.

NOSTALGIC MEMORIES — Clef 695 (1956) **$65**; *reissued* Verve 2045 (1957) **$55**.

TENDERLY — Clef 696 (1956) **$60**; *reissued* Verve 2046 (1957) **$55**; *reissues of* Clef 106.

KEYBOARD — Clef 697 (1956) **$65**; *reissued* Verve 2047 (1957) **$55**; *reissues of* Clef 110.

AN EVENING WITH — Clef 698 (1956) **$65**; *reissued* Verve 2048 (1957) **$55**.

PLAYS COUNT BASIE — Clef 708 (1956) **$65**; *reissued* Verve 8098 (1957) **$55**.

IN A ROMANTIC MOOD (Sings)/with Orchestra — Verve 2002 (1956) with Verve Records, Inc. on bottom of label **$65**; with MGM on bottom of label **$35**.

PASTEL MOODS — Verve 2004 (1956) with Verve Records, Inc. on bottom of label **$60**; with MGM on bottom of label **$30**; *reissue of* Mercury/Clef 119.

ROMANCE (Sings) — Verve 2012 (1956) with Verve Records, Inc. on bottom of label **$60**; with MGM on bottom of label **$30**; *reissue of* Mercury/Clef 145.

SOFT SANDS — Verve 2079 (1957) with Verve Records, Inc. on bottom of label **$60**; with MGM on bottom of label **$30**.

AT THE STRATFORD SHAKESPEAREAN FESTIVAL — Verve 8024 (1956) with Verve Records, Inc. on bottom of label **$50**.

QUARTET — Verve 8072 (1957) with Verve Records, Inc. on bottom of label **$50**; with MGM on bottom of label **$30**.

TRIO AT NEWPORT/with Sonny Stitt and Roy Eldridge — Verve 8239 (1957) with Verve Records, Inc. on bottom of label **$50**; with MGM on bottom of label **$30**; one side of LP only.

TRIO AT THE OPERA HOUSE/with The Modern Jazz Quartet — Verve 8296 (1956) with Verve Records, Inc. on bottom of label **$50**; with MGM on bottom of label **$30**; one side of LP each.

AT THE CONCERTOEBOUW — Verve 8268 (1958) with Verve Records, Inc. on bottom of label **$40**; with MGM on bottom of label **$30**.

ON THE TOWN — Verve 8287 (1958) with Verve Records, Inc. on bottom of label **$40**; with MGM on bottom of label **$30**.

OSCAR PETERSON

piano, vocals - born 1925 Montreal, Quebec, Canada

A child prodigy from Canada, Peterson came to America in 1949 for concerts and tours with Norman Granz' JATP series. He achieved widespread popularity and respect for his phenominal ability on piano in the tradition of earlier masters such as Art Tatum, Earl Hines and Erroll Garner but with his own individual touch. Since this time he has worked in virtually every imaginable context from solo to famous trios over every decade, and in orchestral recordings as well. Peterson is a highly regarded composer, a fine organist and a very good, though rarely heard, singer.

THIS IS/with Armand Samson — RCA Victor 3006 (1950) 10" **$200**; EP 3006 (1950) 2 EPs **$100**.

PIANO SOLOS/with Ray Brown — Mercury/Clef 106 (1952) 10" **$150**; *reissued* Clef 696.

AT CARNEGIE HALL — Mercury/Clef 107 (1952) 10" **$150**.

COLLATES — Mercury/Clef 110 (1952) 10" **$150**; EP 118, EP 123 (1952) **$50 ea.**; *reissued* Clef 697.

QUARTET — Mercury/Clef 116 (1952) **$150**; *reissued* Clef 688.

MY FAIR LADY — Verve 2119 (1958) with Verve Records, Inc. on bottom of label **$40**; with MGM on bottom of label **$30**.

JAZZ PORTRAIT OF SINATRA — Verve 8334 (1959) with Verve Records, Inc. on bottom of label **$40**; with MGM on bottom of label **$30**.

PORGY & BESS — Verve 8340 (1959) with Verve Records, Inc. on bottom of label **$40**; with MGM on bottom of label **$30**.

THE JAZZ SOUL OF — Verve 8351 (1959) with Verve Records, Inc. on bottom of label **$40**; with MGM on bottom of label **$30**.

SWINGING BRASS — Verve 8364 (1959) with Verve Records, Inc. on bottom of label **$45**; with MGM on bottom of label **$30**.

FLORELLO! — Verve 8366 (1959) with Verve Records, Inc. on bottom of label **$40**; with MGM on bottom of label **$30**.

TRIO! LIVE IN CHICAGO — Verve 8420 (1961) with Verve Records, Inc. on bottom of label **$40**; with MGM on bottom of label **$30**.

VERY TALL/with Milt Jackson — Verve 8429 (1961) with MGM on bottom of label **$35**.

WEST SIDE STORY — Verve 8454 (1962) with MGM on bottom of label **$30**.

BURSTING OUT WITH THE ALL STAR BIG BAND — Verve 8476 (1962) with MGM on bottom of label **$35**.

SOUND OF THE TRIO — Verve 8480 (1961) with MGM on bottom of label **$30**.

AFFINITY — Verve 8516 (1963) with MGM on bottom of label **$30**.

NIGHT TRAIN — Verve 8538 (1963) with MGM on bottom of label **$30**.

PLAYS — Verve 8591 (1964) with MGM on bottom of label **$30**.

WITH NELSON RIDDLE — Verve 8562 (1964) with MGM on bottom of label **$30**.

WE GOT REQUESTS — Verve 8606 (1965) with MGM on bottom of label **$30**.

PLAYS THE COLE PORTER SONGBOOK — Verve 2052/6083 (1959) with Verve Records, Inc. on bottom of label **$40**; with MGM on bottom of label **$30**.

PLAYS THE IRVING BERLIN SONGBOOK — Verve 2053/6084 (1959) with Verve Records, Inc. on bottom of label **$40**; with MGM on bottom of label **$30**.

PLAYS THE GEORGE GERSHWIN SONGBOOK — Verve 2054/6085 (1959) with Verve Records, Inc. on bottom of label **$40**; with MGM on bottom of label **$30**.

PLAYS THE DUKE ELLINGTON SONGBOOK — Verve 2055/6086 (1959) with Verve Records, Inc. on bottom of label **$40**; with MGM on bottom of label **$30**.

PLAYS THE JEROME KERN SONGBOOK — Verve 2056/6087 (1959) with Verve Records, Inc. on bottom of label **$40**; with MGM on bottom of label **$30**.

PLAYS THE RICHARD RODGERS SONGBOOK — Verve 2057/6088 (1959) with Verve Records, Inc. on bottom of label **$40**; with MGM on bottom of label **$30**.

PLAYS THE HARRY WARREN SONGBOOK — Verve 2059/6090 (1959) with Verve Records, Inc. on bottom of label **$45**; with MGM on bottom of label **$30**.

PLAYS THE HAROLD ARLEN SONGBOOK — Verve 2060/6091 (1959) with Verve Records, Inc. on bottom of label **$45**; with MGM on bottom of label **$30**.

PLAYS THE JIMMY McHUGH SONGBOOK — Verve 2061/6092 (1959) with Verve Records, Inc. on bottom of label **$45**; with MGM on bottom of label **$30**.

TRIO - PLUS ONE/with Clark Terry — Mercury 20975/60975 (1964) red label **$35**.

OSCAR PETTIFORD
bass, cello - born 1922 Okmulgee, OK died 1960

Pettiford performed in a family band until going with Charlie Barnet in 1943. He quickly gained a reputation for his exceptional ability and soon left Barnet to work in New York with many early bop innovators and some of the best bands around including, and especially, Duke Ellington, Coleman Hawkins and Woody Herman. Pettiford continued to work and record with groups of his own through the 50's which included tours of Europe. He eventually moved to Europe where he remained with his music from the late 50's until his death in 1960.

NEW STARS, NEW SOUNDS/with Serge Chaloff — Mercer 1003 (1951) 10" 100.

OSCAR PETTIFORD/with Harry Babasin — Imperial EP 122 (1953) **$40**.

SEXTET/with Phil Urso — Debut 8 (1953) 10" **$100**.

OSCAR PETTIFORD/with Charlie Rouse — Bethlehem 1003 (1954) 10" **$95**; *reissued* Bethlehem 6 (1955).

BASICALLY DUKE/with Jimmy Cleveland — Bethlehem 1019 (1954) 10" **$95**; *reissued* Bethlehem 2.

OSCAR PETTIFORD/with Bob Brookmeyer — Bethlehem 33 (1955) maroon label **$60**.

JAZZ MAINSTREAM/with Red Mitchell — Bethlehem 2 (1955) one side each **$60**; *reissue* of Bethlehem 1019.

IN HI FI/with Lucky Thompson — ABC Paramount 135 (1956) **$70**.

ORCHESTRA/with Benny Golson — ABC Paramount 227 (1957) **$70**.

LAST RECORDINGS/with Erik Nordstrom — Jazzland 64 (1962) **$40**.

MY LITTLE CELLO — Fantasy 6010/86010 (1964) **$35**.

FLIP PHILLIPS
tenor sax - born 1915 Brooklyn, NY

TENOR SAX STYLINGS — Brunswick 58032 (1954) 10" **$150**.

QUARTET — Mercury 25023 (1950) **$200**.

QUARTET/with Buddy Rich — Mercury/Clef 105 (1952) 10" **$175**; EP 119, EP 120 (1952) **$60 ea.**; *reissued* Clef 634.

COLLATES/with Howard McGhee — Mercury/Clef 109 (1952) 10" **$175**; EP 112, EP 113 (1952) **$60 ea.**; *reissued* Clef 693.

COLLATES - Vol 2/with Ray Brown — Mercury/Clef 133 (1953) 10" **$150**; EP 123 EP 171 (1953) **$50 ea.** *reissued* in part Clef 691.

JUMPING MOOD/with Charlie Shavers — Mercury/Clef 158 (1953) 10" **$150**; EP 173 (1953) **$50**; *reissued* Clef 692.

FLIP PHILLIPS/BUDDY RICH TRIO — Clef 634 (1954) **$95**; EP 253, EP 254 (1954) **$45 ea.**; *reissue* of Clef 105.

QUINTET/with Herb Ellis — Clef 637 (1954) **$80**; EP 260, EP 261, EP 262 (1954) **$35**; *reissued* Clef 740.

FLIP WAILS/with Harry Edison — Clef 691 (1956) **$80**; *reissued* Verve 8075 (1957) with Verve Records, Inc. on bottom of label **$60**; with MGM on bottom of label **$35**; *reissue* inpart of Clef 133.

SWINGIN' WITH FLIP/with Jerome Richardson — Clef 692 (1956) **$80**; *reissued* Verve 8076 (1957) with Verve Records, Inc. on bottom of label **$60**; with MGM on bottom of label **$35**; *reissue* of Clef 158.

FLIP/with Howard McGhee — Clef 693 (1956) **$80**; *reissued* Verve 8077 (1957) with Verve Records, Inc. on bottom of label **$60**; with MGM on bottom of label **$35**; *reissue* of Clef 109.

ROCK WITH FLIP/with Herb Ellis — Clef 740 (1956) **$80**; *reissued* Verve 8116 (1957) with Verve Records, Inc. on bottom of label **$60**; with MGM on bottom of label **$35**; *reissue* of Clef 637.

REVISITED — Sue 1035 (1965) **$40**.

DAVE PIKE
vibes - born 1938 Detroit, MI

IT'S TIME FOR/with Barry Harris — Riverside 360/9360 (1960) blue label mono; black label stereo with Bill Grauer Pro. **$30**.

PIKE'S PEAK/with Bill Evans — Epic 16025/17025 (1961) yellow label **$30**.

BOSSA NOVA CARNIVAL/with Clark Terry and Kenny Burrell — New Jazz 8281 (1962) **$45**.

LIMBO CARNIVAL — New Jazz 8284 (1962) **$30**.

OLIVER! PLAYS THE JAZZ VERSION/with Tommy Flanagan — Moodsville 36 (1963) **$30**.

MANHATTEN LATIN — Decca 4568/74568 (1965) black label with rainbow strip **$15**.

HERB PILHOFER
piano

JAZZ FROM THE NORTH COAST — Zephyr 12013 (1959) **$45**.

THE HERB PILHOFER TRIO: JAZZ — Argo 657 (1960) **$25**.

KING PLEASURE
vocals, composer - born 1922 Oakdale, TN

The first singer to popularize singing lyrics which had been set to well known jazz solos, Pleasure worked and recorded in the early 50's, becoming an important influence on several singers and composers such as Dave Lambert of Lambert, Hendricks and Ross. He did not work or record again until around 1960 and was unable to regain his earlier popularity.

SINGS/with Charlie Ferguson — Prestige 208 (1955) 10" **$125**; *reissued* Prestige 7128 (1957).

KING PLEASURE SINGS/ANNIE ROSS SINGS — Prestige 7128 (1957) yellow label **$75**; *reissue* of Prestige 208 with 4 additional sides by Annie Ross.

GOLDEN DAYS/with Teddy Edwards and Harold Land — Hi Fi Jazz 425 (1960) **$50**.

MR. JAZZ — United Artists 14031/15031 (1962) gray label with silhouette of sax player **$45**.

PONY POINDEXTER
alto, tenor saxes - born 1926 New Orleans, LA

Poindexter obtained national exposure with Billy Eckstine in the late 40's. He then spent most of the 50's on the West Coast around the San Francisco area where he was considered a sort of local legend. Neil Hefti took a phrase he had once heard Poindexter play and used it for a line in an arrangement he wrote for Count Basie. Jon Hendricks put words to it on a Lambert, Hendricks and Ross album and the jazz legend "Little Pony" was born. In the 60's he worked in the group backing the great vocal trio and soon began leading his own group on the East Coast before moving to Europe where he has lived and worked to date.

PONY'S EXPRESS — Epic 16035/17035 (1962) **$60**.

THE BIG ONES — New Jazz 8285 (1962) **$45**.

LUCY ANN POLK
vocals

WITH DAVE PELL — Trend 1008 (1953) 10" **$100**.

LUCKY LUCY ANN/with Marty Paich and Mel Lewis — Mode 115 (1957) **$85**; *reissued* Interlude 504.

EASY LIVIN' — Interlude 504/1004 (1959) **$60**.

TERRY POLLARD
piano, vibes - born 1931 Detroit, MI

TERRY POLLARD — Bethlehem 1015 (1954) 10" **$50**.

HERB POMEROY
trumpet, leader - born 1930 Glouchester, MA

JAZZ IN A STABLE/with V. Haroutunian — Transition 1 (1956) **$95**.

LIFE IS A MANY SPLENDORED GIG/with Boots Mussulli — Roulette 52001 (1958) white label with multicolored pinwheel **$90**.

BAND IN BOSTON/with Charlie Mariano — United Artists 4015/5015 (1959) red label **$90**.

THE BAND AND I/with Irene Kral — United Artists 4016/5016 (1959) red label **$80**.

BILLIE POOLE
vocals

SERMONETTE: THE VOICE OF/with Jimmy Jones Orchestra — Riverside 425/9425 (1962) blue label mono; black label stereo with Bill Grauer Pro. **$50**.

CONFESSIN' THE BLUES/with Junior Mance and Kenny Burrell — Riverside 458/9458 (1962) blue label mono; black label stereo with Bill Grauer Pro. **$50**.

BILL POTTS
composer, piano - born 1928 Arlington, VA

JAZZ SOUL OF PORGY & BESS — United Artists 4032/5032 (1959) red label **$45**.

BYE BYE BIRDIE/with Clark Terry and Phil Woods — Colpix 451 (1963) **$35**.

BUD POWELL
piano, composer - born 1924 New York City, NY
died 1966

Powell was active in and around the jazz scene of New York City in the early 40's and is considered to have been the first modern (bop) pianist. His many recordings under his own name, as well as with other fine musicians, through the 40's and 50's have been very influential. Powell's career was unfortunately very intermittent due to repeated nervous breakdowns and mental problems. In 1959 he moved to France and enjoyed a couple of years of health and work before tuberculosis forced him down into a long recovery period. He returned to the U.S. in 1964, working very little until his death in 1966. Powell was a master on his instrument and is still listed as an influence by a tremendous number of contemporary musicians.

TRIO/with Max Roach — Roost 401 (1952) 10" **$250**; *reissued* Roost 2224.

TRIO/with Art Taylor — Roost 412 (1953) 10" **$250**; *reissued* inpart Roost 2224.

THE AMAZING — Roost 2224 (1958) **$65**; *reissue* of Roost 401 and 412.

JAZZ AT MASSEY HALL - Vol 2/with Charlie Mingus — Debut 3 (1953) 10" **$200**.

BUD POWELL TRIO/with Art Taylor — Norgran 23 (1953) 10" **$90**; EP 41 **$45**; *reissued* Norgran 1064.

JAZZ ORIGINAL/with Max Roach — Norgran 1017 (1954) **$90**; *reissued* Norgran 1098.

JAZZ GIANT/with Max Roach — Norgran 1063 (1955) **$70**; *reissued* Verve 8153 (1957) with Verve Records, Inc. on bottom of label **$65**; with MGM on bottom of label **$35**; *reissues* of Clef 502 and 507.

MOODS/with Art Taylor — Norgran 1064 (1955) **$70**; *reissued* Verve 8154 (1957) with Verve Records, Inc. on bottom of label **$65**; with MGM on bottom of label **$35**; *reissues* of Norgran 23.

PIANO INTERPRETATIONS/with Art Taylor — Norgran 1077 (1955) **$70**; *reissued* Verve 8167 (1957) with Verve Records, Inc. on bottom of label **$65**; with MGM on bottom of label **$35**.

BUD POWELL '57 — Norgran 1098 (1956) **$65**; *reissued* Verve 8185 (1957) with Verve Records, Inc. on bottom of label **$50**; with MGM on bottom of label **$35**; *reissue* of Norgran 1017.

THE AMAZING/with Fats Navarro and Sonny Rollins — Blue Note 5003 (1951) 10" **$150**; *reissued* Blue Note 1503 (1956) with NY address on label **$100**; with NY on label **$65**; with A Division of Liberty on label **$20**.

THE AMAZING/with Fats Navarro and Sonny Rollins — Blue Note 5004 (1951) 10" **$150**; *reissued* Blue Note 1504 (1956) with NY address on label **$100**; with NY on label **$65**; with A Division of Liberty on label **$20**.

BUD POWELL/with Art Taylor — Blue Note 5041 (1953) 10" **$150**; *reissued* Blue Note 1504.

BUD!/with Curtis Fuller — Blue Note 1571 (1957) with NY address on label **$100**; with NY on label **$50**; with A Division of Liberty on label **$20**.

TIME WAITS/with Philly Joe Jones — Blue Note 1598 (1959) with NY address on label **$80**; with NY on label **$45**; with A Division of Liberty on label **$20**.

THE SCENE CHANGES/with Paul Chambers — Blue Note 4009 (1959) with NY address on label **$80**; with NY on label **$45**; with A Division of Liberty on label **$20**.

BUD POWELL TRIO → Mercury/Clef 502 (1953) 10" **$125**; EP 508 (1953) **$50**; *reissued* Norgran 1063.

BUD POWELL PIANO #2 — Mercury/Clef 507 (1953) 10" **$125**; EP 514, EP 515 (1953) **$50 ea.**; *reissued* Norgran 1063.

MOODS — Mercury/Clef 610 (1954) **$75**; *reissued* Verve 8115.

STRICTLY POWELL/with Art Taylor — RCA Victor 1423 (1956) dog on top **$50**; EP 1-1423, EP 2-1423, EP 3-1423 (1957) **$20 ea.**

SWINGIN' WITH/with Art Taylor — RCA Victor 1507 (1957) dog on top **$50**.

THE GENIUS OF — Verve 8115 (1957) with Verve Records, Inc. on bottom of label **$50**; with MGM on bottom of label **$35**; *reissue* of Mercury/Clef 610.

BLUES IN THE CLOSET/with Ray Brown — Verve 8218 (1958) with Verve Records, Inc. on bottom of label **$45**; with MGM on bottom of label **$30**.

THE LONELY ONE — Verve 8301 (1959) with Verve Records, Inc. on bottom of label **$45**; with MGM on bottom of label **$30**.

IN PARIS — Reprise 6098 (1964) **$45**.

A PORTRAIT OF THELONIOUS — Columbia 2292/9092 (1964) red label with one white logo on each side **$45**.

BUD PLAYS BIRD — Roulette 52006 (1958) white label with multicolored pinwheel **$45**.

THE RETURN OF — Roulette 52115 (1965) dark and light orange checked roulette wheel label **$35**.

MEL POWELL

piano, composer - born 1923 New York City, NY

SEPTET/with Buck Clayton — Vanguard 8004 (1953) 10" **$75**.

BANDSTAND/with Mundell Lowe — Vanguard 8015 (1954) 10" **$75**.

BORDERLINE/with Ruby Braff — Vanguard 8501 (1956) maroon label **$35**.

THIGAMAGIG/with Paul Quinichette — Vanguard 8502 (1956) maroon label **$35**.

OUT ON A LIMB/with Al Mattilano — Vanguard 8506 (1956) maroon label **$35**.

EASY SWING — Vanguard 8519 (1958) maroon label **$30**.

JAM SESSION AT CARNEGIE HALL/with Gene Krupa and Buck Clayton — Columbia 557 (1954) red label with Columbia in gold letters on top **$90**; *reissued* Columbia 557 (1956) red label with 3 black logos on each side **$80**; EP 412 (1954) **$40**.

SHELDON POWELL

tenor sax, flute - born 1928 Lawrenceville, VA

PLAYS/with Bob Alexander — Roost 2205 (1956) **$30**.

SEXTET/with Jimmy Cleveland and Freddie Green — Roost 2220 (1956) **$45**.

WE PAID OUR DUES/with Charlie Rouse — Epic 16018/17018 (1961) yellow label **$35**; one side of LP each.

SPECS POWELL
drums - born 1922 New York City, NY

MOVIN' IN/with Jimmy Cleveland and Sahib Shihab — Roulette 52004 (1958) white label with multicolored pinwheel $60.

PRESTIGE JAZZ QUARTET
Teddy Charles, Mal Waldron, Addison Farmer
Jerry Segal

TEO WITH THE PRESTIGE JAZZ QUARTET/with Teo Macero — Prestige 7104 (1957) yellow label $45.

PRESTIGE JAZZ QUARTET — Prestige 7108 (1957) yellow label $45.

*ANDRE PREVIN
piano, conductor, composer - born 1929 Berlin, Germany

ALL STAR JAZZ/with Vido Musso — Monarch 203 (1954) 10" $50.

PLAYS DUKE — Monarch 204 (1954) 10" $50.

PLAYS HARRY WARREN — RCA Victor 3002 (1952) 10" $60; reissued RCA Victor 1356.

GERSHWIN — RCA Victor 1011 (1954) $60.

THREE LITTLE WORDS — RCA Victor 1356 (1957) dog on top $40; reissue of RCA Victor 3002.

LET'S GET AWAY FROM IT ALL/with Red Mitchell — Decca 8134 (1955) black label with silver lettering $45.

HOLLYWOOD AT MIDNIGHT/with Shelly Manne — Decca 8341 (1956) black label with silver lettering $45.

DOUBLE PLAY/with Russ Freeman and Shelly Manne — Contemporary 3537 (1957) yellow label $40; reissued Contemporary 7011 (1958) black label stereo $35.

PAL JOEY/with Red Mitchell and Shelly Manne — Contemporary 3543 (1957) yellow label $30; reissued Contemporary 7543 (1958) black label stereo $25.

GIGI/with Red Mitchell and Shelly Manne — Contemporary 3548 (1957) yellow label $30; reissued Contemporary 7020 (1958) black label stereo $25.

PLAYS VERNON DUKE (Solo) — Contemporary 3558/7558 (1958) yellow label mono; black label stereo $20.

JAZZ: KING SIZE/with Red Mitchell — Contemporary 3570/7570 (1958) yellow label mono; black label stereo $25.

PLAYS JEROME KERN (Solo) — Contemporary 3567/7567 (1959) yellow label mono; black label stereo $25.

WEST SIDE STORY/with Red Mitchell and Shelly Manne — Contemporary 3572/7572 (1959) yellow label mono; black label stereo $25.

LIKE PREVIN/with Red Mitchell — Contemporary 3575/7575 (1960) yellow label mono; black label stereo $25.

PLAYS HAROLD ARLEN (Solo) — Contemporary 3586/7586 (1960) yellow label mono; black label stereo $20.

GIVE MY REGARDS TO BROADWAY/with Red Mitchell — Columbia 1530/8330 (1960) red label with 3 black logos on each side $25.

PLAYS MACK THE KNIFE AND OTHER KURT WEILL MUSIC/with J.J. Johnson — Columbia 1741/8541 (1961) red label with 3 black logos on each side $35.

FOUR TO GO/with Herb Ellis, Ray Brown and Shelly Manne — Columbia 2018/8818 (1963) red label with one white logo on each side $25.

---

*The only LP's within the scope of this book.

RUTH PRICE
vocals - born 1928 Phoenixville, PA

MY NAME IS RUTH PRICE, I SING — Kapp 1006 (1958) $65.

THE PARTY'S OVER — Kapp 1054 (1958) $65.

SING/with Johnny Smith — Roost 2217 (1958) $50.

AT THE MANNE-HOLE/with Shelly Manne and His Men — Contemporary 3590/7590 (1961) yellow label $45.

LIVE AND BEAUTIFUL — Ave 54 (1963) $40.

VITO PRICE
tenor, alto saxes - born 1929 Long Island City, NY

SWINGIN' THE LOOP/with John Howell and Billy Hanley — Argo 631 (1957) $50.

JULIAN PRIESTER
trombone

SPIRITSVILLE/with Charlie Davis — Jazzland 25/925 (1960) $45.

KEEPIN' SWINGIN'/with Jimmy Heath — Riverside 12-316/1163 (1960) blue label mono; black label stereo $60.

ARTHUR PRYSOCK
vocals - born 1929 Spartanburg, SC

I WORRY ABOUT YOU — Old Town 102 (1962) $40.

SINGS ONLY FOR YOU — Old Town 2004 (1962) $40.

COAST TO COAST — Old Town 2005 (1962) $40.

PORTRAIT — Old Town 2006 (1962) $40.

EVERLASTING SONGS FOR EVERLASTING LOVERS — Old Town 2007 (1962) $40.

INTIMATELY YOURS — Old Town 2008 (1962) $40.

DOUBLE HEADER — Old Town 2009 (1962) $40.

STRICTLY SENTIMENTAL — Decca 4581/74581 (1965) black label with rainbow strip **$20.**

SHOWCASE — Decca 4628/74628 (1965) black label with rainbow strip **$20.**

ARTHUR PRYSOCK/COUNT BASIE — Verve 8646/68646 (1965) with MGM on bottom of label and fold out cover **$35.**

JOE PUMA
guitar - born 1927 New York City, NY

A self-taught guitarist, Puma's distinct style was much in demand through the 50's during which time he worked with a large number of bands on the East Coast. He recorded a few LPs to his own credit but also worked as an accompanist for vocalists such as Chris Connor.

QUINTET EAST COAST JAZZ SERIES NO 3/with Don Elliott — Bethlehem 1012 (1954) 10" **$125.**

WILD KITTEN/with Oscar Pettiford — Dawn 1118 (1957) **$60.**

JOE PUMA JAZZ/with Bill Evans — Jubilee 1070 (1957) **$60.**

LIKE TWEET/with Bobby Jaspar and Jerome Richardson — Columbia 1618/8418 (1961) red label with 3 black logos on each side **$45.**

THE QUARTETTE TRES BIEN
Jeter Thompson, Richard Simmons, Albert St. James, Percy James

QUARTETTE TRES BIEN — Norman 102 (1962) **$15.**

KILMANJARO — Norman 107 (1962) **$15.**

BOSS TRES BIEN — Decca 4547/74547 (1964) black label with rainbow strip **$15.**

KILMANJARO — Decca 4548/74548 (1964) black label with rainbow strip **$15.**

SPRING INTO SPRING — Decca 4617/74617 (1965) black label with rainbow strip **$10.**

STEPPING OUT — Decca 4675/74675 (1965) black label with rainbow strip **$10.**

IKE QUEBEC
tenor sax - born 1917 Newark, NJ died 1963

Quebec was a big-toned tenor player who was very popular in the 40's with many of the best big bands like those of Roy Eldridge, Coleman Hawkins and Cab Calloway. Although Quebec did not work in jazz during the 50's, he recorded a few Blue Note LPs in the early 60's.

HEAVY SOUL/with Freddie Roach — Blue Note 4093/84093 (1961) with NY on label **$45;** with A Division of Liberty on label **$20.**

BLUE AND SENTIMENTAL/with Sonny Clark — Blue Note 4098/84098 (1961) with NY on label **$45;** with A Division of Liberty on label **$20.**

IT MIGHT AS WELL BE SPRING/with Freddie Roach — Blue Note 4105/84105 (1962) with NY on label **$45;** with A Division of Liberty on label **$20.**

SOUL SAMBA/with Willie Bobo — Blue Note 4114/84114 (1962) with NY on label **$40;** with A Division of Liberty on label **$20.**

GENE QUILL
alto sax, clarinet - born 1927 Atlantic City, NJ

Quill gained his initial reputation with name bands in the mid-50's and went on to widespread popularity with a group he co-led with Phil Woods in 1957-58. In the Early 60's he worked and recorded with Gerry Mulligan and then with his own group for regular appearances in the New York City area. Quill is considered a very good, Parker-influenced alto sax player with only a few LPs to his own credit.

3 BONES AND A QUILL/with Jimmy Cleveland — Roost 2229 (1958) **$50.**

PHIL AND QUILL WITH PRESTIGE/with Phil Woods — Prestige 7115 (1957) yellow label **$50.**

WOODS-QUILL SEXTET/with Phil Woods — RCA Victor 1284 (1956) dog on top **$50.**

PHIL TALKS WITH QUILL/with Phil Woods — Epic 3521 (1960) yellow label **$40.**

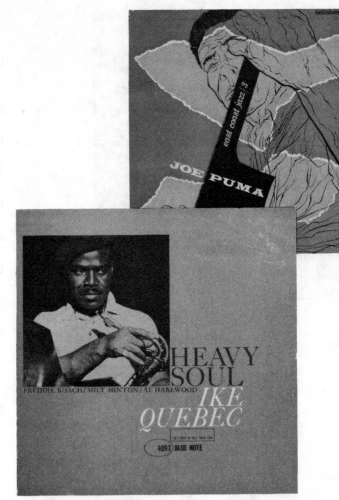

PAUL QUINICHETTE
tenor sax - born 1921 Denver, CO died 1983

Highly respected through his work with a wide variety of well known groups in the 40's, Quinichette's work with Count Basie in the early 50's established him as the stylistic successor to Lester Young to the point of acquiring the nickname "Vice-Pres". He worked and recorded with groups of his own through the remainder of the 50's in addition to occasional jobs with the bands of Benny Goodman and Woody Herman. Quinichette was musically inactive from the early 60's until 1973 when he began playing again in the New York City area.

PRES MEETS VICE-PRES — EmArcy 26021 (1954) 10" **$150;** EP 1-6006 EP 1-6002 (1954) **$60 ea.**

VICE-PRES/with Freddie Green — EmArcy 26022 (1954) 10" **$100;** EP 1-6035 EP 1-6034 (1954) **$60 ea.;** *reissued* EmArcy 36027 (1955) **$45.**

SEQUEL/with Freddie Green — EmArcy 26035 (1954) 10" **$100;** EP 1-6060 (1954) **$50.**

MOODS/with Herbie Mann and Sam Most — EmArcy 36003 (1955) **$65** EP 1-6093, EP 1-6094, EP 1-6095 (1955) **$30 ea.**

THE KID FROM DENVER/with Joe Newman and Thad Jones — Dawn 1109 (1956) **$65.**

BLOW YOUR HORN/with Bennie Green — Decca 8176 (1955) black label with silver lettering **$60;** EP 2291, EP 2292, EP 2293 (1955) **$45 ea.**

ON THE SUNNY SIDE/with Curtis Fuller — Prestige 7103 (1957) yellow label **$75**

FOR BASIE/with Freddie Green — Prestige 7127 (1958) yellow label **$60** *reissued* Swingville 2036 (1962) **$45.**

BASIE REUNION — Prestige 7147 (1958) **$60;** *reissued* Swingville 2037 (1962) **$45.**

CATTIN'/with John Coltrane — Prestige 7158 (1958) yellow label **$60;** *reissue* Prestige 7158 (1964) blue label with logo on right side **$25.**

LIKE BASIE/with Harry Edison — United Artists 4024/5024 (1959) red label **$50**; *reissued* United Artists 4054/5054.

LIKE WHO?/with Harry Edison — United Artists 4054/5054 (1959) red label **$45**; *reissue* of United Artists 4024/5024.

THE CHASE IS ON/with Charlie Rouse — Bethlehem 6021 (1957) maroon label **$45**.

DON RALKE
BONGO MADNESS/with Buddy Collette — Crown 5019 (1957) **$15**.

DON RANDI
piano - born 1937 New York City, NY

FEELIN' LIKE BLUES/with Hershey Hamel and Gene Stone — World Pacific 1297 (1960) **$35**.

WHERE DO WE GO FROM HERE?/with Leroy Vinnegar and Mel Lewis — Verve 8469/68469 (1962) with MGM on bottom of label **$25**.

LAST NIGHT — Verve 8524 (1963) with MGM on bottom of label **$25**.

DON RANDI — Palomar 24002/34002 (1965) **$15**.

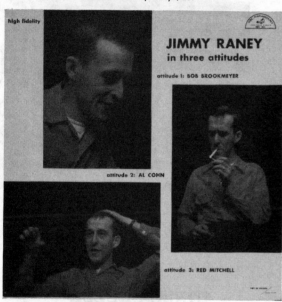

JIMMY RANEY
guitar, composer - born 1927 Louisville, KY

Well known and widely recorded with great groups throughout the 40's and 50's, especially with Stan Getz in the early 50's and again in the early 60's. Raney worked mostly in broadway shows in the early 60's until returning to his hometown of Louisville. Renewed interest in his pleasingly natural approach brought him back again to play and compose through the 60's.

PLAYS/with Red Mitchell — Prestige 156 (1953) 10" **$150**.

IN SWEDEN/with Bengt Hallberg — Prestige 179 (1954) **$150**; *reissued* EmArcy 36121.

QUARTET/with Hall Overton — New Jazz 1101 (1954) 10" **$105**; EP 1701, EP 1702 (1954) **$50 ea.**; *reissued Prestige 201 (1955) 10"* **$95**.

ENSEMBLE/with Phil Woods — New Jazz 1103 (1954) 10" **$105**; *reissued* Prestige 203 (1955) 10" **$95**.

1955/with John Wilson — Prestige 199 (1955) 10" **$95**; *reissued* Prestige 7089.

JIMMY RANEY A. — Prestige 7089 (1956) yellow label **$60**; *reissue* of Prestige 199.

IN THREE ATTITUDES/with Al Cohn, Bob Brookmeyer and Red Mitchell — ABC Paramount 167 (1956) **$65**.

JIMMY RANEY FEATURING BOB BROOKMEYER — ABC Paramount 129 (1956) **$65**.

VISITS PARIS/with Bobby Jaspar — Dawn 1120 (1958) **$60**.

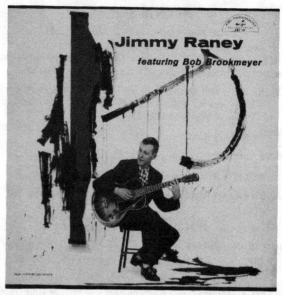

SWINGIN' IN SWEDEN — EmArcy 36121 (1958) **$45**; *reissue* of Prestige 179 one side only.

TWO-JIM AND ZOOT/with Zoot Sims — Mainstream 6013/56013 (1964) **$25**.

*LOU RAWLS
vocals - born 1935 Chicago, IL

LOU RAWLS SINGS-LES McCANN LTD. PLAYS STORMY MONDAY — Capitol 1714 (1962) black label with logo on top **$35**.

BLACK AND BLUE/with Onzy Matthews — Capitol 1824 (1963) black label with logo at top **$35**.

TOBACCO ROAD/with Onzy Matthews — Capitol 2042 (1964) black label with logo on top **$25**.

---

*The only LP's within the scope of this book.

---

*JOHNNIE RAY
vocals - born 1927 Dallas, OR

'TIL MORNING/with Billy Taylor amd Mundell Lowe — Columbia 1225 (1959) red label with 3 black logos on each side **$35**.

---

*The only LP's within the scope of this book.

SONNY RED

alto sax - born 1932 Detroit, MI

A good, swinging Detroit musician, Red teamed up with Curtis Fuller in New York City in 1957. He has remained in this area since, working and recording, often with Donald Byrd or Kenny Dorham.

OUT OF THE BLUE/with Wynton Kelly and Paul Chambers — Blue Note 4032 (1959) with NY address on label $50; with NY on label $40; with A Division of Liberty on label $20.

BREEZIN'/with Barry Harris — Jazzland 32/932 (1960) $35.

THE MODE/with Grant Green — Jazzland 59/959 (1961) $35.

IMAGES/with Blue Mitchell — Jazzland 74/974 (1962) $35.

TWO ALTOS/with Art Pepper — Regent 6069 (1959) green label $60.

FREDDIE REDD

piano, composer - born 1928 New York City, NY

INTRODUCING/with Ron Jefferson — Prestige 195 (1955) 10" $90; *reissued* Prestige 7067.

PIANO EAST-PIANO WEST/with Hampton Hawes — Prestige 7067 (1956) yellow label $65; *reissue* of Prestige 195, 4 sides by Redd only.

SAN FRANCISCO SUITE/with George Tucker — Riverside 12-250 (1958) blue label with Bill Grauer Pro. $35.

THE MUSIC FROM "THE CONNECTION" (Soundtrack) — Blue Note 4027/84027 (1960) with NY address on label $65; with NY on label $45; with A Division of Liberty on label $20.

SHADES OF REDD/with Tina Brooks — Blue Note 4045/84045 (1960) with NY address on label $65; with NY on label $45; with A Division of Liberty on label $20.

VI REDD

vocals, alto sax - born 1928 Los Angeles, CA

Redd played professionally around the Los Angeles area while attending school to obtain a music degree to teach. In the mid-50's she performed with local groups and spent a few years teaching before achieving a more significant musical success in West Coast clubs. This led Redd to tours of Europe and Africa and to work with Dizzy Gillespie and Count Basie. Claiming Charlie Parker, among others, as her inspiration, Redd displays a strong blues feeling in her playing as well as in her singing.

BIRD CALL/with Russ Freeman — United Artists 14016/15016 (1962) gray label with silhouette of sax player $65.

LADY SOUL — Atco 33-157 (1963) $45.

GEORGE REDMAN

drums - born El Paso, TX

THE GEORGE REDMAN GROUP/with Herbie Harper and Bob Gordon — Skylark 20 (1954) $100; EP 115, EP 116 (1954) $50 ea.

DIZZY REECE

trumpet - born 1931 Kingston, Jamacia

CHANGING THE JAZZ/with Terry Shannon — Savoy 12111 (1957) maroon label $45.

LONDON JAZZ/with Sammy Walker — Imperial 9043 (1959) $55.

BLUES IN TRINITY/with Tubby Hayes — Blue Note 4006/84006 (1958) with NY address on label $60; with NY on label $40; with A Division of Liberty on label $20.

STAR BRIGHT/with Hank Mobley — Blue Note 4023/84023 (1959) with NY address on label $50; with NY on label $40; with A Division of Liberty on label $20.

SOUNDIN' OFF/with Walter Bishop — Blue Note 4033/84033 (1962) with NY address on label $50; with NY on label $40; with A Division of Liberty on label $20.

ASIA MINOR/with Cecil Payne — New Jazz 8274 (1962) $35.

LUCY REED

vocals - born 1921 Marshfield, WI

THE SINGING REED — Fantasy 3-212 (1956) $50.

THIS IS — Fantasy 3243 (1957) $50.

*DELLA REESE

vocals - born 1932 Detroit, MI

MELANCHOLY BABY — Jubilee 1026 (1957) $45.

A DATE WITH; AT MR. KELLY'S IN CHICAGO/with Kirk Stuart Trio — Jubilee 1071 (1958) $45.

THE STORY OF THE BLUES/with Sy Oliver — Jubilee 1095 (1958) $45.

WHAT DO YOU KNOW ABOUT LOVE — Jubilee 1109 (1959) $35.

AND THAT REMINDS ME — Jubilee 1116 (1959) $35.

DELLA/with Neal Hefti — RCA Victor 2157 (1960) dog on top $35.

*The only LP's within the scope of this book.

IRENE REID

vocals - born 1930 Savannah, GA

IT'S ONLY THE BEGINNING FOR — MGM 4159 (1964) black label $20.

DJANGO REINHARDT

guitar - born 1910 Liverchies, Belgium died 1953

Reinhardt was a gypsy who played many instruments but became famous for his guitar playing which was unique, in part because of a serious injury to his left hand early in his career. Playing unusual chords and with many single strong melodies, his style was profoundly influential in European jazz. Through recordings with the Quintet of the Hot Club of Paris, his fame spread to the U.S. No

nly was he the first jazz guitarist of international significance, he
as also the first European to influence American jazz musicians
stead of the other way around. Reinhardt's best known work was
ith the Quintet that included Stephane Grapelly.

JANGO REINHARDT/with Gerard Leveque — Jay 3008 (1954) 10" **$80**; *reissued*
on Period recordings.

REAT ARTISTRY/with Maurice Vander — Clef 516 (1953) 10" **$90**; EP 509,
EP 510 (1953) **$40 ea.**; *reissued* Verve 8015.

JANGO REINHARDT: HOT CLUB OF FRANCE/with Joseph Reinhardt — Dial 214
(1950) 10" **$95**; *reissued* on Period recordings.

JANGO REINHARDT: HOT CLUB OF FRANCE/with Joseph Reinhardt — Dial 218
(1950) 10" **$95**; *reissued* on Period recordings.

RANCE: HOT CLUB QUINTET — London 810 (1954) 10" **$80**; *reissued* London
1344 (1956) Swing from Paris added to title **$50**.

E JAZZ HOT — Angel 60003 (1954) 10" **$75**; EP 73006, EP 73007 (1954) **$35 ea.**

JANGO'S GUITAR — Angel 60011 (1954) 10" **$75**.

MEMORIAL ALBUM - Vol 1 — Period 1010 (1954) 10" **$80**; *reissued* Period 1202
(1957) **$60**.

MEMORIAL ALBUM - Vol 2 — Period 1101 (1954) 10" **$80**; *reissued* Period 1202
(1957) **$60**.

MEMORIAL ALBUM - Vol 3 — Period 1102 (1954) 10" **$80**; *reissued* Period 1203
(1957) **$60**.

MEMORIAL ALBUM — Period 1201/3 (1957) 3 LPs **$150**; *reissue* of Dial 214 and
218.

HE BEST OF DJANGO REINHARDT — Period 1204/2204 (1958) **$50**; selections
from Period LPs 1201, 1202, 1203.

ND HIS RHYTHM — Felsted 87005 (1959) **$45**; *reissue* of Clef 516.

JANGO REINHARDT, COLLECTOR'S ITEMS — RCA Victor 1100 (1955) dog on top
$50.

JANGOLOGY — RCA Victor 2319 (1961) dog on top **$35**.

AZZ FROM PARIS/with Dizzy Gillespie — Verve 8015 (1957) with Verve
Records, Inc. on bottom of label **$60**; with MGM on bottom of label **$30**;
reissue of Clef 516 on Django side only.

EST OF — Capitol 10226 (1960) 2 LPs, black label with logo on left side **$60**.

HOT CLUB OF FRANCE — Capitol 2045 (1964) black label with logo on top **$25**.

HE IMMORTAL — Reprise 6075/96075 (1962) **$30**.

HENRI RENAUD
piano, composer - born 1925 Villedieu, Indre, France

ENRI RENAUD ALL STARS/with Sandy Mosse — Contemporary 2502 (1953)
10" **$85**.

DON RENDELL
tenor sax, clarinet - born 1926 Plymouth, England
ROARIN'/with Graham Bond — Jazzland 51/951 (1961) **$40**.

MEL RHYNE
organ
ORGANIZING/with Johnny Griffin and Blue Mitchell — Jazzland 16/916 (1960)
$40.

BUDDY RICH
drums, vocals - born 1917 Brooklyn, NY

Born into a Vaudeville family and working almost since he could
walk, Rich proved to be a prodigy on drums as well as at dancing and
singing. He led his first band when he was 11 years old and,
beginning in 1938, worked with big name jazz bands of increasing
popularity until he was able to start another band of his own in the
late 40's. In addition to working in bands of his own, he toured with
JATP and gigged with other bands intermittently which took him on
world tours and many television appearances. A player of
exceptional ability and taste, Rich has invariably fit into any jazz
context he has encountered.

BUDDY RICH SWINGING/with Benny Carter and George Auld — Norgran 26
(1954) **$100**; EP 38 (1954) **$50**; *reissued* Norgran 1052.

THE SWINGIN' — Norgran 1052 (1955) **$70**; *reissued* Verve 8142 (1957) with
Verve Records, Inc. on bottom of label **$50**.

SING AND SWING WITH/with Herb Ellis — Norgran 1031 (1955) **$65**; EP 135
(1955) **$35**.

BUDDY RICH AND SWEETS EDISON — Norgran 1038 (1955) $70; *reissued* Verve 8129 (1957) with Verve Records, Inc. on bottom of label $50.

THE WAILING/with Ben Webster — Norgran 1078 (1956) $60; *reissued* Verve 8168 (1957) with Verve Records, Inc. on bottom of label $50.

THIS ONE'S FOR BASIE/with Bob Cooper — Norgran 1086 (1956) $60; *reissued* Verve 8176 (1957) with Verve Records, Inc. on bottom of label $50.

SINGS JOHNNY MERCER/with Harry Edison — Verve 2009 (1956) with Verve Records, Inc. on bottom of label $55.

JUST SINGS/with Ben Webster — Verve 2075 (1957) with Verve Records, Inc. on bottom of label $55.

IN MIAMI/with Flip Phillips — Verve 8285 (1958) with Verve Records, Inc. on bottom of label $45.

BLUE CARAVAN/with Rolf Ericson and Sam Most — Verve 8425 (1962) with MGM on bottom of label $30.

BURNIN' BEAT/with Gene Krupa — Verve 8471/68471 (1962) with MGM on bottom of label $30.

GENE KRUPA AND BUDDY RICH — Clef 684 (1956) $100; *reissued* Verve 8069 (1957) with Verve Records, Inc. on bottom of label $80; with MGM on bottom of label $35.

RICH VERSUS ROACH/with Max Roach — Mercury 20448/60133 (1959) black label $60.

RICHCRAFT/with Al Cohn and Benny Golson — Mercury 20451/60136 (1959) black label $60.

THE VOICE IS RICH/BUDDY RICH SINGS — Mercury 20461/60144 (1959) black label $40.

PLAYTIME/with Sam Most — Argo 676 (1960) $35.

ANN RICHARDS
vocals - born 1935 San Diego, CA died 1982

A fine singer who had worked with many West Coast based groups in the early 50's, Richards began working with Stan Kenton in 1955, reaching many new fans and establishing herself on the jazz scene. She married Kenton and, for the most part, discontinued her career until after their separation in the early 60's. Richards made some very fine recordings with Kenton and has a few LPs to her credit. Ms. Richards was considered to be a superb jazz vocalist who, perhaps, did not receive due recognition. She died in 1982 of a gunshot wound and the few recordings she left can be considered collectors items.

I'M SHOOTING HIGH/with Warren Barker — Capitol 1087 (1958) black label with logo on left side $50.

THE MANY MOODS OF/with Bill Holman — Capitol 1406 (1960) black label with logo on left side $40.

TOO MUCH/with Stan Kenton — Capitol 1495 (1961) black label with logo on left side $40.

ANN, MAN!/with Barney Kessel — Atco 33-136 (1961) $35.

JOHNNY RICHARDS
arranger, composer - born 1911 Schenectady, NY died 1968

A multi instrumental child Vaudevillian, Richards, as a young man in the 30's, played, composed and arranged for movies. He then led a band of his own in the early 40's before becoming very much in demand as a composer and arranger for many of the best bands such as Charlie Barnet, Dizzy Gillespie and especially Stan Kenton. Into the 60's he occasionally led groups of his own for club appearances.

SOMETHING ELSE BY/with Charlie Mariano, Buddy Childers and Richie Kamuca — Bethlehem 6011 (1958) maroon label $60.

WIDE RANGE/with Jimmy Cleveland and Gene Quill — Capitol 885 (1957) green label $60; EP 1-885, EP 2-885, EP 3-885 (1957) $25 ea.

EXPERIMENTS IN SOUND/with Jimmy Cleveland and Gene Quill — Capitol 981 (1958) green label $55.

THE RITES OF DIABLO/with Seldon Powell and Ernie Royal — Roulette 52008 (1958) white label with multicolored pinwheel $50.

MY FAIR LADY — Roulette 52114 (1965) dark and light orange checked roulette wheel label $25.

JEROME RICHARDSON
saxes, woodwinds - born 1920 Oakland, CA

Extremely talented on several instruments, Richardson played in many Bay Area groups in the 40's and first gained national exposure through his work with Lionel Hampton and continued with Earl Hines in the early 50's. Later, he toured with Quincy Jones, Chico Hamilton and worked as a freelance musician.

MIDNIGHT OIL/with Jimmy Cleveland — New Jazz 8205 (1958) $55.

ROAMIN' WITH RICHARDSON/with Charlie Persip — New Jazz 8226 (1959) $45.

GOING TO THE MOVIES/with Les Spann — United Artists 14006/15006 (1962) gray label with silhouette of sax player $35.

*MAVIS RIVERS
vocals

WE REMEMBER MILDRED BAILEY/with Red Norvo — Vee Jay 1132 (1964) $25.

MAVIS/with Jack Sheldon and Bill Perkins — Reprise 2002/92002 (1961) $45.

MEETS SHORTY ROGERS — Reprise 6074 (1962) $35.

*The only LP's within the scope of this book.

SAM RIVERS

tenor sax - born 1930 El Reno, OK

capable player who worked around the Boston area before
becoming well known for his work through the 50's with Jaki Byard,
Herb Pomeroy and Gigi Gryce. In the 60's, Rivers' style continued to
evolve becoming freer and more intense. He has recorded throughout
his career with various groups and under his own name on a variety
of labels.

FUCHSIA SWING SONG/with Jaki Byard — Blue Note 4184/84184 (1964) with NY
on label **$45**; with A Division of Liberty on label **$20**.

CONTOURS/with Freddie Hubbard and Herbie Hancock — Blue Note 4206/
84206 (1965) with NY on label **$45**; with A Division of Liberty on label
$20.

RIVERSIDE JAZZ STARS

*Jimmy Heath, Blue Mitchell, Clark Terry
George Dorsey, Ernie Royal, Arthur Clarke
Bobby Timmons, Ron Carter, Al Heath*

EAN — Riverside 397/9397 (1961) blue label mono; black label stereo with
Bill Grauer Pro. **$45**.

FREDDIE "FREDERICK" ROACH

organ, composer - born 1931 Bronx, NY

DOWN TO EARTH/with Kenny Burrell — Blue Note 4113/84133 (1962) with NY
on label **$40**; with A Division of Liberty on label **$20**.

MO' GREENS PLEASE/with Conrad Lester — Blue Note 4128/84128 (1962) with
NY on label **$40**; with A Division of Liberty on label **$20**.

GOOD MOVE/with Hank Mobley — Blue Note 4158/84158 (1963) with NY on
label **$35**; with A Division of Liberty on label **$20**.

BROWN SUGAR/with Joe Henderson — Blue Note 4168/84168 (1964) with NY
address on label **$35**; with A Division of Liberty on label **$20**.

ALL THAT'S GOOD/with Conrad Lester — Blue Note 4190/84190 (1964) with NY
on label **$35**; with A Division of Liberty on label **$20**.

MAX ROACH

drums - born 1925 Brooklyn, NY

One of the pioneers of be-bop drumming along with Kenny Clarke,
Roach began working on 42nd St. with Charlie Parker while still in
his teens. Through the 40's he was much sought after and worked
with most of the major stars of the time. In the 50's with groups of his
own, Roach proved to be a major innovator. His groups included the
finest musicians available; Clifford Brown and Sonny Rollins as
examples. Further, Roach was the first jazz musician to extensively
explore unusual time signatures and his studies of third world
rhythms led to some of the drum groups he headed during the 60's. In

addition to these contributions, Roach has served as teacher, lecturer
and clinician since the 50's and has a wide variety of recordings still
available.

MAX ROACH SEXTET — Debut EP 451 (1953) **$50**.

QUARTET/with Hank Mobley and Gigi Gryce — Debut 13 (1953) 10" **$90**.

MAX ROACH QUINTET/with Art Blakey — Blue Note 5010 (1952) 10" **$90**; three
sides only.

PLUS FOUR/with Sonny Rollins and Kenny Dorham — EmArcy 36098 (1956)
with drummer logo **$65**; *reissued* EmArcy 80000 (1958) stereo **$45**.

JAZZ IN 3/4 TIME/with Sonny Rollins and Kenny Dorham — EmArcy 36108
(1957) with drummer logo **$65**; *reissued* EmArcy 80002 (1958) stereo
$45.

FOUR PLAYS CHARLIE PARKER/with Hank Mobley and Kenny Dorham —
EmArcy 36127/80019 (1958) EmArcy within Mercury logo **$50**.

ON THE CHICAGO SCENE/with Booker Little and George Coleman — EmArcy
36132 (1958) EmArcy within Mercury logo **$50**.

PLUS FOUR NEWPORT/with Ray Draper and Booker Little — EmArcy 36140/
80010 (1958) EmArcy within Mercury logo **$45**.

WITH THE BOSTON PERCUSSION ENSEMBLE/with compositions by H.
Farberman — EmArcy 36144/80015 (1958) EmArcy within Mercury
logo **$45**.

RICH VERSUS ROACH/with Buddy Rich — Mercury 20448/60133 (1959) black
label **$60**.

QUIET AS IT'S KEPT/with Tommy and Stanley Turrentine — Mercury 20491/
60170 (1960) black label **$60**.

MOON-FACED AND STARRY-EYED/with Abbey Lincoln — Mercury 20539/60215
(1960) black label **$60**.

PARISIAN SKETCHES/with Stanley Turrentine — Mercury 20760/60760 (1962)
black label **$50**.

THE MANY SIDES OF MAX/with George Coleman — Mercury 20911/60911
(1964) red label **$50**.

DRUMMIN' THE BLUES/with Stan Levey — Liberty 3064 (1957) green label with lighthouse on label **$60.**

MAX/with Hank Mobley — Argo 623 (1958) **$45.**

AWARD WINNING DRUMMER/with Booker Little and George Coleman — Time 70003 (1960) **$55.**

MAX ROACH — Time 2087 **$50**; same LP as 70003 but in stereo and title changed.

WE INSIST/with Coleman Hawkins — Candid 8002/9002 (1960) **$50.**

DEEDS NOT WORDS/with Booker Little and Ray Draper — Riverside 12-280/ 1122 (1958) blue label mono; black label stereo **$50**; *reissued* Jazzland 79/979.

CONVERSATION — Jazzland 79/979 (1962) **$35.**

PERCUSSION BITTER SWEET/with Booker Little — Impulse 8 (1961) orange label **$35.**

IT'S TIME/with Abbey Lincoln and Clifford Jordan — Impulse 16 (1962) orange label **$35.**

SPEAK BROTHER, SPEAK/with Clifford Jordan — Fantasy 6007 (1963) **$40.**

TRIO: FEATURING THE LEGENDARY HASAAN — Atlantic 1435 (1965) with logo on right side **$25.**

HOWARD ROBERTS
guitar - born 1929 Phoenix, AZ

Primarily a self-taught musician, Roberts began working in the Los Angeles area about 1950 with many name bands in addition to studio work of all types. He had several popular recordings in the 60's which helped him continue to work outside the studio. He can be found as a sideman with many quality artists and is an outstanding single performer.

MR. ROBERTS PLAYS GUITAR/with Bob Enevoldsen — Verve 8192 (1957) with Verve Records, Inc. on bottom of label **$45.**

GOOD PICKIN'S/with Bill Holman — Verve 8305 (1959) with Verve Records, Inc. on bottom of label **$45.**

COLOR HIM FUNKY — Capitol 1887 (1963) black label with logo on top **$30.**

H.R. IS A DIRTY GUITAR PLAYER — Capitol 1961 (1963) black label with logo on top **$30.**

SOMETHING'S COOKIN' — Capitol 2214 (1964) black label with logo on top **$25.**

GOODIES — Capitol 2400 (1965) black label with logo on top **$20.**

BETTY ROCHE
vocals - born 1920 Wilmington, DE

Early exposure with the Savoy Sultans led Roche to work with Duke Ellington's Orchestra which included his premier at Carnegie Hall of Black, Brown and Beige in 1944. She worked with Ellington in the early 40's and then again in the early 50's, recording with him and achieving considerable recognition as one of the finest singers to ever perform with him. Following a period of inactivity, she recorded again on her own in 1956 but with little popular success and has retired since for a period of time.

TAKE THE A TRAIN/with Conte Candoli — Bethlehem 64 (1956) maroon label **$80.**

SINGIN' AND SWINGIN'/with Jimmy Forrest and Bill Jennings — Prestige 7187 (1960) yellow label **$75.**

LIGHTLY AND POLITELY/with Jimmy Neely — Prestige 7198 (1961) yellow label **$75.**

RED RODNEY
trumpet - born 1927 Philadelphia, PA

Rodney began working in his teens with bands like those of Tommy Dorsey, Les Brown, Gene Krupa, Woody Herman and Claude Thornhill. After several months with Charlie Parker in 1950, he was considered to be one of the best new style players around. Unfortunately, due to personal problems, he was unable to fully capitalize on his popularity with a few exceptions.

RED RODNEY/with Jimmy Ford — Prestige 122 (1952) 10" **$95.**

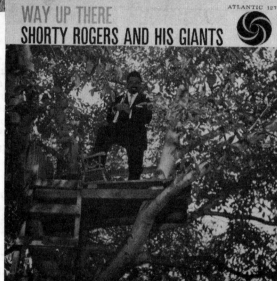

MODERN MUSIC FROM CHICAGO/with Ira Sullivan — Fantasy 3-208 (1955) **$60** EP 4047 (1955) **$30.**

1957/with Ira Sullivan — Signal 1206 (1957) **$55**; *reissued* Savoy 12148.

RED RODNEY — Savoy 12148 (1959) **$40**; *reissue* of Signal 1206.

RETURNS/with Billy Root — Argo 643 (1959) **$40.**

BOB ROGERS
vibes

ALL THAT AND THIS TOO/with Bill Perkins — Indigo 1501 (1961) **$30.**

SHORTY ROGERS
trumpet, fluegelhorn, composer - born 1924 Great Barrington, MA

Very popular on the West Coast with the bands of Red Norvo and Woody Herman in the 40's as both player and arranger, Rogers moved on to work with Stan Kenton in the early 50's and Howard Rumsey in 1953. He had his own combo in the mid-50's and pursued his interest in writing and arranging for movies and television. In the early 50's, Rogers was one of the busiest men on the music scene, playing with groups of his own, performing, writing and arranging for other groups and working in studios and recording companies. He has continued to work primarily in a studio context in the years since.

**Personal Note: The LP Gospel Mission is not a jazz endeavor; however, it will be listed here solely for collecting purposes. There will be no price given.

MODERN SOUNDS/with Art Pepper — Capitol H294 (1951) 10" **$200**; EP 2-294 (1951) **$60**; *reissued* Capitol T691.

MODERN SOUNDS/with Gerry Mulligan — Capitol T691 (1956) green label **$70**; *reissued* Capitol 2025 (1963) tan and black label, one side each **$40**; Rogers' side is a *reissue* of Capitol H294 (1951).

**GOSPEL MISSION — Captiol 1960 (1963).

SHORTY ROGERS' GIANTS/with Art Pepper and Jimmy Giuffre — RCA Victor 3137 (1953) 10" **$105**; *reissued* RCA Victor 1195 (1955) dog on top **$85**.

COOL AND CRAZY/with Bob Cooper and Art Pepper — RCA Victor 3138 (1953) 10" **$105**; *reissued* RCA Victor 3138 (1956) dog on top **$80**.

COURTS THE COUNT/with Zoot Sims and Bob Cooper — RCA Victor 1004 (1954) dog on top **$90**; EP 1004 (1954) **$45**.

COLLABORATION/with Bob Cooper and Jimmy Giuffre — RCA Victor 1018 (1954) **$90**; EP 901 (1954) **$45**; *reissued* RCA Victor 1334 (1956) **$65**.

EAST COAST-WEST COAST/with Zoot Sims and Lennie Niehaus — RCA Victor 1020 (1954) dog on top **$95**; one side Rogers, flipside is Al Cohn.

AND HIS GIANTS/with Jimmy Giuffre and Shelly Manne — RCA Victor 1195 (1955) **$85**.

WHEREVER THE FIVE WINDS BLOW/with Jimmy Giuffre — RCA Victor 1326 (1957) dog on top **$55**.

THE BIG SHORTY ROGERS EXPRESS/with Charlie Mariano, Art Pepper and Jack Montrose — RCA Victor 1350 (1957) dog on top **$55**.

PLAYS RICHARD RODGERS/with Bill Perkins, Jack Montrose and Pepper Adams — RCA Victor 1428 (1957) dog on top **$55**.

PORTRAIT OF SHORTY/with Richie Kamuca and Herbie Geller — RCA Victor 1564 (1957) dog on top **$50**.

GIGI GOES JAZZ/with Bill Holman and Mel Lewis — RCA Victor 1696 (1958) dog on top **$50**.

AFRO-CUBAN INFLUENCE/with Bob Cooper and Frank Rosolino — RCA Victor 1763 (1958) dog on top **$35**.

CHANCES ARE IT SWINGS/with Richie Kamuca and Conte Candoli — RCA Victor 1975 (1959) dog on top **$45**.

THE WIZARD OF OZ/with Bud Shank and Jimmy Giuffre — RCA Victor 1997 (1959) dog on top **$35**.

THE SWINGIN' NUTCRACKER/with Bill Perkins and Art Pepper — RCA Victor 2110 (1960) dog on top **$30**.

THE SWINGING MR. ROGERS/with Jimmy Giuffre — Atlantic 1212 (1955) black label **$65**; EP 538, EP 539, EP 540 (1955) **$25 ea.**; *reissued* Atlantic 1212 with logo on right side **$35**.

MARTIANS COME BACK/with Jimmy Giuffre and Bud Shank — Atlantic 1232 (1956) black label with green LP cover **$65**; *reissued* Atlantic 1232 with logo on right side **$35**.

ROGERS IN STEREO — Atlantic 1232 (1958) black label with red LP cover, stereo **$40**; *reissue* in part of Atlantic 1232 and 1270.

WAY UP THERE/with Barney Kessel and Bud Shank — Atlantic 1270 (1956) black label **$50**; *reissued* Atlantic 1270 with logo on right side **$35**.

MEETS TARZAN (Soundtrack Tarzan the Ape Man)/with Bob Cooper and Bill Perkins — MGM 3798 (1960) **$35**.

4TH DIMENSION IN SOUND/with Bud Shank — Warner Brothers 1443 (1961) **$30**.

BOSSA NOVA/with Bud Shank — Reprise 6050/96050 (1962) **$30**.

JAZZ WALTZ/with Bob Cooper and Bill Perkins — Reprise 6060/96060 (1962) **$30**.

GENE ROLAND
trumpet, composer - born 1921 Dallas, TX

JAZZVILLE - Vol 4/with Paul Quinichette — Dawn 1122 (1957) **$40**; one side only.

SWINGIN' FRIENDS/with Al Cohn and Zoot Sims — Brunswick 54114 (1963) black label with rainbow arrow **$50**.

JOE ROLAND
vibes - born 1920 New York City, NY

JOE ROLAND QUARTET/with Ron Jefferson — Savoy 15034 (1954) 10" **$70**; *reissued* Savoy 12039.

JOE ROLAND QUARTET/with Freddie Redd — Savoy 15047 (1954) 10" **$70**; *reissued* Savoy 12039.

JOLTIN' JOE ROLAND — Savoy 12039 (1956) **$40**; *reissue* of Savoy 15034 and 15047.

JOE ROLAND QUINTET/with Freddie Redd — Bethlehem 17 (1955) maroon label **$40**.

SONNY ROLLINS
tenor sax - born 1929 New York City, NY

A fiery player who first gained recognition around New York City in the early 50's, Rollins worked with the best including Miles Davis and Max Roach before forming his own groups in the later 50's. These groups were usually pianoless trios leaving much room for Rollins to develop his solos. Through his works with others, his own groups and his many recordings, Rollins became very popular but, as he would several times later in his career, took a couple of years off to practice his instrument and explore other interests. Often after these breaks he would indeed bring new ideas and attempts at stretching or adapting his style but his general line of development can be traced beginning in the 60's. He continues to be an important musician and an exciting performer.

SONNY ROLLINS/with Kenny Drew — Prestige 137 (1952) 10" **$150**; *reissued* Prestige 7029.

QUINTET/with Kenny Dorham — Prestige 186 (1954) 10" **$150**; *reissued* Prestige 7058.

QUARTET/with Thelonious Monk — Prestige 190 (1954) 10" **$150**; *reissued* in part Prestige 7058.

WORKTIME/with Ray Bryant — Prestige 7020 (1956) yellow label $80; *reissued* Prestige 7246 (1962) yellow label $45.

WITH THE MODERN JAZZ QUARTET — Prestige 7029 (1956) yellow label $75; *reissue* of Prestige 137.

PLUS FOUR/with Clifford Brown — Prestige 7038 (1956) yellow label with original cover $80; *reissued* yellow label with abstract cover $20.

TENOR MADNESS/with John Coltrane — Prestige 7047 (1956) yellow label $75.

MOVIN' OUT — Prestige 7058 (1956) yellow label $75; *reissue* of Prestige 186 with part of Prestige 190.

SAXOPHONE COLOSSUS/with Tommy Flanagan — Prestige 7079 (1956) yellow label $75.

ROLLINS PLAYS FOR BIRD/with Kenny Dorham — Prestige 7095 (1956) yellow label $50.

TOUR DE FORCE/with Earl Coleman — Prestige 7126 (1957) yellow label $45.

SONNY BOY — Prestige 7207 (1961) yellow label $45.

SONNY AND THE ALL STARS — Prestige 7269 (1962) yellow label $45.

SONNY ROLLINS/with Donald Byrd — Blue Note 1542 (1957) with NY address on label $65; with NY on label $40; with A Division of Liberty on label $20.

SONNY ROLLINS - Vol 2/with J.J. Johnson — Blue Note 1558 (1957) with NY address on label $65; with NY on label $40; with A Division of Liberty on label $20.

A NIGHT AT THE VILLAGE VANGUARD/with Elvin Jones — Blue Note 1581 (1957) with NY address on label $65; **with NY on label $40**; with A Division of Liberty on label $20.

NEWK'S TIME/with Wynton Kelly — Blue Note 4001 (1958) with NY address on label $65; with NY on label $40; with A Division of Liberty on label $20.

WAY OUT WEST/with Ray Brown and Shelly Manne — Contemporary 3530 (1957) yellow label $65; *reissued* Contemporary 7017 (1958) black label, stereo $50.

AND THE CONTEMPORARY LEADERS/with Barney Kessel and Shelly Manne — Contemporary 3564/7504 (1958) yellow label mono; black label stereo $60.

THE SOUND OF SONNY/with Sonny Clark — Riverside 12-241 (1957) blue label with Bill Grauer Pro. $60; *reissued* Riverside 1124 (1958) black label with Bill Grauer Pro. $45; *reissued* Jazzland 72.

FREEDOM SUITE/with Max Roach — Riverside 12-258 (1958) blue label with Bill Grauer Pro. $50; EP 136 (1958) $30; *reissued* Jazzland 86.

SONNY'S TIME — Jazzland 72/972 (1962) $35; *reissue* of Riverside 12-241.

SHADOW WALTZ — Jazzland 86/986 (1962) $35; *reissue* of Riverside 12-258.

AND THE BIG BRASS/with Clark Terry — Metrojazz 1002 (1958) $50; *reissued* Verve 8430.

AT MUSIC INN/with The Modern Jazz Quartet — Metrojazz 1011 (1958) $50; Teddy Edwards does a couple of sides on this LP.

PLAYS/with Jimmy Cleveland — Period 1204 (1957) $60; one side only.

THE BRIDGE/with Jim Hall — RCA Victor 2527 (1962) dog on top $40.

WHAT'S NEW — RCA Victor 2572 (1962) dog on top $40.

OUR MAN IN JAZZ/with Don Cherry — RCA Victor 2612 (1963) dog on top $40.

SONNY MEETS HAWK/with Coleman Hawkins — RCA Victor 2712 (1963) dog on top $40.

SONNY ROLLINS BRASS/SONNY ROLLINS TRIO — Verve 8430/68430 (1962) with MGM on bottom of label $35; *reissue* of Metrojazz 1002.

FRANK ROSOLINO
trombone, vocals - born 1926 Detroit, MI

Rosolino's musical background led to playing in an Army band in the mid-40's followed by several years with various name bands, eventually leading his own group in the early 50's. He then worked with Stan Kenton for a couple of years, during which time he gained some national recognition. In demand for studio work in California, Rosolino has lived there working in a wide variety of contexts including studio work, television bands, clinics and many concert and club appearances.

KENTON PRESENTS/with Charlie Mariano — Capitol H6507 (1954) 10" $100; EP 1-6507, EP 2-6507 (1954) $50 ea.; *reissued* Capitol T6507 (1955) green label $85.

FRANKLY SPEAKING/with Charlie Mariano — Capitol T6509 (1955) green label $85.

I PLAY TROMBONE/with Sonny Clark — Bethlehem 26 (1956) maroon label $75.

QUINTET/with Richie Kamuca — Mode 107 (1957) $75; *reissued* Interlude 500/1000.

THE LEGEND OF — Interlude 500/1000 (1959) $60.

TURN ME LOOSE/with Victor Feldman — Reprise 6016/96016 (1961) $45.

ANNIE ROSS
vocals, songwriter - born 1930 Surrey, England

Born in England and raised in the U.S., Miss Ross was a child actress and singer. She studied and achieved both professions with varying degrees of success and first attracted attention in the jazz world with her vocal version of a Wardell Gray solo on the song Twisted. This eventually led to her being one of the founding members of the extremely popular and influential Lambert, Hendricks and Ross vocal group in the late 50's. After illness forced her out of the group, she recovered and has since worked both as an actress and singer in England and Europe. Ross is possessor of an unusual vocal quality of a wide range which she has used to great effect in many contexts, especially in the Lambert, Hendricks and Ross collaborations.

ANNIE ROSS SINGS A SONG WITH MULLIGAN/with Gerry Mulligan — World Pacific 1253/1020 (1959) $80; *reissued* Kimberly 2018/11018 (1963) $45.

GYPSY/with Conte Candoli and Frank Rosolino — World Pacific 1276/1028 (1959) $80.

A GASSER/with Zoot Sims — World Pacific 1285 (1959) $80.

KING PLEASURE SINGS/ANNIE ROSS SINGS — Prestige 7128 (1957) yellow label $75; EP 1301 (1952) $45; Ross sings 4 sides on this LP from EP 1301.

ARNOLD ROSS
piano, leader, composer - born 1921 Boston, MA

ARNOLD ROSS — Discovery 2006 (1954) $45.

RONNIE ROSS
baritone sax - born 1933 Calcutta, India

Extremely well known in England through his work with big name bands of that country in the 50's and for his work with visiting American musicians. Ross came to America in the late 50's to work with various groups and is highly thought of by all who worked with him. In the 60's he led groups of his own and worked with some of the best European big bands including Clarke-Boland.

THE JAZZ MAKERS/with Allan Ganley — Atlantic 1333 (1960) with logo on right side $45.

CHARLIE ROUSE
tenor sax - born 1924 Washington, DC

Rouse gained extensive experience with Billy Eckstine, Dizzy Gillespie and Duke Ellington in the 40's and then worked in New York City with various groups which included co-leading Les Jazz Modes with Julius Watkins. Always a strong player, he is probably best known for his work with Thelonious Monk from 1959 where he played extensively in every major jazz aspect. He made many recordings that demonstrate his complete understanding of Monk's music while displaying his own abilities.

TAKIN' CARE OF BUSINESS/with Blue Mitchell and Walter Bishop — Jazzland 19/919 (1960) **$40.**

YEAH!/with Dave Bailey — Epic 16012/17012 (1960) yellow label **$35.**

WE PAID OUR DUES/with Seldon Powell — Epic 16018/17018 (1961) yellow label **$35**; Rouse is on one side only.

BOSSA NOVA BACCHANAL/with Kenny Burrell — Blue Note 4119/84119 (1962) with NY on label **$40**; with A Division of Liberty on label **$20.**

JIMMY ROWLES
piano - born 1918 Spokane, WA

Earning early recognition through work with Ben Webster, Rowles then worked with who's who of jazz including Lester Young, Billie Holiday, Benny Goodman, Woody Herman, Tommy Dorsey and Bob Crosby during the 40's. Working California since the early 50's, Rowles has done studio work for television and movies and has gained a reputation as perhaps the most sensitive of accompanists through his long association with many big name singers.

RARE, BUT WELL DONE/with Red Mitchell — Liberty 3003 (1956) **$50.**

LET'S GET ACQUAINTED WITH JAZZ...FOR PEOPLE WHO HATE JAZZ!/with Pete Candoli and Harold Land — Tampa 8 (1957) **$50**; *reissued* Interlude 515.

UPPER CLASSMEN — Interlude 515/1015 (1959) **$40**; *reissue* of Tampa 8.

WEATHER IN A JAZZ VANE/with Bob Enevoldsen and Herb Geller — Andex 3007 (1958) **$40.**

KINDA GROOVY!/with Howard Roberts — Capitol 1831 (1962) black label with logo on top **$20.**

ERNIE ROYAL
trumpet - born 1921 Los Angeles, CA died 1983

ACCENT ON TRUMPET/with Billy Taylor — Urania 1203 (1955) **$55.**

*PETE RUGOLO
leader, composer - born 1915 San Piero, Patti, Sicily

FOR HI FI BUGS — EmArcy 36082 (1956) with drummer logo **$45.**

OUT ON A LIMB — EmArcy 36115 (1958) EmArcy within Mercury logo **$45.**

PERCUSSION AT WORK/with Buddy Childers and Herbie Harper — EmArcy 36122 (1958) EmArcy within Mercury logo **$40.**

PLAYS KENTON/with Bud Shank and Bob Cooper — EmArcy 36143 (1958) EmArcy within Mercury logo **$40.**

MUSIC FROM RICHARD DIAMOND — EmArcy 36162 (1958) EmArcy within Mercury logo **$40.**

BRASS IN HI FI/with Pete Candoli and Barney Kessel — Mercury 20261/60044 (1958) black label **$40.**

*The only LP's within the scope of this book.

HOWARD RUMSEY
bass, leader - born 1917 Brawley, CA

A good, swinging bass player, Rumsey's reputation as the bassist for the original Stan Kenton Band in 1944 allowed him to play extensively on the West Coast with many greats in the mid to late 40's. Beginning in 1949 he ran the Lighthouse in California, working as a sit-in performer for almost every well known local musician and with some of the most famous jazz musicians who visited there. As time went on he hired the best local groups and featured famous musicians and groups on tour, many of whom have used the club for live recordings. Through Rumsey's work, both as a bass player and a club owner, the Lighthouse started as a place to jam and eventually became one of the best known jazz clubs in the world.

SUNDAY JAZZ AT THE LIGHTHOUSE/with Bob Cooper — Lighthouse 301 (1953) 10" red vinyl **$100.**

SUNDAY JAZZ AT THE LIGHTHOUSE - Vol 2/with Jimmy Giuffre — Lighthouse 302 (1953) 10" red vinyl **$100.**

JAZZ ROLLS-ROYCE/with Bob Cooper — Lighthouse S300 (1957) **$65**; *reissued* Omega 5 (1960) **$40.**

LIGHTHOUSE ALL STARS - Vol 2/with Bob Cooper and Jimmy Giuffre — Contemporary 2501 (1953) 10" **$90**; EP 4006 (1953) **$40.**

LIGHTHOUSE ALL STARS - Vol 3/with Bob Cooper and Shorty Rogers — Contemporary 2506 (1953) 10" **$90**; EP 4002, EP 4008 (1953) **$40 ea.**; *reissued* Contemporary 3508 (1955) yellow label with lighthouse **$60.**

LIGHTHOUSE ALL STARS - Vol 4/with Bob Cooper and Bud Shank — Contemporary 2510 (1954) 10" **$90**; *reissued* Contemporary 3520.

LIGHTHOUSE ALL STARS - Vol 5/with Bob Cooper and Bob Gordon — Contemporary 2515 (1954) 10" **$90**; EP 4022, EP 4023, EP 4024 (1954) with lighthouse on label **$40 ea.**; *reissued* Contemporary 3517.

LIGHTHOUSE ALL STARS - Vol 6/with Bob Cooper and Frank Rosolino — Contemporary 3504 (1955) **$60**; EP 4015 (1955) yellow label with lighthouse **$35.**

LIGHTHOUSE AT LAGUNA/with Hampton Hawes Trio — Contemporary 3509 (1955) yellow label with lighthouse **$60.**

MUSIC FOR LIGHTHOUSEKEEPING - Vol 8/with Bob Cooper and Conte Candoli — Contemporary 3528 (1956) yellow label with lighthouse **$50**; *reissued* Contemporary 7008 (1958) black label, stereo **$40.**

IN THE SOLO SPOTLIGHT - Vol 5 — Contemporary 3517 (1956) yellow label with lighthouse **50**; *reissue* of Contemporary 2515.

OBOE/FLUTE - Vol 4 — Contemporary 3520 (1956) yellow label with lighthouse **50**; *reissue* of Contemporary 2510.

SUNDAY JAZZ A LA LIGHTHOUSE/with Bob Cooper and Jimmy Giuffre — Contemporary 3501 (1955) yellow label with lighthouse **$65.**

DOUBLE OR NOTHIN'/with Charlie Persip's Jazz Statemen — Liberty 3045/7014 (1957) green label with lighthouse **$50.**

JAZZ STRUCTURES/with Bob Cooper and Bud Shank — Philips 200-012/600-012 (1961) black label with rainbow strip **$40.**

JIMMY RUSHING
vocals - born 1903 Oklahoma City, OK died 1972

Rushing came to prominence with the Count Basie Band for whom he sang from 1935-50. During this time, he appeared with them on radio, in movies and hundreds of recordings. His voice and style were the model for many now famous singers and his success and popularity afforded him his own band after he left Basie. Following work with his group, Rushing continued as a single and became very popular with younger fans who were discovering blues in the late 50's. The resurgence in blues popularity was not confined to the U.S. and Rushing carried on steadily, recording and touring on many occasions through the 60's.

GOING TO CHICAGO/with Buddy Tate — Vanguard 8011 (1954) 10" **$80**; *reissued* Vanguard 8518 (1957) maroon label **$45.**

LISTEN TO THE BLUES/with Buddy Tate and Freddie Green — Vanguard 8505 (1955) maroon label **$60**; *reissued* Jazztone 1244 (1957) **$45.**

IF THIS AIN'T THE BLUES/with Buddy Tate — Vanguard 8513 (1957) maroon label **$50**; *reissued* Vanguard 2008 (1958) stereo **$45.**

THE JAZZ ODYSSEY/with Buck Clayton — Columbia 963 (1957) red label with 3 black logos on each side **$45.**

LITTLE JIMMY RUSHING AND THE BIG BRASS/with Buddy Tate and Coleman Hawkins — Columbia 1152/8060 (1958) red label with 3 black logos on each side **$35.**

RUSHING LULLABIES/with Buddy Tate — Columbia 1401/8196 (1959) red label with 3 black logos on each side **$35.**

BRUBECK AND RUSHING/with Dave Brubeck Quartet — Columbia 1553/8353 (1960) red label with 3 black logos on each side **$45.**

AND THE SMITH GIRLS/with Buck Clayton — Columbia 1605/8405 (1961) red label with 3 black logos on each side **$35.**

TWO SHADES OF BLUE/with Jack Dupree — Audio Lab 1512 (1959) **$35.**

FIVE FEET OF SOUL/with Zoot Sims — Colpix 446 (1963) **$20.**

GEORGE RUSSEL
drums, composer - born 1923 Cincinnati, OH

THE JAZZ WORKSHOP/with Art Farmer and Bill Evans — RCA Victor 1372 (1956) dog on top **$85**; *reissued* RCA Victor 2534 (1961) dog on top **$45.**

NEW YORK, N.Y./with John Coltrane, Al Cohn and Bob Brookmeyer — Decca 9216/79216 (1958) black label with silver lettering **$60.**

JAZZ IN THE SPACE AGE/with Bill Evans and Dave Young — Decca 9219/79219 (1960) black label with silver lettering **$50.**

AT THE FIVE SPOT/with Dave Young — Decca 9220/79220 (1960) black label with silver lettering **$60.**

IN KANSAS CITY/with Dave Young — Decca 4183/74183 (1960) black label with silver lettering **$60.**

STRATUSPHUNK/with Dave Young — Riverside 341/9341 (1960) blue label mono; black label stereo with Bill Grauer Pro. **$45.**

EZZ-THETICES/with Eric Dolphy and Don Ellis — Riverside 375/9375 (1961) blue label mono; black label stereo with Bill Grauer Pro. **$35.**

THE STRATUS SEEKERS — Riverside 412/9412 (1962) blue label mono; black label stereo with Bill Grauer Pro. **$45.**

THE OUTER VIEW — Riverside 440/9440 (1963) blue label mono; black label stereo with Bill Grauer Pro. **$40.**

RUSSIAN JAZZ QUARTET
Boris Midney, Igor Berukshtis, Roger Kellaway Grady Tate

HAPPINESS — Impulse 80 (1964) orange label **$35.**

BILL RUSSO

composer, trombone - born 1928 Chicago, IL

A RECITAL IN NEW AMERICAN MUSIC/with Kenny Mann and Don Hanby — Dee Gee 1001 (1952) 10" **$75.**

THE WORLD OF ALCINA/with Sandy Mosse — Atlantic 1241 (1955) black label **$50.**

SCHOOL OF REBELLION/with Frank Socolow — Roulette 52045 (1960) dark and light orange checked roulette wheel label **$30.**

SEVEN DEADLY SINS/with Tony Ferina — Roulette 52063 (1961) dark and light orange checked roulette wheel label **$30.**

STEREOPHONY — FM 302 (1963) **$30.**

AARON SACHS

clarinet, tenor sax - born 1923 Bronx, NY

AARON SACHS QUINTET/with Urbie Green — Bethlehem 1008 (1954) 10" **$105;** *reissued* Bethlehem 7.

WE BROUGHT OUR AXES/with Hand D'Amico — Bethlehem 7 (1955) maroon label **$60;** *reissue* of Bethlehem 1008, Sach's sides only.

JAZZVILLE - Vol 3/with Jimmy Cleveland — Dawn 1114 (1957) **$60.**

CLARINET AND CO./with Aaron Bell — Rama 1004 (1957) **$60.**

FATS SADI

vibes - born 1926 Andenne, Belgium

THE SWINGING FATS SADI COMBO/with Bobby Jaspar — Blue Note 5061 (1954) 10" **$200.**

A.K. SALIM

arranger, composer - born 1922 Chicago, IL

FLUTE SUITE/with Herbie Mann and Frank Wess — Savoy 12102 (1956) maroon label **$60.**

PRETTY FOR THE PEOPLE/with Johnny Griffin, Kenny Dorham and Pepper Adams — Savoy 12118 (1957) maroon label **$55.**

BLUE SUITE/with Phil Woods and Sahib Shihab — Savoy 12132 (1958) maroon label **$50.**

SAL SALVADOR

guitar, composer - born 1925 Monson, MA

Already an accomplished guitar player, Salvador was moved towards jazz by hearing Charlie Christian recordings. In the late 40's he worked in New York City, often as accompanist for singers. By the early 50's he was working with Stan Kenton, afterwhich he led his

own combos and big bands through the 50's with occasional recording sessions.

QUINTET/with John Williams — Blue Note 5053 (1954) 10" **$95.**

KENTON PRESENTS/with Eddie Costa — Capitol H6505 (1954) 10" **$95;** EP 1-6505, EP 2-6505 (1954) **$30 ea.;** *reissued* Capitol T6505 (1955) green label **$60.**

SHADES OF/with Eddie Costa and Phil Woods — Bethlehem 39 (1956) maroon label **$50.**

FRIVOLOUS/with Eddie Costa — Bethlehem 59 (1956) maroon label **$40.**

TRIBUTE TO THE GREATS/with Eddie Costa — Bethlehem 74 (1957) maroon label **$40.**

COLORS IN SOUND/with Orchestra — Decca 9210/79210 (1958) maroon label with silver lettering **$45.**

BEAT FOR THIS GENERATION/with Orchestra — Decca 4026/74026 (1959) black label with silver lettering **$45.**

QUARTET/with Ray Sterling — Jazz Unlimited: Gold Crest 1001 (1961) **$35.**

YOU AIN'T HEARD NOTHIN' YET/with Charlie Mariano — Dauntless 6307/4307 (1963) **$40.**

MUSIC TO STOP SMOKING BY — Roulette 25262 (1965) dark and light orange checked roulette wheel label **$20.**

PHARAOH SANDERS

tenor sax - born 1940 Little Rock, AK

PHARAOH — ESP Disk 1003 (1965) **$15.**

SANDOLE BROTHERS

Dennis Sandole/guitar - born 1917 Philadelphia, PA
Adolphe Sandole/piano - born 1925 Philadelphia, PA

BROTHERS SANDOLE: MODERN MUSIC FROM PHILADELPHIA/with Art Farmer and George Barrows — Fantasy 3-209 (1956) **$65;** EP 4048 (1956) **$30.**

SANTOS BROTHERS

JAZZ FOR TWO TRUMPETS — Metro Jazz 1015 (1958) **$35.**

LEON SASH

accordion, vibes, guitar - born 1922 Chicago, IL died 1979

QUARTET/with Lee Morgan — Storyville 917 (1956) **$50.**

AT NEWPORT/with Toshiko Akiyoshi — Verve 8236 (1958) with Verve Records, Inc. on bottom of label **$35.**

SAUTER-FINEGAN

Eddie Sauter - composer, leader
born 1914 Brooklyn, NY
Bill Finegan - composer, leader, piano
born 1917 Newark, NJ

NEW DIRECTIONS IN MUSIC — RCA Victor 3115 (1953) 10" **$70.**

INSIDE/with Nick Travis, Sonny Russo and Ralph Burns — RCA Victor 1003 (1954) silver label, dog on top **$50.**

THE SOUND — RCA Victor 1009 (1954) silver label, dog on top **$50.**

CONCERT JAZZ — RCA Victor 1051 (1955) silver label, dog on top **$50.**

SONS OF — RCA Victor 1104 (1955) dog on top **$40.**

ADVENTURE IN TIME — RCA Victor 1210 (1956) dog on top **$40.**

UNDER ANALYSIS — RCA Victor 1341 (1957) dog on top **$35.**

STRAIGHT DOWN THE MIDDLE — RCA Victor 1497 (1957) dog on top **$35.**

SAXOPHONES INCORPORATED

Zoot Sims, Seldon Powell, Al Cohn, Phil Woods,
Gene Quill, Hal McKusick, Herb Geller,
Coleman Hawkins, George Auld

SAXOPHONES INCORPORATED — Warner Brothers 1336 (1959) **$75.**

JOE SAYE

piano - born 1923 Glasgow, Scotland

SCOTCH ON THE ROCKS/with Herbie Mann and Mundell Lowe — EmArcy 36072 (1956) drummer logo **$35.**

A WEE BIT OF JAZZ/with Herbie Mann — EmArcy 36112 (1957) drummer logo **$35.**; *reissued* Mercury 60052 (1958) **$20.**

A DOUBLE SHOT OF/with Spencer Sinatra and Barry Galbraith — EmArcy 36147/80022 (1958) EmArcy within Mercury logo **$30.**

*HAL SCHAEFER

piano, composer - born 1925 New York City, NY

THE JAZZ WORKSHOP/with Nick Travis and Urbie Green — RCA Victor 1199 (1955) dog on top **$55.**

---

*The only LP's within the scope of this book.

GUNTHER SCHULLER

arranger, composer - born 1925 Jackson Heights, NY

JOHN LEWIS PRESENTS: JAZZ ABSTRACTIONS — Atlantic 1365 (1960) with logo on right side **$25.**

THORNEL SCHWARTZ

guitar - born 1927 Philadelphia, PA

SOUL COOKIN'/with Bill Leslie — Argo 704 (1962) **$35.**

SCOOBY DOO GROUP

Dave Pell, John Ewing, John Anderson,
Raymond Martinez, Plas Johnson, Ad Alshibrod,
Irving Ashby, Jewel Grant, Ernie Freeman

JERRY LEIBER PRESNETS: SCOOBY DOO — Zephyr 12002 (1959) **$45.**

BOBBY SCOTT

piano, composer, vocals - born 1937 Bronx, NY

Scott was a musical prodigy as a child, studying with Mortiz and Dubussy and making his debut when 11 years old. In the next few years, he worked with several name bands of the road including Louis Prima and Gene Krupa. While still in his teens he had a commercial hit as a singer but was unable to repeat that success and continued with his music studies. During this period he became very interested

in composing and arranging, which he did with Quincy Jones and in subsequent studio work for movies and television.

GREAT SCOTT/with Whitey Mitchell — Bethlehem 1004 (1954) 10" **$65.**

THE COMPOSITIONS - Vol 1/with Hal McKusick — Bethlehem 1009 (1954) 10" **$65.**; *reissued* Bethlehem 8 (1955) **$45.**

THE COMPOSITIONS - Vol 2/with Charlie Mariano — Bethlehem 1029 (1954) 10" **$65.**; *reissued* Bethlehem 8 (1955) **$45.**

SCOTT FREE — ABC Paramount 102 (1956) **$35.**

AND TWO HORNS/with Marty Flax — ABC Paramount 148 (1957) **$45.**

THE COMPLETE MUSICIAN/with Orchestra — Atlantic 1341 (1960) with logo on right side **$25.**

A TASTE OF HONEY/with Frank Socolow — Atlantic 1355 (1960) with logo on right side **$25.**

WHEN THE FEELING HITS YOU — Mercury 20767/60767 (1961) black label **$20.**

JOYFUL NOISES — Mercury 20701/60701 (1962) black label **$20.**

CLIFFORD SCOTT

saxes, flute, clarinet - born 1928 San Antonio, TX

OUT FRONT/with Les McCann — Pacific Jazz 66 (1963) **$35.**

CLIFFORD SCOTT/with Burt Kendrix — World Pacific 1811 (1963) **$35.**

LAVENDER SAX — World Pacific 1825 (1964) **$35.**

*HAZEL SCOTT

piano, vocals - born 1920 Port of Spain, Trinidad
died 1981

Due to her musical upbringing Ms. Scott was professional from childhood, eventually working in shows and society clubs in the 30's. She is credited with recordings, some movies and considerable work in the New York City area during the 40's, continuing intermittently into the mid-50's.

LATE SHOW/with Red Callender — Capitol 364 (1952) 10" **$40.**

RELAXED PIANO MOODS/with Max Roach and Charlie Mingus — Debut 16 (1955) 10" **$40.**

---

*The only LP's within the scope of this book.

JIMMY SCOTT

vocals

VERY TRULY YOURS — Savoy 12027 (1957) maroon label **$30.**

IF YOU ONLY KNEW — Savoy 14003 (1958) maroon label **$30.**

FABULOUS — Savoy 12150 (1959) maroon label **$30.**

SHIRLEY SCOTT
organ - born 1934 Philadelphia, PA

Scott first worked in jazz with Eddie "Lockjaw" Davis in an organ/tenor group of the type that has long been popular. Their collaboration continued from 1956-60 and during this time she often recorded with Davis as well as on her own. Scott then married saxist Stanley Turrentine and worked with him in a very similar situation until their divorce. She has since worked in New York City with her own group and often with Harold Vick. Ms. Scott has always been a powerful organ player throughout her career.

GREAT SCOTT — Prestige 7143 (1958) yellow label **$40.**

SCOTTIE — Prestige 7155 (1959) yellow label **$40.**

PLAYS THE DUKE — Prestige 7163 (1959) yellow label **$40.**

SOUL SEARCHING — Prestige 7173 (1959) yellow label **$40.**

MUCHO MUCHO — Prestige 7182 (1960) yellow label **$40.**

HIP SOUL/with Stan Turner — Prestige 7205 (1961) yellow label **$60;** *reissued* Prestige 7205 (1965) blue label with logo on right side **$30.**

HIP TWIST/with Stanley Turrentine — Prestige 7226 (1961) yellow label **$60;** *reissued* Prestige 7226 (1965) blue label with logo on right side **$30.**

PLAYS HORACE SILVER — Prestige 7240 (1961) yellow label **$35.**

HAPPY TALK — Prestige 7262 (1962) yellow label **$35.**

SOUL IS WILLING/with Stanley Turrentine — Prestige 7267 (1962) yellow label **$40;** *reissued* Prestige 7267 (1965) blue label with logo on right side **$30.**

LATIN DOLL — Prestige 7283 (1963) yellow label **$35.**

DRAG 'EM OUT — Prestige 7305 (1964) yellow label **$35.**

SOUL SHOUTIN'/with Stanley Turrentine — Prestige 7312 (1964) yellow label **$40;** *reissued* Prestige 7312 (1965) blue label with logo on right side **$30.**

TRAVELIN' LIGHT/with Kenny Burrell — Prestige 7328 (1965) blue label with logo on right side **$30.**

BLUE FLAMES/with Stanley Turrentine — Prestige 7338 (1965) blue label with logo on right side **$35.**

FOR MEMBERS ONLY/with Oliver Nelson Orchestra — Impulse 51 (1963) orange label **$25.**

GREAT SCOTT — Impulse 67 (1964) orange label **$25.**

EVERYBODY LOVES A LOVER/with Stanley Turrentine — Impulse 73 (1965) orange label **$35.**

QUEEN OF THE ORGAN/with Stanley Turrentine — Impulse 81 (1965) orange label **$35.**

SHIRLEY SCOTT TRIO — Moodsville 5 (1960) **$45.**

LIKE COZY — Moodsville 19 (1960) **$45.**

TONY SCOTT
clarinet, saxes, piano, composer - born 1921 Morristown, NJ

Inspired by Benny Goodman and others, young Scott was a fine clarinetist and soon proved equally capable on many instruments. He worked with several groups during the 40's and 50's, along with many of the best bop stars. In addition, he played piano for jazz vocalists and, from 1954, worked and recorded with groups of his own. From the late 50's to the mid-60's, Scott toured, played, recorded and studied music of the Far East, not returning to the U.S. until the mid-60's.

MUSIC AFTER MIDNIGHT/with Philly Joe Jones — Brunswick 58040 (1953) 10" **$75;** *reissued* Brunswick 54021.

QUARTET/with Osie Johnson 58056 (1954) 10" **$75;** *reissued* Brunswick 54021.

JAZZ FOR GI'S/with Milt Hinton — Brunswick 58057 (1954) 10" **$75.**

IN HI FI — Brunswick 54021 (1957) **$55;** *reissue* of Brunswick 58040 and 58056.

SCOTT'S FLING — RCA Victor 1022 (1955) dog on top **$50.**

BOTH SIDES OF/with Mundell Lowe — RCA Victor 1268 (1956) dog on top **$50;** EP 741 (1956) **$20.**

THE TOUCH OF/with Orchestra — RCA Victor 1353 (1957) dog on top **$60;** EP 941, EP 942, EP 943 (1956) **$20 ea.**

THE COMPLETE/with Orchestra — RCA Victor 1452 (1957) dog on top **$40.**

TONY SCOTT SEXTET — RCA Victor EP 596 (1954) **$30.**

52ND STREET SCENE/with Red Rodney — Coral 57239/757239 (1958) maroon label **$65.**

GYPSY/with Mundell Lowe — Signature 6001 (1959) **$40.**

FREE BLOWN JAZZ/with Jim Knepper — Carlton 12/113 (1959) **$50.**

THE MODERN ART OF JAZZ/with Clark Terry — Seeco 425/4150 (1959) **$40.**

HI FI LAND OF JAZZ — Seeco 428 (1959) **$40.**

SOUTH PACIFIC/with Dick Hyman — ABC Paramount 235 (1958) **$40.**

MY KIND OF JAZZ — Perfect 12010/14010 (1960) **$50.**

AL SEARS
tenor sax - born 1910 Macomb, IL

Sears worked with name bands as early as the 20's, forming a band of his own in the 30's and moved on to team up with Lionel Hampton and Duke Ellington in the 40's. Through the 50's Sears expanded on his musical endeavors and was involved in music publishing in New York City. During this same time, he continued to play and some of his best known work is with Duke Ellington and the Johnny Hodges Group.

DANCE MUSIC WITH A SWING BEAT/with Joe Thomas — Audio Lab 1540 (1959) **$50.**

SWING'S THE THING/with Wendell Marshall — Swingville 2018 (1960) **$45.**

PAUL SERRANO
trumpet - born 1932 Chicago, IL

BLUES HOLIDAY/with Bunky Green and Jodie Christian — Riverside 359/9359 (1960) blue label mono; black label stereo with Bill Grauer Pro. **$30.**

BUD SHANK
alto sax, flute, composer - born 1926 Dayton, OH

During the late 40's in California, Shank studied with Shorty Rogers and worked with several good West Coast groups in the years that followed including Charlie Barnet and Stan Kenton. In the early 50's he appeared as a regular with Howard Rumsey at the Lighthouse. Since the late 50's, Shank has worked a great deal in Los Angeles studios for movies and television pieces in addition to continued work and recordings with his own groups. Easily, he is one of the best flutists in jazz is also extremely good on the alto sax.

QUINTET/with Shorty Rogers — Nocturne 2 (1953) 10" **$125;** EP 3, EP 4 (1953) **$50** ea.; *reissued* Pacific Jazz 1205.

AND THREE TROMBONES/with Bob Enevoldsen, Stu Williamson and Maynard Ferguson — Pacific Jazz 14 (1954) 10" **$95;** EP 4-23 (1954) **$40;** *reissued* Pacific Jazz 1213.

BUD SHANK AND BOB BROOKMEYER — Pacific Jazz 20 (1955) 10" **$95;** *reissued* Pacific Jazz 1213.

BUD SHANK - SHORTY ROGERS — Pacific Jazz 1205 (1955) **$65;** EP 4-34 (1955) **$40;** *reissued* World Pacific 1205 (1958) **$50;** *reissues* of Nocturne 2.

STRINGS AND TROMBONES/with Bob Brookmeyer — Pacific Jazz 1213 (1956) **$65;** *reissued* Kimberly 2025/11025.

THE BUD SHANK QUARTET/with Claude Williamson — Pacific Jazz 1215 (1956) **$60;** EP 4-44 (1956) **$30;** *reissued* World Pacific 1215 (1958) **$45.**

JAZZ AT CAL-TECH/with Bob Cooper — Pacific Jazz 1219 (1956) **$65;** *reissued* World Pacific 1219 (1958) **$50.**

FLUTE 'N OBOE/with Bob Cooper — Pacific Jazz 1226 (1957) **$55;** *reissued* World Pacific 1226 (1958) **$45.**

QUARTET/with Claude Williamson — Pacific Jazz 1230 (1957) **$55;** *reissued* World Pacific 1230 (1958) **$45.**

JAZZ SWINGS BROADWAY/with Chico Hamilton Quintet, Stu Williamson Quintet and Russ Freeman Trio — Pacific Jazz 404 (1957) **$55;** *reissued* World Pacific 404 (1958) **$45;** *reissued* Kimberly 2024/11024.

THE SWING'S TO TV/with Bob Cooper — Pacific Jazz 411 (1957) **$55;** *reissued* World Pacific 411/1002 (1958) **$45.**

NEW GROOVE/with Carmell Jones — Pacific Jazz 21 (1961) **$35.**

BAREFOOT ADVENTURE (Soundtrack)/with Carmell Jones — Pacific Jazz 35 (1961) **$30.**

BOSSA NOVA JAZZ SAMBA/with Clare Fischer — Pacific Jazz 58 (1962) **$30.**

BRASAMBA/with Clare Fischer — Pacific Jazz 64 (1963) **$30.**

AND HIS BRAZILIAN FRIENDS — Pacific Jazz 89 (1965) **$30.**

I'LL TAKE ROMANCE/with Orchestra — World Pacific 1251 (1958) **$45.**

SLIPPERY WHEN WET/with Bill Bean — World Pacific 1265 (1959) **$40.**

LATIN CONTRASTS — World Pacific 1281 (1959) **$30.**

FLUTE 'N ALTO — World Pacific 1286 (1960) **$30.**

KOTO 'N FLUTE — World Pacific 1299 (1960) **$30.**

BRAZILLIANCE - Vol 2/with Laurindo Almeida — World Pacific 1419 (1962) **$25.**

BRAZILLIANCE - Vol 3/with Laurindo Almeida — World Pacific 1425 (1962) **$25.**

SWINGING BROADWAY — Kimberly 2024/11024 (1963) **$20;** *reissue* of Pacific Jazz 404 and World Pacific 404.

THE TALENTS OF — Kimberly 2025/11025 (1963) **$20;** *reissue* of Pacific Jazz 1213.

BUD SHANK/with Bob Enevoldsen — Crown 5311 (1963) **$20;** *reissue* of Pacific Jazz matter.

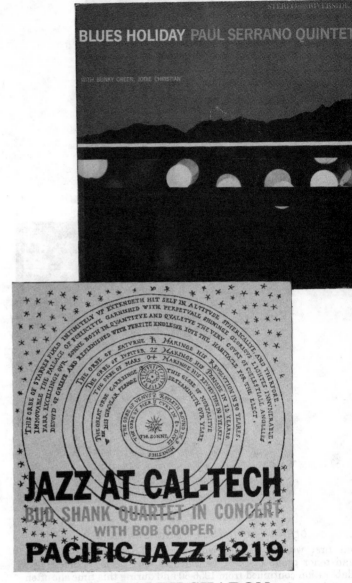

RALPH SHARON
piano, composer - born 1923 London, England

EASY JAZZ/with J.R. Monterose — London 1488 (1955) **$50.**

MR. AND MRS. JAZZ/with Sue Sharon and Jack Montrose — Bethlehem 13 (1955) maroon label **$50.**

TRIO — Bethlehem 41 (1956) maroon label **$30.**

JAZZ AROUND THE WORLD/with Lucky Thompson — Rama 1001 (1957) **$50.**

2:38 A.M./with Candido — Argo 635 (1958) **$30.**

CHARLIE SHAVERS
trumpet, vocals, composer
born 1917 New York City, NY died 1971

Shavers' first recognition was due to him being an important member of one of the most tasteful small groups in the early 40's, The John Kirby Sextet. His unique sound and style added significantly to the groups considerable success. He then began an association with the Tommy Dorsey Orchestra that would last on-and-off from the mid-40's well into the 60's.

THE MOST INTIMATE — Bethlehem 1021 (1954) **$60;** EP 109 (1954) **$15;** *reissued* Bethlehem 5002 (1958) **$45;** *reissued* Aamco 310 (1959) **$30**

GERSHWIN, SHAVERS AND STRINGS — Bethlehem 27 (1955) maroon label **$40.**

THE COMPLETE/with Maxine Sullivan — Bethlehem 67 (1957) maroon label **$40**

CHARLIE DIGS PAREE/with Ray Bryant — MGM 3765 (1959) yellow label **$20.**

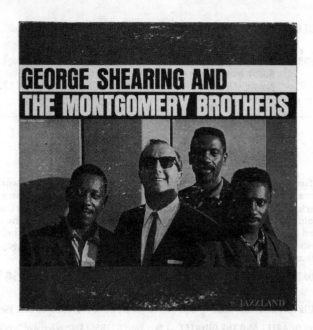

HARLIE DIGS DIXIE — MGM 3809 (1960) yellow label **$20.**

UT OF NO WHERE — Everest 5070/1070 (1959) **$20.**

ERE COMES CHARLIE — Everest 5108/1108 (1960) **$20.**

IKE CHARLIE — Everest 5127/1127 (1960) **$20.**

XCITEMENT UNLIMITED/with Jerome Richardson — Capitol 1883 (1963) black label with logo on top **$25.**

GENE SHAW
trumpet - born 1926 Detroit, MI

After gaining experience around the Detroit area, Shaw went to New York and worked with many great name groups including Charlie Mingus for whom he worked in the mid-50's. While with Mingus he made several recordings, one being Tijuana Moods which is now considered a classic.

REAKTHROUGH/with Sherman Morrison — Argo 707 (1962) **$40.**

EBUT IN BLUES/with Jay Peters — Argo 726 (1963) **$35.**

ARNIVAL SKETCHES/with Richard Evans — Argo 743 (1964) **$35.**

*GEORGE SHEARING
piano, composer - born 1919 London, England

UINTET/with Marie Hyams — Discovery 3002 (1950) 10" **$35;** *reissued* Savoy 12093.

IANO SOLO/with Cozy Cole — Savoy 15003 (1950) **$35.**

IDNIGHT ON CLOUD 69/with Marie Hyams — Savoy 12093 (1957) maroon label **$15;** *reissue* of Discovery 3002.

OUCH OF GENIUS/with Don Elliott — MGM 90 (1951) 10" **$25;** EP 90 (1951) **$5;** *reissued* MGM 3265 (1955) **$15.**

I HEAR MUSIC/with Joe Roland — MGM 155 (1951) 10" **$25;** EP 1455 (1951) **$5;** *reissued* MGM 3266 (1955) **$15.**

WHEN LIGHTS ARE LOW/with Marie Hyams — MGM 226 (1952) 10" **$25;** *reissued* MGM 3264 (1955) **$15.**

EVENING WITH/with Marie Hyams — MGM 252 (1953) 10" **$25;** *reissued* MGM 3222 (1955) **$15.**

SHEARING CARAVAN — MGM 3175 (1955) **$15;** EP 1088 (1955) **$5.**

SHEARING IN HI FI — MGM 3293 (1955) **$15;** EP 1185 (1955) **$5.**

THE SHEARING SPELL/with Johnny Rae — Capitol 648 (1955) green label **$15;** EP 1-648, EP 2-648, EP 3-648 (1955) **$5 ea.**

LATIN ESCAPADE/with Emile Richards — Capitol 737 (1956) green label **$15;** EP 1-737, EP 2-737, EP 3-737 (1956) **$5 ea.**

BLACK SATIN/with Toots Thielemans — Capitol 858 (1956) green label **$15;** EP 1-858, EP 2-858, EP 3-858 (1956) **$5 ea.**

SHEARING PIANO (Solo) — Capitol 909 (1957) green label **$15;** EP 1-909, EP 2-909 (1957) **$5 ea.**

IN THE NIGHT/with Dakota Staton — Capitol 1003 (1957) green label **$45;** *reissued* Capitol 1003 (1958) black label with logo on left side **$35;** *reissued* Capitol 1003 (1962) black label with logo on top **$20.**

ON STAGE/with Toots Thielemans — Capitol 1187 (1958) black label **$15.**

LATIN AFFAIR/with Toots Thielemans — Capitol 1275 (1959) black label with logo on left side **$15.**

WHITE SATIN/with Toots Thielemans — Capitol 1334 (1959) black label with logo on left side **$15.**

BEAUTY AND THE BEAT/with Peggy Lee — Capitol 1219 (1959) black label with logo on left side **$40;** *reissued* Capitol 1219 (1962) black label with logo on top **$20.**

THE SWINGIN'S MUTUAL/with Nancy Wilson — Capitol 1524 (1960) black label with logo on left **$40;** *reissued* Capitol 1524 (1962) black label with logo on top **$20.**

MOOD LATINO/with Warren Chasen — Capitol 1567 (1961) black label with logo on left **$10.**

NAT KING COLE SINGS, GEORGE SHEARING PLAYS — Capitol 1675 (1961) black label with logo on left **$30;** *reissued* Capitol 1675 (1963) black label with logo on top **$20.**

SAN FRANCISCO SCENE/with Warren Chasen — Capitol 1715 (1961) black label with logo on left **$10.**

JAZZ MOMENTS/with Vernell Fournier — Capitol 1827 (1962) black label with logo on top **$10.**

BOSSA NOVA/with Vernell Fournier — Capitol 1873 (1962) black label with logo on top **$10.**

OUT OF THE WOODS/with Paul Horn — Capitol 2272 (1965) black label with logo on top **$25.**

GEORGE SHEARING AND THE MONTGOMERY BROTHERS/with Wes, Monk and Buddy Montgomery — Jazzland 55/955 (1961) original cover with picture of them all together **$35;** cover with picture of a girl **$25.**

---

*The only LP's within the scope of this book.

JACK SHELDON

trumpet - born 1931 Jacksonville, FL

After playing in Army bands in California, Sheldon worked considerably around the Los Angeles area. During this time he performed at the Lighthouse and with many groups including Curtis Counce, Stan Kenton, Mel Torme and Benny Goodman in the 50's and again in the mid-60's. In addition to his musical career, Sheldon also appeared on television as an actor, sang and did comedy on albums.

QUARTET/with Walter Norris — Jazz West 1 (1954) 10" **$100;** EP 1 (1954) **$50;** *reissued* Jazz West 6.

QUINTET/with Zoot Sims — Jazz West 2 (1955) 10" **$100;** *reissued* Jazz West 6.

THE QUARTET AND THE QUINTET — Jazz West 6 (1956) **$80;** *reissue* of Jazz West 1 and 2.

JACK'S GROOVE — Gene Norman Presents 60 (1961) **$10.**

A JAZZ PROFILE OF RAY CHARLES/with Marty Paich — Reprise 2004/92004 (1961) **$35.**

OUT/with Howard Roberts — Capitol 1851 (1962) black label with logo on top **$20.**

OOOO, BUT IT'S GOOD — Capitol 1963 (1963) black label with logo on top **$20.**

TOMMY SHEPARD

trombone - born 1923 Chicago, IL

SHEPARD'S FLOCK/with Al Cohn and Nick Travis — Coral 57110 (1957) **$75.**

ARCHIE SHEPP

tenor sax, composer - born 1937 Ft. Lauderdale, FL

ARCHIE SHEPP - BILL DIXON QUARTET — Savoy 12178 (1962) maroon label **$35.**

ARCHIE SHEPP — Impulse 71 (1964) orange label **$30.**

FIRE MUSIC — Impulse 86 (1965) orange label **$30.**

SAHIB SHIHAB

alto, baritone saxes, flute - born 1925 Savannah, GA

After adequate experience in big bands, Shihab's first recordings and widespread recognition came with performing with Fletcher Henderson in the mid-40's. He then worked with Roy Eldridge and eventually moved on to Thelonious Monk, Tadd Dameron, Art Blakey and Dizzy Gillespie for the remainder of the 40's. During his work with Illinois Jacquet in the early 50's he toured Europe and, after finding things difficult in the U.S., in the late 50's moved to Scandinavia where he worked extensively through the 60's. Shihab is a good bop player who has developed into a fine composer and arranger.

JAZZ SAHIB/with Benny Golson — Savoy 12124 (1957) maroon label **$50.**

SUMMER DAWN/with Ake Persson — Argo 742 (1963) **$40.**

*DINAH SHORE

vocals

DINAH SINGS SOME BLUES WITH RED/with Red Norvo Quintet — Capitol 1354 (1959) black label with logo on left side **$35.**

---

*The only LP's within the scope of this book.

WAYNE SHORTER

tenor sax - born 1933 Newark, NJ

Originally influenced by Sonny Rollins, Shorter demonstrated an increasingly strong individual concept evident in his work with Maynard Ferguson, Horace Silver and, from 1959-63, Art Blakey's Jazz Messengers. His recordings with Blakey included compositions of his own and revealed his increasing range of expression on the tenor sax.

INTRODUCING/with Lee Morgan — Vee Jay 3006/1018 (1960) maroon label **$50;** *reissued* Vee Jay 3006/1018 (1962) black label **$40.**

WAYNING MOMENTS/with Freddie Hubbard — Vee Jay 3029 (1961) black label **$40.**

NIGHT DREAMER/with Lee Morgan — Blue Note 4173/84173 (1964) with NY on label **$40;** with A Division of Liberty on label **$20.**

JU JU/with McCoy Tyner — Blue Note 4182/84182 (1964) with NY on label **$40;** with A Division of Liberty on label **$20.**

THE SIGNATURES
vocal group and musicians
Bunny Phillips, Ruth Alcivar, Lee Humes, Bob Alcivar,
Hal Curtis

THEIR VOICES AND INSTRUMENTS — Whippet 702 (1957) **$60.**

SING IN — Warner Brothers 1250 (1959) **$45.**

PREPARE TO FLIP! — Warner Brothers 1353 (1959) **$40.**

HORACE SILVER
piano, composer - born 1928 Norwalk, CT

A swinging player with a gospel sound to his style, Silver worked with notable groups in the early 50's including Stan Getz, Art Blakey, Coleman Hawkins, Lester Young and others before forming a group of his own. With this group he played jazz standards and his own compositions which received much attention and resulted in considerable work and popularity for Silver. He has continued to work, record and tour with groups of varying instrumentation in addition to his usual quintet.

HORACE SILVER TRIO "NEW FACES - NEW SOUNDS"/with Art Blakey — Blue Note 5018 (1953) 10" **$90;** *reissued* Blue Note 1520 (1956) with NY address on label **$60;** with NY on label **$45.**

HORACE SILVER TRIO/with Art Blakey — Blue Note 5034 (1954) 10" **$90;** *reissued* Blue Note 1520 (1956) with NY address on label **$60;** with NY on label **$45.**

HORACE SILVER QUINTET/with Hank Mobley and Kenny Dorham — Blue Note 5058 (1955) 10" **$125;** *reissued* Blue Note 1518.

HORACE SILVER QUINTET/with Hank Mobley and Kenny Dorham — Blue Note 5062 (1955) 10" **$125;** *reissued* Blue Note 1518.

AND THE JAZZ MESSENGERS — Blue Note 1518 (1956) with NY address on label **$80;** with NY on label **$45;** with A Division of Liberty on label **$20;** *reissue* of Blue Note 5058 and 5062.

SIX PIECES OF SILVER/with Hank Mobley — Blue Note 1539 (1956) with NY address on label **$70;** with NY on label **$45;** with A Division of Liberty on label **$20.**

THE STYLINGS OF/with Hank Mobley and Art Farmer — Blue Note 1562 (1957) with NY address on label **$65;** with NY on label **$45;** with A Division of Liberty on label **$20.**

FURTHER EXPLORATIONS/with Clifford Jordan — Blue Note 1589 (1958) with NY address on label **$65;** with NY on label **$45;** with A Division of Liberty on label **$20.**

FINGER POPPIN'/with Blue Mitchell — Blue Note 4008 (1959) with NY address on label **$60;** with NY on label **$45;** with A Division of Liberty on label **$20.**

BLOWING THE BLUES AWAY/with Blue Mitchell — Blue Note 4017/84017 (1959) with NY address on label **$60;** with NY on label **$45;** with A Division of Liberty on label **$20.**

HORACE SCOPE/with Junior Cook — Blue Note 4042/84042 (1960) with NY address on label **$50;** with NY on label **$45;** with A Division of Liberty on label **$20.**

DOIN' THE THING "AT THE VILLAGE GATE"/with Junior Cook — Blue Note 4076/84076 (1961) with NY on label **$45;** with A Division of Liberty on label **$20.**

THE TOKYO BLUES/with Junior Cook — Blue Note 4110/84110 (1962) with NY on label **$45;** with A Division of Liberty on label **$20.**

SILVER SERENADE/with Junior Cook — Blue Note 4131/84131 (1963) with NY on label **$45;** with A Division of Liberty on label **$20.**

SONG FOR MY FATHER/with Carmell Jones and Joe Henderson — Blue Note 4185/84185 (1964) with NY on label **$40;** with A Division of Liberty on label **$20.**

SILVER'S BLUE/with Hank Mobley and Joe Gordon — Epic 3326 (1956) yellow label **$75;** *reissued* Epic 16006 (1958) stereo **$65.**

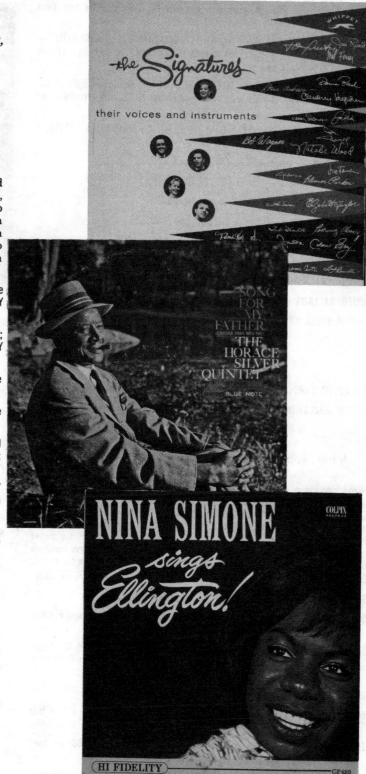

NORMAN SIMMONS
piano, composer - born 1929 Chicago, IL

TRIO — Argo 607 (1956) **$30.**

NINA SIMONE
vocals, piano, composer - born 1933 Tyron, NC

Ms. Simone used her musical background to begin as an accompanist for other vocalists and began singing professionally herself in New York City during the late 50's. She had a hit recording of I Love You Porgy in 1959 which resulted in continued recordings and appearances through the 60's. Ms. Simone sings jazz and many other styles of music but her rich voice and powerful personality come

145

through in everything and are especially effective in her jazz endeavors.

JAZZ AS PLAYED IN AN EXCLUSIVE SIDE STREET CLUB "LITTLE GIRL BLUE" — Bethlehem 6028 (1959) maroon label **$45**; EP 134, EP 135, EP 136 (1959) **$10 ea.**; *reissued* Bethlehem 6028 (1961).

THE ORIGINAL...AND BEST OF "LITTLE GIRL BLUE" — Bethlehem 6028 (1961) maroon label **$30**; same record as above retitled and in rechanneled stereo.

AND HER FRIENDS — Bethlehem 6041 (1959) maroon label **$30**; EP 137 (1959) **$10**.

THE AMAZING — Colpix 407 (1959) gold label **$25**.

NINA AT TOWN HALL — Colpix 409 (1959) gold label **$25**.

AT NEWPORT — Colpix 412 (1960) gold label **$25**.

FORBIDDEN FRUIT — Colpix 419 (1961) gold label **$25**.

AT THE VILLAGE GATE — Colpix 421 (1961) gold label **$25**.

SINGS ELLINGTON — Colpix 425 (1962) gold label **$25**.

IN CONCERT — Philips 200-135/600-135 (1964) **$20**.

BLUES: BALLADS — Philips 200-148/600-148 (1964) **$20**.

I PUT A SPELL ON YOU — Philips 200-172/600-172 (1965) **$20**.

CAROLE SIMPSON
vocals

ALL ABOUT CAROLE — Capitol 878 (1957) green label **$40**.

SINGIN' AND SWINGIN' — Tops 1732 (1960) **$30**.

ZOOT SIMS
tenor, soprano, alto, baritone saxes - born 1925 Inglewood, CA

Sims has been a well-known tenorman since the mid-40's when he began his professional career with big bands which included Benny Goodman, Woody Herman, Stan Kenton and many others. He co-led a group with Al Cohn and has since worked constantly with Cohn, his own groups or as sideman with many other groups. Sims' most collectable LPs are with Al Cohn but he has many fine recordings otherwise. His very smooth, light, Lester Young-style is a favorite.

ZOOT SIMS QUARTET/with Gerald Wiggins — Discovery 3015 (1953) 10" **$200**.

SWINGIN'/with Art Blakey — Prestige 117 (1952) 10" **$150**.

QUARTET/with John Lewis — Prestige 118 (1952) 10" **$150**; *reissued* Prestige 7026 (1956) yellow label **$75**.

ZOOT SIMS/with Al Cohn and Kai Winding — Prestige 138 (1953) 10" **$200**; EP 1348 (1953) **$90**; *reissued* Prestige 7022 (see Stan Getz - The Brothers).

ZOOT SIMS/with Chester Slater — Prestige EP 1306 (1953) **$50**.

ZOOT SIMS IN HOLLYWOOD — Prestige 202 (1955) 10" **$85**; *reissue* of New Jazz 1102.

ZOOT SIMS/with Kenny Drew — New Jazz 1102 (1954) 10" **$100**; *reissued* Prestige 202 and New Jazz 8280.

GOOD OLD ZOOT — New Jazz 8280 (1962) **$35**; *reissue* of New Jazz 1102 and Prestige 202.

THE MODERN ART OF JAZZ/with Bob Brookmeyer — Dawn 1102 (1956) **$60**; *reissued* Seeco 452/4520 (1960) **$35**.

GOES TO JAZZVILLE/with John Williams — Dawn 1115 (1956) **$60**.

ZOOT — Argo 608 (1958) with LP cover in color **$40**; *reissued* with black and white cover **$20**.

PLAYS ALTO, TENOR AND BARITONE/with John Williams — ABC Paramount 155 (1956) **$70**; Sims sings one side on this LP.

PLAYS FOUR ALTOS/with George Handy — ABC Paramount 198 (1957) **$70**.

ZOOT/with Nick Travis — Riverside 12-228 (1956) white label with Bill Grauer Pro. (1956) **$75**; *reissued* (1958) blue label club Bill Grauer Pro. **$60**; *reissued* Jazzland 2 (1960) **$35**;.

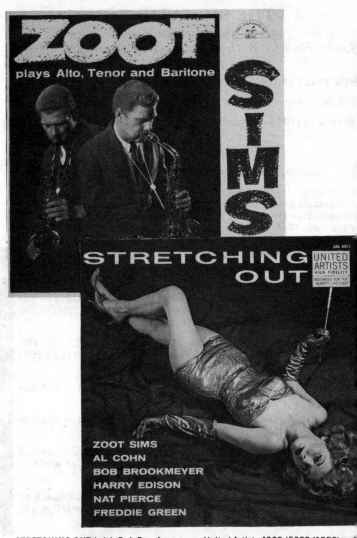

STRETCHING OUT/with Bob Brookmeyer — United Artists 4023/5023 (1959) red label **$60**.

A NIGHT AT THE HALF NOTE/with Al Cohn and Phil Woods — United Artists 4040/5040 (1959) red label **$45**.

IN PARIS — United Artists 14013/15013 (1962) gray label with silhouette of sax player **$40**.

CHOICE/with Russ Freeman — Pacific Jazz 20 (1961) **$40**.

DOWN HOME/with Dave McKenna — Bethlehem 6051 (1960) maroon label **$45**.

NEW BEAT BOSSA NOVA/with Phil Woods and Gene Quill — Colpix 435 (1962) gold label **$45**.

NEW BEAT BOSSA NOVA - Vol 2/with Jim Hall and Spencer Sinatra — Colpix 437 (1963) gold label **$45**.

THE SIX
Johnny Glasel, Bob Wilber, Eddie Phyfe

AN EVENING OF JAZZ/with Tommy Goodman, Porky Cohen and Bob Peterson — Norgran 25 (1954) 10" **$90**; *reissued* Norgran 1065 (1955) **$75**; *reissued* Verve 8155 (1957) with Verve Records, Inc. on bottom of label **$60**.

THE SIX/with Bob Hammar, Sonny Truitt and Bill Britto — Bethlehem 28 (1955) maroon label **$60**.

THE VIEW FROM JAZZBO'S HEAD/with Bob Hammar, Sonny Truitt and Bill Britto — Bethlehem 57 (1956) maroon label **$60**.

DON SLEET
trumpet

ALL MEMBERS/with Jimmy Heath — Jazzland 45/945 (1961) **$35**.

CAROL SLOANE
vocals - born 1937 Providence, RI

OUT OF THE BLUE/with Nick Travis and Bob Brookmeyer — Columbia 1766/8566 (1962) red label with 1 white logo on each side **$20.**

LIVE AT 30TH ST. — Columbia 1923/8723 (1963) red label with 1 white logo on each side **$20.**

THE SMART SET
vocal group

A NEW EXPERIENCE IN VOCAL STYLES/with Jimmy Joyce — Warner Brothers 1203 (1958) gold label **$30.**

BILL SMITH
composer, clarinet - born 1926 Sacramento, CA

FOLK JAZZ/with Shelly Manne — Contemporary 3591/7591 (1961) **$30.**

BUSTER SMITH
alto sax - born 1904 Ellis County, TX

THE LEGENDARY — Atlantic 1323 (1960) black label with 4 page booklet **$55.**

JIMMY SMITH
organ - born 1925 Norristown, PA

After putting together his first trio in 1955, Smith rose to popularity quickly with his unique and swinging style on the organ. He appeared in clubs and at festivals throughout the U.S. and made many recordings in the 50's and 60's. His style has been very influential and has spawned many imitators.

A NEW SOUND, A NEW STAR — Blue Note 1512 (1956) with NY address on label **$40;** with NY on label **$30;** with A Division of Liberty on label **$20.**

A NEW SOUND, A NEW STAR (The Champ) — Blue Note 1514 (1956) with NY address on label **$40;** with NY on label **$30;** with A Division of Liberty on label **$20.**

AT THE ORGAN — Blue Note 1525 (1956) with NY address on label **$40;** with NY on label **$30;** with A Division of Liberty on label **$20;** the cover is Smith pointing his finger.

AT CLUB BABY GRAND — Blue Note 1528 (1956) with NY address on label **$40;** with NY on label **30;** with A Division of Liberty on label **$20.**

AT CLUB BABY GRAND - Vol 2 — Blue Note 1529 (1956) with NY address on label **$40;** with NY on label **$30;** with A Division of Liberty on label **$20.**

A DATE WITH/with Hank Mobley, Lou Donaldson and Donald Byrd — Blue Note 1547 (1957) with NY address on label **$70;** with NY on label **$45;** with A Division of Liberty on label **$20.**

A DATE WITH - Vol 2/with Hank Mobley, Lou Donaldson and Donald Byrd — Blue Note 1548 (1957) with NY address on label **$70;** with NY on label **$45;** with A Division of Liberty on label **$20.**

AT THE ORGAN (All Day Long)/with Lou Donaldson and Kenny Burrell — Blue Note 1551 (1957) with NY address on label **$65;** with NY on label **$45;** with A Division of Liberty on label **$20;** with Smith at organ on cover.

AT THE ORGAN - Vol 2/with Lou Donaldson — Blue Note 1552 (1957) with NY address on label **$65;** with NY on label **$45;** with A Division of Liberty on label **$20;** with Smith at organ on cover.

THE SOUNDS OF — Blue Note 1556 (1957) with NY address on label **$40;** with NY on label **$30;** with A Division of Liberty on label **$20.**

PLAYS PRETTY JUST FOR YOU — Blue Note 1563 (1957) with NY address on label **40;** with NY on label **$30;** with A Division of Liberty on label **$20.**

GROOVIN' AT SMALL'S PARADISE — Blue Note 1585 (1958) with NY address on label **$40;** with NY on label **$30;** with A Division of Liberty on label **$20.**

GROOVIN' AT SMALL'S PARADISE — Blue Note 1586 (1958) with NY address on label **40;** with NY on label **$30;** with A Division of Liberty on label **$20.**

HOUSE PARTY/with Lee Morgan, Tina Brooks and Lou Donaldson — Blue Note 4002 (1959) with NY address on label **$60;** with NY on label **$45;** with A Division of Liberty on label **$20.**

THE SERMON/with Lee Morgan, Tina Brooks and Lou Donaldson — Blue Note 4011 (1959) with NY address on label **$60;** with NY on label **$45;** with A Division of Liberty on label **$20.**

CRAZY BABY — Blue Note 4030/84030 (1960) with NY address on label **$40;** with NY on label **$30;** with A Division of Liberty on label **$20.**

HOME COOKIN'/with Kenny Burrell — Blue Note 4050/84050 (1960) with NY address on label **$40;** with NY on label **$30;** with A Division of Liberty on label **$20.**

MIDNIGHT SPECIAL/with Stanley Turrentine — Blue Note 4078/84078 (1961) with NY on label **$45;** with A Division of Liberty on label **$20.**

PLAYS FATS WALLER — Blue Note 4100/84100 (1961) with NY on label **$30;** with A Division of Liberty on label **$20.**

BACK AT THE CHICKEN SHACK/with Stanley Turrentine — Blue Note 4117/84117 (1961) with NY on label **$45;** with A Division of Liberty on label **$30.**

ROCKIN' THE BOAT/with Lou Donaldson — Blue Note 4141/84141 (1963) with NY on label **$45;** with A Division of Liberty on label **$20.**

PRAYER MEETIN'/with Stanley Turrentine — Blue Note 4164/84164 (1963) with NY on label **$45;** with A Division of Liberty on label **$20.**

BASHIN', THE UNPREDICTABLE/with Phil Woods and George Barrow — Verve 8472/68472 (1962) with MGM on bottom of label **$35.**

HOBO FLATS/with Oliver Nelson Orchestra — Verve 8544/68544 (1963) with MGM on bottom of label **$20.**

ANY NUMBER CAN WIN/with Orchestra — Verve 8552/68552 (1965) with MGM on bottom of label **$15.**

BLUE BASH/with Kenny Burrell — Verve 8553/68553 (1963) with MGM on bottom of label **$25.**

WHO'S AFRAID OF VIRGINIA WOOLF? — Verve 8583/68583 (1964) with MGM on bottom of label **$10.** (A)

THE CAT/with Lalo Schifrin — Verve 8587/68587 (1964) with MGM on bottom of label **$25.**

CHRISTMAS '64 — Verve 8604/68604 (1964) with MGM on bottom of label **$45.**

MONSTER — Verve 8618/68618 (1965) with MGM on bottom of label **$10.**

ORGAN GINGER SWING/with Kenny Burrell — Verve 8628/68628 (1965) with MGM on bottom of label **$20.**

JOHNNY "HAMMOND" SMITH
organ - born 1933 Louisville, KY

ALL SOUL/with Thornel Schwartz — New Jazz 8221 (1960) **$45.**

THAT GOOD FEELIN'/with Thornel Schwartz — New Jazz 8229 (1960) **$45.**

TALK THAT TALK/with Oliver Nelson — New Jazz 8241 (1961) **$45.**

GETTIN' THE MESSAGE/with Lem Winchester — Prestige 7217 (1960) yellow label **$45;** *reissued* Prestige 7217 (1965) blue label with logo on right side **$30.**

STIMULATION/with Fred McCoy — Prestige 7203 (1961) yellow label **$45;** *reissued* Prestige 7203 (1965) blue label with logo on right side **$30.**

COOKS WITH GATOR TAIL/with Willis Jackson — Prestige 7239 (1962) yellow label **$50;** *reissued* Prestige 7239 (1965) blue label with logo on right side **$30.**

THE STINGER/with Houston Person — Prestige 7408 (1965) blue label with logo on right side **$30.**

BLACK COFFEE/with Seldon Powell — Riverside 442/9442 (1962) blue label mono; black label stereo with Bill Grauer Pro. **$35.**

MR. WONDERFUL/with Houston Person — Riverside 466/9466 (1963) blue label mono; black label stereo with Bill Grauer Pro. **$35.**

JOHNNY SMITH
guitar - born 1922 Birmingham, AL

For the most part, Smith was a self-taught guitarist who obtained a large amount of experience early in his career. He was a staff musician with N.B.C. in the late 40's until he achieved a commercial hit in 1952 with Moonlight In Vermont. Following that success, he worked with his own jazz group in New York City through the 60's producing several more recordings. Smith is an extremely capable player whose jazz work is primarily on the guitar.

JOHNNY SMITH QUINTET/with Stan Getz — Roost 410 (1952) 10" **$95;** EP 303, EP 305 (1952) **$45 ea.;** *reissued* Roost 2211.

JOHNNY SMITH QUINTET/with Stan Getz — Roost 413 (1953) 10" **$95;** EP 310, EP 311 (1953) **$45 ea.;** *reissued* Roost 2211.

IN A MELLOW MOOD — Roost 421 (1953) 10" **$50;** *reissued* Roost 2215.

PLAYS JIMMY VAN HEUSEN — Roost 2201 (1955) **$40;** *reissued* Roost 2250 (1962) **$25.**

QUARTET — Roost 2203 (1955) **$40.**

MOONLIGHT IN VERMONT/with Stan Getz — Roost 2211 (1956) **$65;** *reissue* of Roost 410 and 413.

MOODS — Roost 2215 (1956) **$35;** *reissue* of Roost 421.

NEW QUARTET — Roost 2216 (1956) **$35.**

FOURSOME — Roost 2223 (1956) **$35.**

FOURSOME - Vol 2 — Roost 2228 (1957) **$35.**

FLOWER DRUM SONG — Roost 2231 (1958) **$35.**

EASY LISTENING — Roost 2233 (1959) **$35.**

FAVORITES — Roost 2237 (1959) **$35.**

DESIGNED FOR YOU — Roost 2238 (1960) **$30.**

DEAR LITTLE SWEETHEART — Roost 2239 (1960) **$30.**

GUITAR AND STRINGS — Roost 2242 (1960) **$30.**

PLUS THE TRIO — Roost 2243 (1960) **$30.**

SOUND OF THE JOHNNY SMITH GUITAR — Roost 2246 (1961) **$30.**

MAN WITH THE BLUE GUITAR — Roost 2248 (1962) **$25.**

GUITAR WORLD — Roost 2254 (1963) **$20.**

REMINISCING — Roost 2259 (1965) **$20.**

ANNOTATIONS OF THE MUSES/with Johnny Richards — Legende 1401 (1954) 10" **$65.**

LOUIS SMITH
trumpet - born 1931 Memphis, TN

HERE COMES/with Duke Jordan — Blue Note 1584 (1958) with NY address on label **$85.**

SMITHVILLE/with Charlie Rouse and Sonny Clark — Blue Note 1594 (1958) with NY address on label **$85.**

OSBORNE SMITH
vocals

EYES OF LOVE/with Richard Evans — Argo 4000 (1960) **$40.**

STUFF SMITH
violin - born 1909 Portsmouth, OH

TOWN HALL CONCERT/with Krupa and Ventura Trio — Commodore 20,028 (1950) 10" **$200.**

STUFF SMITH/with Oscar Peterson — Verve 2041 (1957) with Verve Records, Inc. on bottom of label **$50;** *reissued* Verve 8206 (1958) with Verve Records, Inc. on bottom of label **$40.**

WILLIE SMITH
alto sax - born 1908 Charleston, SC

ALTO SAX ARTISTRY/with Billy May - Mercury 25075 (1950) 10" **$150**; *reissued* EmArcy 26000.

RELAXIN' AFTER HOURS — EmArcy 26000 (1954) 10" **$100**; EP 1-6008 (1954) **$50**.

FRANK SOCOLOW
tenor sax - born 1923 Brooklyn, NY Died 1981

SOUNDS BY SOCOLOW/with Eddie Bert and Sal Salvador — Bethlehem 70 (1957) maroon label **$75**.

LES SPANN
guitar - born 1932 Pine Bluff, AK

GEMINI/with Tommy Flanagan — Jazzland 35/935 (1961) **$35**.

*JO STAFFORD
vocals

JO + JAZZ/with Ben Webster and Johnny Hodges — Columbia 1561/8361 (1960) red label with 3 black logos on each side **$50**.

The only LP's within the scope of this book.

MARY STALLINGS
vocals - born 1938 San Francisco, CA

CAL TJADER PLAYS, MARY STALLINGS SINGS/with Paul Horn — Fantasy 3325/ 8068 (1961) red vinyl **$50**.

*KAY STARR
vocals - born 1922 Dougherty, OK

SONGS BY/with Dave Cavanaugh - Capitol H211 (1952) 10" **$75**; Capitol CCF211 7" 3 record box set (1949) **$40**; *reissued* Capitol T211 (1955) green label **$60**.

JAZZ SINGER — Capitol 1438 (1960) black label with logo on left side **$35**.

SWINGIN' WITH THE STARR — Liberty 9001 (1956) **$50**; *reissued* Coronet 106.

SINGIN' KAY STARR - SWINGIN' ERROLL GARNER — Modern 1203 (1956) **$45**; *reissued* Crown 5003 (1957) one side each with liner notes on cover **$40**.

THEM THERE EYES — Rondo-Lette 3 (1958) **$45**.

KAY STARR SINGS — Coronet 106 (1963) **$15**; *reissue* of Liberty 9001.

The only LP's within the scope of this book.

DAKOTA STATON
vocals - born 1932 Pittsburgh, PA

Staton came to national prominence in the mid-50's through her many recordings which featured her impressive voice and warm personal style. She has continued to do club and concert appearances and to record.

THE LATE LATE SHOW/with Hank Jones — Capitol 876 (1957) green label **$65**; *reissued* Capitol 876 (1959) black label with logo on left side **$45**; *reissued* Capitol 876 (1962) black label with logo on top **$20**.

IN THE NIGHT/with George Shearing Quintet — Capitol 1003 (1958) green label **$55**; *reissued* Capitol 1003 (1959) black label with logo on left side **$45**; *reissued* Capitol 1003 (1962) black label with logo on top **$20**.

DYNAMIC! — Capitol 1054 (1958) black label with logo on left side **$50**; *reissued* Capitol 1054 (1962) black label with logo on top **$20**.

CRAZY HE CALLS ME — Capitol 1170 (1958) black label with logo on left side **$50**; EP 1-1170, EP 2-1170 (1958) **$25 ea.**; *reissued* Capitol 1170 (1962) black label with logo on top **$20**.

HAVE VIOLIN WILL SWING/with Red Callender — Verve 8282 (1958) with Verve Records, Inc. on bottom of label **$40**.

CAT ON A HOT FIDDLE/with Red Mitchell — Verve 8339/6097 (1959) with Verve Records, Inc. on bottom of label **$40**.

DIZZY GILLESPIE AND STUFF SMITH — Verve 8214 (1958) with Verve Records, Inc. on bottom of label **$50**.

SWEET SWINGIN' STUFF/with Johnny Letman — 20th Century Fox 3008 (1959) **$30**.

SWINGIN' STUFF - EmArcy 26008/66008 (1965) gray label with EmArcy logos in circle **$25**.

149

TIME TO SWING/with Jerome Richardson and Joe Wilder — Capitol 1241 (1959) black label with logo on left side **$40**; *reissued* Capitol 1241 (1962) black label with logo on top **$20**.

MORE THAN THE MOST/with Sid Feller — Capitol 1325 (1959) black label with logo on left side **$40**; *reissued* Capitol 1325 (1962) black label with logo on top **$20**.

SINGS BALLADS AND THE BLUES/with Eddie Wilcox — Capitol 1387 (1959) black label with logo on left side **$40**; *reissued* Capitol 1387 (1963) black label with logo on top **$20**.

SOFTLY/with Benny Carter — Capitol 1427 (1960) black label with logo on left side **$35**; *reissued* Captiol 1427 (1963) black label with logo on top **$20**.

DAKOTA/with Benny Carter — Capitol 1490 (1960) black label with logo on left side **$35**; *reissued* Capitol 1427 (1963) black label with logo on top **$20**.

ROUND MIDNIGHT/with Benny Carter — Capitol 1597 (1960) black label with logo on left side **$35**; *reissued* Capitol 1597 (1963) black label with logo on top **$20**.

DAKOTA AT STORYVILLE/with Norman Simmons — Capitol 1649 (1961) black label with logo on left side **$30**; *reissued* Capitol 1649 (1963) black label with logo on top **$20**.

FROM DAKOTA WITH LOVE/with Matthew Gee — United Artists 3292/6292 (1963) gray label with silhouette of sax player **$30**.

LIVE AND SWINGING/with Howard McGhee and Billy Mitchell — United Artists 3312/6312 (1963) gray label with silhouette of sax player **$30**.

WITH STRINGS — United Artists 3355/6355 (1964) gray label with silhouette of sax player **$30**.

BETTY ST. CLAIRE
vocals - born Columbus, OH

COOL AND CLEARER — Jubilee 23 (1954) 10" **$75**.

WHAT IS THERE TO SAY? — Jubilee 1011 (1956) **$50**.

AT BASIN ST. EAST — Seeco 456 (1960) **$30**.

HERBIE STEWARD
alto, tenor, baritone saxes - born 1926 Los Angeles, CA

SO PRETTY/with Orchestra — Ava 9 (1962) **$40**.

HELYNE STEWART
LOVE MOODS/with Art Pepper, Teddy Edwards and Jack Sheldon — Contemporary 3601/7601 (1961) yellow label **$50**.

SAM STEWART
bass - born 1914 Englewood, NJ

BLOWIN' SINGIN' — Savoy 12067 (1956) maroon label **$40**.

TOM STEWART
tenor sax, trumpet - born 1931 Bridgeport, CT

SEXTETTE-QUINTET — ABC Paramount 117 (1956) **$40**.

SONNY STITT
tenor, alto, baritone saxes - born 1924 Boston, MA
died 1982

Stitt was thought by many to be copying Charlie Parker but subsequent research has shown that he developed a similar approach prior to meeting or hearing Parker. Their admiration for each other was well known and it is not surprising that Stitt first gained attention through his work with another well known Parker collaborator, Dizzy Gillespie. He toured extensively with JATP and was also popular for a series of recordings he made with Gene Ammons. He has recorded often all through his career in many different contexts and is considered by many to be one of the finest altoists since Parker. Stitt died at the age of 58.

ALL STAR SERIES: BE-BOP/with Kenny Dorham and Bud Powell — Savoy 9006 (1953) 10" **$95**.

NEW TRENDS OF JAZZ/with Kenny Dorham — Savoy 9014 (1953) 10" **$95**.

SONNY STITT PLAYS/with Bud Powell — Prestige 103 (1951) 10" **$100**; *reissued* Prestige 7024 and 7248.

BATTLE OF SAXES/with Gene Ammons — Prestige 107 (1951) 10" **$150**; EP 1316 (1950) **$70**.

MR. SAXOPHONE/with Kenny Drew — Prestige 111 (1951) 10" **$100**; EP 1346 (1951) **$50**; *reissued* Prestige 7077.

FAVORITES/with Duke Jordan — Prestige 126 (1952) 10" **$95**; *reissued* Prestige 7133.

FAVORITES/with Junior Mance — Prestige 148 (1953) 10" **$95**; *reissued* Prestige 7077.

SONNY STITT WITH BUD POWELL AND J.J. JOHNSON — Prestige 7024 (1956) yellow label **$80**; *reissue* of Prestige 103.

KALEIDOSCOPE — Prestige 7077 (1956) yellow label **$75**; *reissue* of Prestige 111.

STITT'S BITS — Prestige 7133 (1957) yellow label **$75**; *reissue* of Prestige 126.

MEETS JACK McDUFF — Prestige 7244 (1962) yellow label **$55**.

SOUL SHACK/with Jack McDuff — Prestige 7297 (1963) yellow label **$50**.

NUTHER FU'THER/with Jack McDuff — Prestige 7244 (1963) yellow label **$45**.

PRIMITIVO SOUL — Prestige 7302 (1964) yellow label **$40**.

SHANGRI LA — Prestige 7332 (1965) blue label with logo on right side **$35**.

SOUL PEOPLE/with Booker Ervin and Don Patterson — Prestige 7372 (1965) blue label with logo on right side **$35**.

ARRANGEMENTS FROM THE PEN OF JOHNNY RICHARDS/with Kai Winding and Horace Silver — Roost 415 (1952) 10" **$200**.

JAZZ AT THE HI HAT — Roost 418 (1952) 10" **$200**.

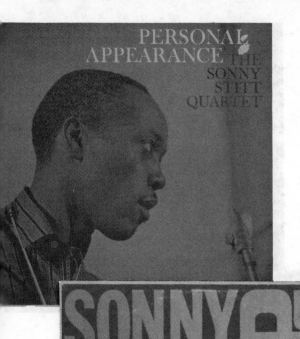

SITS IN WITH THE OSCAR PETERSON TRIO — Verve 8344/6108 (1959) with Verve Records, Inc. on bottom of label **$60**.

BLOWS THE BLUES/with Leroy Vinnegar — Verve 8374/68374 (1959) with Verve Records, Inc. on bottom of label **$50**.

SAXOPHONE SUPREMACY/with Mel Lewis — Verve 8377/68377 (1959) **$50**.

SWINGS THE MOST/with Lou Levy — Verve 8389/68380 (1959) with Verve Records, Inc. on bottom of label **$50**.

SENSUAL SOUNDS/with Orchestra — Verve 8451/68451 (1962) with MGM on bottom of label **$35**.

EARLY MODERN/with Kai Winding — Jazztone 1231 (1956) **$45**; *reissued* Jazztone 1263 (1957) **$40**; *reissue* of Roost matter.

SONNY STITT — Argo 629 (1958) **$35**.

BURNIN'/with Barry Harris — Argo 661 (1961) **$35**.

AT THE D.J. LOUNGE/with John Board — Argo 683 (1961) **$35**.

REARIN' BACK/with Ronald Mathews — Argo 709 (1962) **$35**.

MOVE ON OVER — Argo 730 (1964) **$35**.

MY MAIN MAN — Argo 744 (1965) **$35**.

INTER ACTION/with Zoot Sims — Cadet 760 (1965) dark and light blue label with Cadet in pink and white on top **$20**.

AND THE TOP BRASS/with Jimmy Cleveland and Tadd Dameron — Atlantic 1395 (1962) with logo on right side **$35**.

STITT PLAYS BIRD — Atlantic 1418 (1964) with logo on right side **$30**.

THE MATADORS MEET THE BULL: STITT/with Eddie Lockjaw Davis — Roulette 25339 (1965) dark and light orange checked roulette wheel label **$30**.

NOW/with Hank Jones — Impulse 43 (1963) orange label **$30**.

SALT AND PEPPER/with Paul Gonsalves — Impulse 52 (1964) orange label **$35**.

MY MOTHER'S EYES/with Charlie Kynard — Pacific Jazz 71 (1963) **$35**.

LOW FLAME/with Don Patterson — Jazzland 71/971 (1962) **$45**.

BILLY STRAYHORN
piano, composer - born 1915 Dayton, OH

TRIO/with Duke Ellington — Mercer 1001 (1951) 10" **$150**.

SEPTET/with Johnny Hodges — Felsted 7008/2008 (1959) **$60**.

PEACEFUL SIDE OF/with Choirs — United Artists 14010/15010 (1962) gray label with silhouette of sax player **$35**.

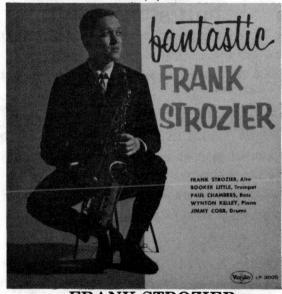

FRANK STROZIER
alto sax - born 1937 Memphis, TN

Well known around the Chicago area in the mid-50's, Strozier went to New York City where he was first recorded. He then worked with Roy Haynes in the early 60's before venturing to the West Coast. Strozier

---

ATTLE OF BIRDLAND/with Eddie Davis — Roost 1203 (1956) **$50**.

LAYS ARRANGEMENTS OF QUINCY JONES/with Sheldon Powell — Roost 2204 (1956) **$40**.

ONNY STITT/with Freddie Green — Roost 1208 (1956) **$40**.

7 MINUTES AND 48 SECONDS — Roost 2219 (1956) **$50**.

WITH THE NEW YORKERS — Roost 2226 (1957) **$40**.

HE SAXOPHONE OF — Roost 2230 (1959) **$40**.

TTLE BIT OF STITT — Roost 2235 (1959) **$40**.

ONNY SIDE OF STITT — Roost 2240 (1960) **$40**.

TITTSVILLE — Roost 2244 (1960) **$40**.

UNNY SIDE UP — Roost 2245 (1960) **$40**.

EELINS' — Roost 2247 (1962) **$35**.

N ORBIT — Roost 2252 (1963) **$35**.

OES LATIN — Roost 2253 (1963) **$35**.

EW YORK JAZZ/with Ray Brown — Verve 8219 (1957) with Verve Records, Inc. on bottom of label **$65**.

ERSONAL APPEARANCE/with Bobby Timmons — Verve 8324 (1959) with Verve Records, Inc. on bottom of label **$65**.

NLY THE BLUES/with Roy Eldridge — Verve 8250 (1957) with Verve Records, Inc. on bottom of label **$65**.

LAYS JIMMY GIUFFRE ARRANGEMENTS/with Jack Sheldon — Verve 8309/6041 (1959) with Verve Records, Inc. on bottom of label **$60**.

ARD SWING/with Lennie McBrowne — Verve 8306/6038 (1959) with Verve Records, Inc. on bottom of label **$60**.

is very respected for his ability on the alto and has recorded with many fine groups including Shelly Manne in the mid-60's.

FANTASTIC/with Booker Little — Vee Jay 1007/3005 (1960) maroon label **$50**; *reissued* Vee Jay 1007/3005 (1962) black label **$40**.

LONG NIGHT/with George Coleman — Jazzland 56/956 (1961) **$40**.

MARCH OF THE SIAMESE CHILDREN/with Harold Mabern — Jazzland 70/970 (1962) **$40**.

IDREES SULIEMAN
trumpet - born 1923 St. Petersburg, FL

COOLIN'/with Teddy Charles — New Jazz 8216 (1958) **$45**.

IRA SULLIVAN
trumpet - born 1931 Washington, D.C.

Sullivan came from a musical family, learning trumpet from his father and saxophone from his mother. He was a professional from an early age and grew to prominence around Chicago in the late 40's. Most of his work and recording was done in this area with groups and as sideman on pieces by other musicians.

BILLY TAYLOR INTRODUCES — ABC Paramount 162 (1957) **$50**.

QUINTET: BLUE STROLL/with Johnny Griffin — Delmark 402 (1961) **$40**.

BIRD LIVES!/with Nicky Hill and Jodie Christian — Vee Jay 3033 (1962) black label **$40**.

MAXINE SULLIVAN
vocals - born 1911 Homestead, PA

Sullivan worked considerably with Claude Thornhill before going with John Kirby's group with whom she achieved much popularity in 1938 from the recording Loch Lomond. She was also married to John Kirby from 1937 to 41. Sullivan was a very good singer and was in several movies in addition to her continued club appearances and recordings through the mid-50's.

MAXINE SULLIVAN/with Charlie Shavers — Period 1909 (1955) **$60**.

MAXINE SULLIVAN/with Charlie Shavers — Period 1207 (1956) **$60**.

FLOW GENTLY, SWEET RHYTHM/with Charlie Shavers — Jazztone 1229 (1956) **$45**; *reissue* of Period matter.

THE COMPLETE CHARLIE SHAVERS WITH MAXINE SULLIVAN — Bethlehem 67 (1957) maroon label **$40**.

PHIL SUNKEL
trumpet, cornet, composer - born 1925 Zanesville, OH

JAZZ BAND — ABC Paramount 136 (1956) **$75**.

JAZZ CONCERTO GROSSO/with Bob Brookmeyer and Gerry Mulligan — ABC Paramount 225 (1958) **$75**.

REINHOLD SVENSSON
piano, organ - born 1919 Husum, Sweden died 1968

MODERN PIANOS/with Bengt Hallberg — Prestige 174 (1954) 10" **$80**.

SEXTET: NEW SOUNDS OF SWEDEN — Prestige 155 (1953) 10" **$90**.

PIANO: NEW SOUNDS OF SWEDEN — Prestige 129 (1952) 10" **$50**.

PIANO: NEW SOUNDS OF SWEDEN — Prestige 106 (1951) 10" **$50**.

SYLVIA SYMS
vocals - born 1919 New York City, NY

A highly respected singer who was appreciated and encouraged by Benny Carter early in her career, Syms worked in New York City in clubs through the 40's and 50's. In 1956 Syms' big hit was I Could Have Danced All Night.

SONGS BY/with Barbara Carroll — Atlantic 137 (1953) 10" **$80**; *reissued* Atlantic 1243 (1956) black label **$50**; *reissued* Atlantic 1243 (1960) with logo on right side **$30**.

AFTER DARK — Version 103 (1954) 10" **$60**.

SINGS — Decca 8188 (1955) black label with silver lettering **$40**.

SONG OF LOVE — Decca 8639 (1958) black label with silver lettering **$35**.

THE FABULOUS — 20th Century Fox 4123 (1964) **$20**.

SYLVIA IS!/with Kenny Burrell — Prestige 7439 (1965) blue label with logo on right side **$45**.

THE SYNANON BAND
Greg Dykes, Dave Allen, Arnold Ross, Joe Pass, Ronald Clark, Bill Crawford, Candy Latston

SOUNDS OF SYNANON — Pacific Jazz 48 (1962) **$50**; musicians are narcotic addicts in self-help Synanon Home for the Cure.

BUDDY TATE
tenor sax - born 1925 Sherman, TX

Tate gained early experience with artists such as John Kirby and was in Count Basie's first band in Kansas City during the early 30's. He continued to work with Basie from 1939-49 and his big, warm sound found him great popularity. This resulted in several recordings with Basie and, from the early 50's, he led a band of his own in New York City which took him on tours of Europe.

SWINGING LIKE TATE/with Ben Richardson — Felsted 7004/2004 (1958) **$40**.

TATE'S DATE/with Ben Richardson — Swingville 2003 (1960) **$30**.

TATE-A-TATE/with Clark Terry — Swingville 2014 (1960) **$30**.

GROOVIN' WITH — Swingville 2029 (1961) **$30**.

DUANE TATRO
tenor sax, arranger, composer - born 1927 Van Nuys, CA

JAZZ FOR MODERNS/with Lennie Niehaus, Bill Holman and Jimmy Giuffre — Contemporary 3514 (1956) yellow label **$60**.

ART TATUM
piano - born 1910 Toledo, OH died 1956

Tatum was well known in his hometown through appearing in clubs and on the radio. He went to New York City in 1932 where his exceptional technique and ideas quickly gained him recognition as a master of his instrument. From that time, until his death in 1956, Tatum worked and recorded consistently, usually with a trio or as a solo. His recorded works reveal the reason he made such an impression on his contemporaries and why he is still regarded as one of the best pianists to ever play jazz.

ART TATUM TRIO/with Tiny Grimes — Dial 206 (1948) 10" **$75**; *reissued* Roost 2213 and Jazztone 1203.

ART TATUM TRIO AND PIANO SOLOS/with Tiny Grimes — Stinson 40 (1950) 10" **$75**.

ART TATUM TRIO — Folkway 33 (1954) 10" **$65**; *reissued* Folkway 2293 (1962) 10" **$40**.

ART TATUM TRIO — Brunswick 58013 (1950) 10" **$75**; EP 71020, EP 71021 (1950) **$35 ea.**; Brunswick 9-7003 (1950) 4 record 7" box set **$45**; *reissued* Brunswick 54004.

PIANO SOLOS — Brunswick 58023 (1950) 10" **$75**; Brunswick 9-7006 (1950) 4 record 7" box set **$45**.

HERE'S ART TATUM — Brunswick 54004 (1954) **$50**.

PIANO SOLOS — Decca 5086 (1950) 10" **$70**; Decca 9-304 (1950) 4 record 7" box set **$45**; *reissued* Decca 8715.

THE ART OF TATUM — Decca 8715 (1957) **$50**.

TATUM CONCERT — Columbia 6301 (1950) 10" **$70**; Columbia 4-12 (1950) 4 record 7" box set **$45**; *reissued* Columbia 2565 (1956) 10" **$45**; *reissued* Harmony 7006 (1957) **$35**.

TATUM PIANO — Rem 2 (1950) 10" **$60**.

ART TATUM ALBUM — Capitol H216 (1950) 10" **$70**; EP 216 (1950) 2 records **$40**; *reissued* Capitol T216 (1955) green label **$60**.

ENCORES — Capitol H269 (1950) 10" **$75**; EP 269 (1950) 2 records **$35**; *reissued* Capitol T216.

ART TATUM TRIO — Capitol H408 (1953) 10" **$65**.

ART TATUM — Capitol T216 (1955) green label **$50**.

PIANO DISCOVERIES — 20th Century Fox 3029 (1960) **$25**; *reissued* 20th Century Fox 102.

PIANO DISCOVERIES — 20th Century Fox 3033 (1960) **$25**; *reissued* 20th Century Fox 102.

PIANO DISCOVERIES — 20th Century Fox 102-2 (1961) 2 LPs **$45**; *reissue* of 20th Century Fox 3029 and 3033.

GIANTS OF THE PIANO/with Erroll Garner — Roost 2213 (1956) **$45**; one side each.

KINGS OF THE KEYBOARD/with Erroll Garner — Jazztone 1203 (1956) **$40**; one side each.

THE GENIUS OF #1 — Clef 612 (1953) **$50**; EP 264, EP 265, EP 266 (1953) **$15 ea.**; *reissued* Verve 8036 (1957) with Verve Records, Inc. on bottom of label **$40**.

THE GENIUS OF #2 — Clef 613 (1953) **$50**; EP 271 (1953) **$15**; *reissued* Verve 8037 (1957) with Verve Records, Inc. on bottom of label **$40**.

THE GENIUS OF #3 — Clef 614 (1953) **$50**; EP 267, EP 269 (1953) **$15 ea.**; *reissued* Verve 8038 (1957) with Verve Records, Inc. on bottom of label **$40**.

THE GENIUS OF #4 — Clef 615 (1953) **$50**; EP 270, EP 271, EP 272 (1953) **$15 ea.**; *reissued* Verve 8039 (1957) with Verve Records, Inc. on bottom of label **$40**.

THE GENIUS OF #5 — Clef 618 (1953) **$50**; EP 273, EP 274 (1953) **$15 ea.**; *reissued* Verve 8040 (1957) with Verve Records, Inc. on bottom of label **$40**.

THE GENIUS OF #6 — Clef 657 (1955) **$45**; EP 349, EP 350, EP 351 (1955) **$15 ea.**; *reissued* Verve 8055 (1957) with Verve Records, Inc. on bottom of label **$40**.

THE GENIUS OF #7 — Clef 658 (1955) **$45**; EP 352, EP 353 (1955) **$15 ea.**; *reissued* Verve 8056 (1957) with Verve Records, Inc. on bottom of label **$40**.

THE GENIUS OF #8 — Clef 659 (1955) **$45**; EP 354, EP 355, EP 356 (1955) **$15 ea.**; *reissued* Verve 8057 (1957) with Verve Records, Inc. on bottom of label **$40**.

THE GENIUS OF #9 — Clef 660 (1955) **$45**; EP 357, EP 358 (1955) **$15**; *reissued* Verve 8058 (1957) with Verve Records, Inc. on bottom of label **$40**.

THE GENIUS OF #10 — Clef 661 (1955) **$45**; EP 359, EP 360 (1955) **$15**; *reissued* Verve 8059 (1957) with Verve Records, Inc. on bottom of label **$40**.

THE GENIUS OF #11 — Clef 712 (1956) **$45**; *reissued* Verve 8095 (1957) with Verve Records, Inc. on bottom of label **$40**.

THE ART TATUM, LOUIS BELLSON, BENNY CARTER TRIO — Clef 643 (1955) **$75**; EP 318, EP 319, EP 320 (1955) **$30 ea.**; *reissued* Verve 8013.

THE ART TATUM, ROY ELDRIDGE, JOHN SIMMONS, ALVIN STOLLER QUARTET — Clef 679 (1955) **$75**; *reissued* Verve 8064 (1957) with Verve Records, Inc. on bottom of label **$65**.

ART TATUM - Vol 1 — Verve 8101/5 (1957) 5 LP box set with Verve Records, Inc. on bottom of label **$95**.

ART TATUM - Vol 2 — Verve 8102/5 (1957) 5 LP box set with Verve Records, Inc. on bottom of label **$95**.

THE THREE GIANTS/with Carter and Bellson — Verve 8013 (1957) with Verve Records, Inc. on bottom of label **$65**; *reissue* of Clef 643.

PRESENTING — Verve 8118 (1957) with Verve Records, Inc. on bottom of label **$40**.

THE ART TATUM - BEN WEBSTER QUARTET — Verve 8220 (1957) with Verve Records, Inc. on bottom of label **$65**.

MAKIN' WHOOPEE/with Benny Carter — Verve 8227 (1958) with Verve Records, Inc. on bottom of label **$65**.

THE ART TATUM - BUDDY DeFRANCO QUARTET — Verve 8229 (1958) with Verve Records, Inc. on bottom of label **$45**.

THE IMCOMPARABLE — Verve 8332 (1959) with Verve Records, Inc. on bottom of label **$40**.

THE GREATEST PIANO OF THEM ALL — Verve 8323 (1959) with Verve Records, Inc. on bottom of label **$40**.

MORE OF THE GREATEST PIANO — Verve 8347 (1960) with Verve Records, Inc. on bottom of label **$30**.

STILL MORE OF THE GREATEST PIANO — Verve 8360 (1960) with Verve Records, Inc. on bottom of label **$30**.

AN ALL STAR TRIBUTE TO TATUM — American Recording Society 424 (1957) **$60**.

ART TAYLOR
drums - born 1929 New York City, NY

TAYLOR'S WAILERS/with Donald Byrd and Jackie McLean — Prestige 7117 (1957) yellow label **$65.**

TAYLOR'S TENORS/with Frank Foster and Charlie Rouse — New Jazz 8219 (1959) **$45.**

A.T.'S DELIGHT/with Stanley Turrentine — Blue Note 4047 (1960) with NY address on label **$50.**

BILLY TAYLOR
piano, composer - born 1921 Greenville, NC

In the 40's Taylor worked with many name groups including Ben Webster, Dizzy Gillespie and Stuff Smith among others. He toured with Don Redman in 1946 and worked as the house pianist at Birdland. In the 50's, Taylor led his own groups and became increasingly involved in radio D.J. work as well as teaching through the 60's. Throughout his career and in all of his recordings, Taylor has demonstrated a command of many styles and a great deal of taste and swing.

BILLY TAYLOR PIANO/with John Hardee — Savoy 9035 (1951) 10" **$80.**

PIANO PANORAMA/with John Collins — Atlantic 113 (1951) 10" **$70**; EP 517, EP 532 (1951) **$30** ea.; *reissued* Atlantic 1277.

THE BILLY TAYLOR TOUCH — Atlantic 1277 (1957) black label **$40.**

ONE FOR FUN — Atlantic 1329 (1959) black label **$40.**

JAZZ AT STORYVILLE/with Charlie Mingus — Roost 406 (1952) 10" **$75**; *reissued* in part Roost 2222.

TAYLOR MADE JAZZ/with Chuck Wayne — Roost 409 (1952) 10" **$75**; *reissued* Roost 2222 (1958) **$45.**

TRIO — Prestige 139 (1952) 10" **$85**; *reissued* Prestige 7015 (1956) yellow label **$60.**

TRIO — Prestige 165 (1953) 10" **$85**; EP 1336 (1953) **$40**; *reissued* Prestige 7016 (1956) yellow label **$60.**

TRIO — Prestige 168 (1953) 10" **$85**; EP 1333, EP 1335 (1953) **$40** ea.; *reissued* Prestige 7016.

PLAYS D.J. THEME — Prestige 184 (1954) 10" **$75**; *reissued* Prestige 7071.

BILLY TAYLOR WITH CANDIDO — Prestige 188 (1954) 10" **$75**; EP 1344 (1954) **$35**; *reissued* Prestige 7051 (1956) yellow label **$55.**

AT TOWN HALL — Prestige 194 (1954) 10" **$75**; *reissued* Prestige 7093 (1956) yellow label **$55.**

A TOUCH OF — Prestige 7001 (1955) yellow label **$65.**

CROSS SECTION — Prestige 7071 (1956) yellow label **$55**; *reissue* of Prestige 184.

THE ORIGINAL JAZZ SCORE OF "KWAMINA"/with Frank Wess, Phil Woods and Jimmy Cleveland — Mercury 20654/60654 (1961) **$40.**

IMPROMPTU/with Jim Hall — Mercury 20722/60722 (1962) **$35.**

TAYLOR MADE JAZZ/with Johnny Hodges — Argo 650 (1957) **$35.**

WITH FOUR FLUTES/with Frank Wess, Herbie Mann, Jerome Richardson and Phil Bodner — Riverside 12-306/1151 (1959) blue label mono; black label stereo with Bill Grauer Pro. **$45.**

TRIO UPTOWN — Riverside 12-319/1168 (1960) blue label mono; black label stereo with Bill Grauer Pro. **$30.**

WARMING UP — Riverside 12-339/1195 (1960) blue label mono; black label stereo with Bill Grauer Pro. **$30.**

EVERGREENS — ABC Paramount 112 (1956) **$40.**

AT THE LONDON HOUSE — ABC Paramount 134 (1956) **$40.**

INTRODUCES IRA SULLIVAN — ABC Paramount 162 (1956) **$60.**

MY FAIR LADY LOVES JAZZ/with Jimmy Cleveland, Ernie Royal and Tony Ortega — ABC Paramount 177 (1957) **$55.**

THE NEW TRIO — ABC Paramount 226 (1957) **$30.**

INTERLUDE — Moodsville 16 (1961) **$40.**

RIGHT HERE, RIGHT NOW/with Oliver Nelson Orchestra — Capitol 2039 (1963) black label with logo on top **$30.**

MIDNIGHT PIANO — Capitol 2302 (1965) black label with logo on top **$30.**

CECIL TAYLOR
piano, composer - born 1933 New York City, NY

JAZZ ADVANCE/with Stan Lacy — Transition 19 (1956) **$75.**

LOOKING AHEAD — Contemporary 3562/7562 (1958) yellow label mono; black label stereo **$60.**

LOVE FOR SALE/with Bill Barron — United Artists 4046/5046 (1959) red label **$50.**

HARD DRIVING JAZZ/with John Coltrane — United Artists 14014 (1962) **$35**; also issued under John Coltrane titled Coltrane Time.

WORLD OF/with Archie Shepp — Candid 8006/9006 (1960) **$50.**

CLARK TERRY
trumpet, flugelhorn - born 1920 St. Louis, MO

CLARK TERRY/with Cecil Payne — EmArcy 36007 (1955) drummer logo **$50**; EP 1-6107, EP 1-6108 (1955) **$25** ea.

SERENADE TO A BUS SEAT/with Johnny Griffin — Riverside 12-137 (1957) blue label with Bill Grauer Pro. **$50.**

Jeannie Thomas sings some of the songs most frequently requested by members of our Armed Forces during her singing tour of our Military Installations.

DUKE WITH A DIFFERENCE/with Johnny Hodges — Riverside 12-246/1108 (1957) blue label mono; black label stereo with Bill Grauer Pro. **$50.**

IN ORBIT/with Thelonious Monk — Riverside 12-271 (1958) blue label with Bill Grauer Pro. **$50.**

TOP AND BOTTOM BRASS/with Jimmy Jones — Riverside 12-295/1137 (1959) blue label mono; black label stereo with Bill Grauer Pro. **$50.**

OUT ON A LIMB/with Mike Simpson — Argo 620 (1957) **$35.**

COLOR CHANGES/with Yusef Lateef and Seldon Powell — Candid 8009/9009 (1960) **$60.**

MORE/with Ben Webster — Cameo 1064 (1963) **$40.**

TREAD YE LIGHTLY/with Seldon Powell — Cameo 1071 (1963) **$35.**

EVERYTHING'S MELLOW/with Junior Mance — Moodsville 20 (1961) **$40.**

PLAYS THE JAZZ VERSION "ALL AMERICAN"/with George Barrow — Moodsville 26 (1962) **$40.**

WHAT MAKES SAMMY SWING/with Urbie Green — 20th Century Fox 3137/4137 (1963) **$35.**

THE HAPPY HORN OF/with Phil Woods and Ben Webster — Impulse 64 (1964) orange label **$35.**

JEANNIE THOMAS
vocals - born Deep Creek, VA

SINGS FOR THE BOYS/with Klaus Ogermann — Strand 1030 (1961) **$20.**

RENE THOMAS
guitar - born 1927 Liége, Belgium

GUITAR GROOVE/with J.R. Monterose — Jazzland 27/927 (1960) **$40.**

LES THOMPSON
accordion

JUST JAZZ/with Dexter Gordon and Wardell Gray — RCA Victor 3102 (1952) 10" **$150.**

LUCKY THOMPSON
tenor, soprano saxes - born 1924 Detroit, MI

Thompson was very popular with many groups in New York City including Lionel Hampton and Billy Eckstine during the early 40's. He was then widely recorded on the West Coast with many of bop's best during the late 40's, and with his own group from the early 50's. While working with Stan Kenton, he toured Europe and, finding it to his liking, was soon living and working there from 1957-62. He returned to the U.S. to continue his work and recording for the remainder of the 60's. Thompson has been one of the few musicians to continue to evolve from his early style through his work with so many great contemporaries.

JUNIOR JAZZ AT THE AUDITORIUM/with Howard McGhee — Top 928 (1954) 10" **$75.**

LUCKY THOMPSON FEATURING OSCAR PETTIFORD - Vol 1 — ABC Paramount 111 (1956) **$50.**

LUCKY THOMPSON FEATURING OSCAR PETTIFORD - Vol 2 — ABC Paramount 171 (1957) **$50.**

ACCENT ON TENOR/with Billy Taylor — Urania 1206 (1955) **$60.**

LUCKY THOMPSON — Dawn 1113 (1957) **$60.**

LUCKY STRIKES — Transition 21 (1957) **$60.**

PLAYS JEROME KERN AND NO MORE — Moodsville 39 (1963) **$45.**

LUCKY STRIKES — Prestige 7365 (1965) blue label with logo on right side **$35.**

HAPPY DAYS ARE HERE AGAIN — Prestige 7394 (1965) blue label with logo on right side **$35.**

LUCKY IS BACK! — Rivoli 40 (1965) **$45.**

KINFOLK'S CORNER — Rivoli 44 (1965) **$45.**

SIR CHARLES THOMPSON
organ, composer - born 1918 Springfield, OH

AND HIS ALL STARS/with Charlie Parker, Dexter Gordon and Leo Parker — Apollo 103 (1950) 10" **$150.**

SEXTET/with Joe Newman — Vanguard 8003 (1954) 10" **$60.**

QUARTET/with Freddie Green — Vanguard 8006 (1954) 10" **$40.**

AND HIS BAND/with Coleman Hawkins — Vanguard 8009 (1954) 10" **$80.**

TRIO — Vanguard 8018 (1955) 10" **$40.**

AND THE SWING ORGAN/with Percy France — Columbia 1364/8205 (1960) red label with 3 black logos on each side **$30.**

ROCKIN' RHYTHM/with Tiny Grimes — Columbia 1663/8463 (1961) red label with 3 black logos on each side **$30.**

TERI THORNTON
vocals - born 1936 Detroit, MI

DEVIL MAY CARE/with Clark Terry and Seldon Powell — Riverside 352/9352 (1960) blue label mono; black label stereo with Bill Grauer Pro. **$45.**

SINGS "SOMEWHERE IN THE NIGHT"/with Larry Wilcox — Dauntless 4306/6306 (1963) **$45.**

SINGS "OPEN HIGHWAY"/with Larry Wilcox — Columbia 2094/8894 (1963) red label with 1 white logo on each side **$25.**

THREE SOULS

Henry Cain - piano, Albert Coleman - drums,
Will Scott - bass

ALMOST LIKE BEING IN LOVE — Argo 4005 (1963) **$35**.

DANGEROUS DAN EXPRESS — Argo 4036 (1964) **$30**.

SOUL SOUNDS — Argo 4044 (1965) **$30**.

THE THREE SOUNDS

Gene Harris - piano, Andrew Simpkins - bass,
Bill Dowdy - drums

INTRODUCING — Blue Note 1600 (1958) with NY address on label **$50**; with NY on label **$40**; with A Division of Liberty on label **$20**.

BOTTOMS UP — Blue Note 4014 (1959) with NY address on label **$50**; with NY on label **$40**; with A Division of Liberty on label **$20**.

GOOD DEAL — Blue Note 4020 (1959) with NY address on label **$50**; with NY on label **$40**; with A Division of Liberty on label **$20**.

MOODS — Blue Note 4044/84044 (1960) with NY address on label **$50**; with NY on label **$40**; with A Division of Liberty on label **$20**.

FEELIN' GOOD — Blue Note 4072/84072 (1960) with NY address on label **$45**; with NY on label **$40**; with A Division of Liberty on label **$20**.

HERE WE COME — Blue Note 4088/84088 (1960) with NY on label **$40**; with A Division of Liberty on label **$20**.

HEY THERE — Blue Note 4102/84102 (1962) with NY on label **$40**; with A Division of Liberty on label **$20**.

IT JUST GOT TO BE — Blue Note 4120/84120 (1962) with NY on label **$40**; with A Division of Liberty on label **$20**.

BLACK ORCHID — Blue Note 4155/84155 (1962) with NY on label **$35**; with A Division of Liberty on label **$20**.

THE 3 SOUNDS — Verve 8513/68513 (1962) with MGM on label **$35**.

JAZZ ON BROADWAY — Mercury 20776/60776 (1962) **$25**.

SOME LIKE IT MODERN — Mercury 20839/60839 (1963) **$25**.

LIVE AT LIVING ROOM — Mercury 20921/60921 (1963) **$25**.

THREE MOODS — Limelight 82014/86014 (1965) fold out cover **$25**.

BEAUTIFUL FRIENDSHIP — Limelight 82026/86026 (1965) fold out cover **$25**.

BOBBY TIMMONS

piano - born 1935 Philadelphia, PA died 1974

THIS HERE IS — Riverside 12-317/1164 (1960) blue label mono; black label stereo with Bill Grauer Pro. **$35**.

SOUL TIME/with Blue Mitchell — Riverside 334/9334 (1960) blue label mono; black label stereo with Bill Grauer Pro. **$45**.

EASY DOES IT — Riverside 363/9363 (1961) blue label mono; black label stereo with Bill Grauer Pro. **$35**.

TRIO IN PERSON — Riverside 391/9391 (1961) blue label mono; black label stereo with Bill Grauer Pro. **$35**.

SWEET AND SOULFUL SOUNDS — Riverside 422/9422 (1962) blue label mono; black label stereo with Bill Grauer Pro. **$35**.

BORN TO BE BLUE — Riverside 468/9468 (1963) blue label mono; black label stereo with Bill Grauer Pro. **$35**.

LITTLE BAREFOOT SOUL — Prestige 7335 (1965) blue label with logo on right side **$25**.

CHUN-KING — Prestige 7351 (1965) blue label with logo on right side **$25**.

*CAL TJADER

vibes, drums, piano, composer - born 1925 St. Louis, MO
died 1982

Tjader grew up on the West Coast and received early recognition for his work as a drummer for Dave Brubeck in the late 40's, and later

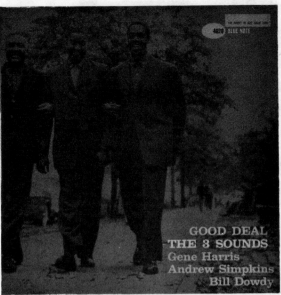

GOOD DEAL
THE 3 SOUNDS
Gene Harris
Andrew Simpkins
Bill Dowdy

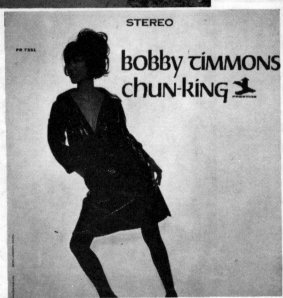

STEREO
bobby timmons
chun-king

playing vibes and drums with George Shearing until 1954. Since that time Tjader worked and recorded with groups of his own in many different configurations, usually featuring a strong Latin touch. Tjader made many recordings of Latin tunes or his own compositions quite often with Latin rhythms, and was a very sensitive interpreter of ballads who could swing in any context.

CAL TJADER TRIO/with John Marabuto — Fantasy 3-9 (1953) 10" **$60**.

RITMO CALIENTE/with Jerome Richardson — Fantasy 3-17 (1954) 10" **$75**; EP 4021, EP 4022 (1954) **$30 ea.**; *reissued* Fantasy 3216 (1955) **$50**; *reissued* 8077 (1958) **$35**.

TJADER PLAYS TJAZZ/with Brew Moore and Sonny Clark — Fantasy 3211 (1955) **$60**; EP 4049, EP 4050 (1955) **$30 ea.**; *reissued* Fantasy 3278/8097 (1962) **$30**.

JAZZ AT THE BLACKHAWK/with Vince Guaraldi — Fantasy 3241 (1957) **$35**; EP 4069 (1957) **$15**; *reissued* Fantasy 8026 (1958) **$20**.

LATIN KICK/with Brew Moore — Fantasy 3250 (1957) **$60**; EP 4067, EP 4068 (1957) **$30 ea.**; *reissued* Fantasy 8033 (1958) **$50**.

CAL TJADER - STAN GETZ SEXTET/with Vince Guaraldi — Fantasy 3266/8005 (1958) **$50**; *reissued* Fantasy 3348/8348 (1965) **$20**.

SAN FRANCISCO MOODS/with Eddie Duran — Fantasy 3271/8017 (1958) **$30**

LATIN FOR LOVERS/with Paul Horn — Fantasy 3279/8016 (1958) **$35**.

NIGHT AT BLACKHAWK/with Joe Silva — Fantasy 3283/8026 (1959) **$30**.

CONCERT BY THE SEA/with Paul Horn — Fantasy 3295/8035 (1959) **$35**.

DEMASADO CALIENTE/with Tony Terran — Fantasy 3309/8053 (1960) **$30**.

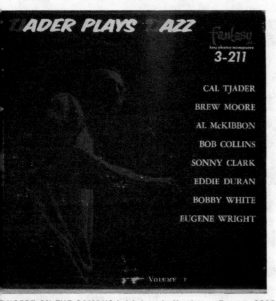

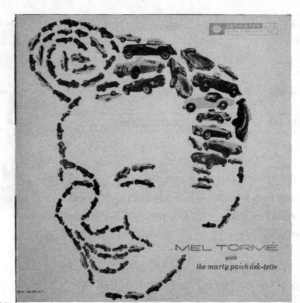

CONCERT ON THE CAMPUS/with Lonnie Hewitt — Fantasy 3299/8044 (1960) $30.

WEST SIDE STORY/with Paul Horn and Red Callender — Fantasy 3310/8054 (1960) $35.

PLAYS HAROLD ARLEN/with Buddy Motsinger — Fantasy 3330/8072 (1961) $30.

LIVE AND DIRECT — Fantasy 3315/8059 (1961) $30.

CONCERT BY THE SEA - Vol 2 — Fantasy 3341/8098 (1961) $30.

GREATEST HITS — Fantasy 3366/8366 (1965) $30.

IN A LATIN BAG/with Paul Horn — Verve 8419/68419 (1961) with MGM on bottom of label $25.

SATURDAY NIGHT, SUNDAY NIGHT AT THE BLACKHAWK — Verve 8459/68459 (1962) with MGM on bottom of label $25.

SEVERAL SHADES OF JADE/with Clark Terry and Jimmy Raney — Verve 8507/6-8507 (1963) with MGM on bottom of label $25.

BREEZE FROM THE EAST/with Jerry Dogion — Verve 8575/6-8575 (1963) with MGM on bottom of label $25.

SOUL SAUCE/with Donald Byrd — Verve 8614/68614 (1965) with MGM on bottom of label $25.

CAL TJADER QUARTET — Savoy 9036 (1954) 10" $60; EP 8100, EP 8111 (1954) $30 ea.; reissued Savoy 12054.

VIB-RATIONS/with Don Elliott — Savoy 12054 (1956) maroon label $40; reissue of Savoy 9036.

---

*The only LP's within the scope of this book.

*MEL TORME

vocals, composer - born 1925 Chicago, IL

Torme has been a professional singer, musician and actor from childhood and was performing in big name bands as a teenager. A popular recording artist and gifted composer and arranger from the late 40's to date, Torme has continued to record award winning albums and make night club and television appearances in addition to writing his autobiography.

SONGS — MGM 552 (1952) 10" $60; MGM K79 (1952) 4 record 7" box set $35.

AT THE CRESCENDO "1954" — Coral 57012 (1954) maroon label $60.

MUSICAL SOUNDS/with Sonny Burke — Coral 57044 (1954) maroon label $45.

IT'S A BLUE WORLD/with Orchestra — Bethlehem 34 (1955) maroon label $40.

WITH THE MARTY PAICH DEK-TETTE/with Bob Cooper and Bud Shank — Bethlehem 52 (1956) maroon label $45.

SINGS FRED ASTAIRE/with Pete Candoli and Jack Montrose — Bethlehem 6013 (1958) maroon label $45.

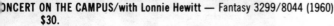

CALIFORNIA SUITE/with Marty Paich — Bethlehem 6016 (1958) maroon label $40.

AT THE CRESCENDO/with Don Fagerquist — Bethlehem 6020 (1958) maroon label $45; different from Coral 57012.

SONG FOR ANY TASTE — Bethlehem 6031 (1959) maroon label $40.

TORME/with Marty Paich — Verve 2105/6015 (1958) with Verve Records, Inc. at bottom of label $40.

BACK IN TOWN/with Marty Paich, Jack Sheldon and Art Pepper — Verve 2120/6083 (1959) with Verve Records, Inc. on bottom of label $50.

SWINGS SHUBERT ALLEY/with Art Pepper and Bill Perkins — Verve 2132/6146 (1960) with Verve Records, Inc. on bottom of label $45.

SWINGIN' ON THE MOON/with Russ Garcia — Verve 2144/62144 (1960) with MGM on bottom of label $35.

MY KIND OF MUSIC — Verve 8440/68440 (1961) with MGM on bottom of label $35.

I DIG THE DUKE, I DIG THE COUNT/with Jack Sheldon and Bill Perkins — Verve 8491/68491 (1961) with MGM on bottom of label $35.

SINGS — Strand 1076 (1960) $30.

AT THE RED HILL — Atlantic 8066 (1962) with logo on right side $35.

COMIN' HOME BABY/with Shorty Rogers and Claus Ogerman — Atlantic 8069 (1962) with logo on right side $45.

SUNDAY IN NEW YORK/with Shorty Rogers — Atlantic 8091 (1963) with logo on right side **$35.**

THAT'S ALL — Columbia 2318/9118 (1964) red label with 1 white logo on each side **$25.**

I WISHED ON THE MOON — Metro 523 (1965) **$20.**

---

*The only LP's within the scope of this book.

CY TOUFF
bass trumpet - born 1927 Chicago, IL

OCTET & QUINTET/with Russ Freeman — Pacific Jazz 1211 (1956) **$60.**

HAVIN' A BALL — World Pacific 410 (1958) **$45;** *reissue* of Pacific Jazz 1211.

TOUFF ASSIGNMENT — Argo 641 (1959) **$35.**

NICK TRAVIS
trumpet - born 1925 Philadelphia, PA

Travis was a well known and respected trumpet man who backed several big name bands in the 40's and 50's. He recorded with many of these bands including Ernie Lawrence, Bill Holman, Al Cohn, Zoot Sims and the Sauter-Finegan Band. In the late 50's he worked as a staff musician in New York television and produced the only recording to his own credit.

THE PANIC IS ON/with Al Cohn and Johnny Williams — RCA Victor 1010 (1954) **$95;** EP 1010 (1954) 3 records **$50.**

JEANNIE TREVOR
vocals - born St. Louis, MO

SINGS! POW! — Mainstream 56075/6075 (1965) comic cover **$25.**

LENNIE TRISTANO
piano, composer - born 1919 Chicago, IL died 1978

Tristano is an extremely talented player who is best known for his experimental and progressive ideas. His approach to playing is intellectual and is an extension of earlier influences such as Earl Hines that has been carried to new conclusions by Tristano. His cerebral approach has always had many adherents and has been influential through constant teaching in his own studio as well as through his recordings.

LENNIE TRISTANO/with Lee Konitz — Prestige EP 1308 (1950) **$50;** *reissued* Prestige 101, listed under Lee Konitz.

LENNIE TRISTANO PLAYS/with Lee Wiley — Allegro-Elite 4049 (1954) 10" **$75;** one side only.

HOLIDAY IN PIANO/with Arnold Ross — EmArcy 26029 (1953) 10" **$75;** one side only.

LENNIE TRISTANO/with Lee Konitz — Atlantic 1224 (1955) black label **$75;** EP 568, EP 569 (1955) **$35 ea.**

THE NEW TRISTANO (Solo) — Atlantic 1357 (1960) with logo on right side **$30.**

TROMBONE SCENE
Jimmy Cleveland, Urbie Green, Eddie Bert, Frank Reheck, Sonny Russo, Willie Dennie, Jimmy Knepper, Tommy Mitchell (trombones)

TROMBONE SCENE — Vik 1087 (1957) **$50;** EP 1087 (1957) **$25.**

THE TROMBONES, INC.
Herbie Harper, Jimmy Cleveland, Frank Rosolini, Bob Brookmeyer, Benny Green, Melba Liston, etc.

TROMBONES, INC. — Warner Brothers 1272 (1959) **$45.**

*BOBBY TROUP
vocals, piano, composer - born 1918 Harrisburg, PA

BOBBY/with Bob Enevoldsen — Capitol H484 10" (1953) **$75;** *reissued* Capitol T484 (1955) green label **$50.**

SINGS JOHNNY MERCER/with Bob Enevoldsen — Bethlehem 19 (1955) maroon label **$40.**

THE DISTINCTIVE STYLE OF — Bethlehem 35 (1955) maroon label **$30.**

ESCAPADE: "REVIEWS THE JAZZ SCENE"/with Howard Rumsey, Ziggy Elman, Johnny Otis, Jack Teagarden and Jack Costanzo — Liberty 9005 (1957) **$60.**

DO RE MI — Liberty 3026 (1957) **$40;** music and conversations.

AND HIS TRIO — Liberty 3002 (1956) **$35.**

BOBBY SWINGS TENDERLY/with Bob Enevoldsen — Mode 111 (1957) **$50;** *reissued* Interlude 501/1001.

COOL — Interlude 501/1001 (1959) **$40;** *reissue* of Mode 111.

STARS OF JAZZ/with Bob Cooper, Buddy Childers and Richie Kamuca — RCA Victor 1959 (1959) dog on top **$45.**

---

*The only LP's within the scope of this book.

STANLEY TURRENTINE
tenor sax - born 1934 Pittsburgh, PA

LOOK OUT/with George Tucker — Blue Note 4039/84039 (1960) with NY address on label **$60;** with NY on label **$40;** with A Division of Liberty on label **$20.**

BLUES HOUR/with The Three Sounds — Blue Note 4057/84057 (1960) with NY address on label **$65;** with NY on label **$40;** with A Division of Liberty on label **$20.**

COMIN' YOUR WAY/with Tommy Turrentine — Blue Note 4065/84065 (1961) with NY address on label **$65;** with NY on label **$40;** with A Division of Liberty on label **$20.**

AT MINTON'S - Vol 1/with Grant Green — Blue Note 4069/84069 (1961) with NY address on label **$60**; with NY on label **$40**; with A Division of Liberty on label **$20**.

AT MINTON'S - Vol 2/with Grant Green — Blue Note 4070/84070 (1961) with NY address on label **$60**; with NY on label **$40**; with A Division of Liberty on label **$20**.

EARLY BELOVED/with Shirley Scott — Blue Note 4081/84081 (1961) with NY on label **$40**; with A Division of Liberty on label **$20**.

THAT'S WHERE IT'S AT/with Les McCann — Blue Note 4096/84096 (1962) with NY on label **$40**; with A Division of Liberty on label **$20**.

NEVER LET ME GO/with Shirley Scott — Blue Note 4129/84129 (1962) with NY on label **$35**; with A Division of Liberty on label **$20**.

CHIP OFF THE OLD BLOCK/with Blue Mitchell — Blue Note 4150/84150 (1963) with NY on label **$30**; with A Division of Liberty on label **$20**.

HUSTLIN'/with Shirley Scott — Blue Note 4162/84162 (1964) with NY on label **$30**; with A Division of Liberty on label **$20**.

STAN THE MAN — Time 52086/2086 (1963) **$60**.

TIGER TAIL — Mainstream 56041/6041 (1965) **$25**.

TOMMY TURRENTINE
trumpet - born 1928 Pittsburgh, PA

Elder brother of Stanley Turrentine, Tommy played and recorded with the groups of Benny Carter, Charlie Mingus, Earl Bostic and Max Roach as well as with working in groups and recording with his brother.

TOMMY TURRENTINE/with Stanley Turrentine and Julian Priester — Time 70008 (1960) **$60**.

RICHARD TWARDZIK
piano - born 1931 Danvers, MA died 1955

RICHARD TWARDZIK TRIO/with Russ Freeman Trio — Pacific Jazz 1212 (1956) **$45**; *reissued* World Pacific 1212 (1958) **$35**; *reissued* Pacific Jazz 37.

THE LAST SET — Pacific Jazz 37 (1961) **$20**.

TEDDY TYLE
tenor sax

MOON SHOT/with Tony Gottusa — Golden Crest 3060 (1959) **$45**.

McCOY TYNER
piano, composer - born 1938 Philadelphia, PA

INCEPTION/with Elvin Jones — Impulse 18 (1962) orange label **$20**.

REACHING FOURTH/with Roy Hayes — Impulse 33 (1962) orange label **$20**.

NIGHT OF BALLADS/with Steve Davis — Impulse 39 (1963) orange label **$30**.

LIVE AT NEWPORT/with Clark Terry and Charlie Mariano — Impulse 48 (1963) orange label **$35**.

TODAY AND TOMORROW/with John Gilmore and Frank Strozier — Impulse 63 (1964) orange label **$35**.

PLAYS ELLINGTON — Impulse 79 (1965) orange label **$25**.

PHIL URSO
tenor sax - born 1925 Jersey City, NJ

URSO - BROOKMEYER QUINTET/with Bob Brookmeyer — Savoy 15041 (1954). 10" **$95**; EP 8059, EP 8118 (1954) **$40 ea.**; *reissued* Savoy 12056.

PHILOSOPHY OF URSO — Savoy 12056 (1955) **$35**; *reissue* of Savoy 15041.

SENTIMENTAL JOURNEY — Regent 6003 (1956) **$35**.

BILLY USSELTON
tenor sax - born 1926 New Castle, PA

HIS FIRST ALBUM/with Bob Burgess — Kapp 1051 (1957) **$55**.

*SARAH VAUGHAN
vocals - born 1934 Newark, NJ

Ms. Vaughan has always demonstrated an outstanding vocal quality from her work with the Earl Hines Band in the early 40's and in subsequent work as a solo artist in clubs, concerts and recordings. She was held highly in the 40's by bop artists for her unique abilities of interpretation and made many popular recordings in the 50's and 60's.

SARAH VAUGHAN SINGS — Atlantic EP 527 (1955) **$35**.

HOT JAZZ/with Dizzy Gillespie, Charlie Parker and Leonard Feather — Remington 1024 (1953) 10" **$100**; *reissue* of 78 RPM Continental records of the 40's.

TENDERLY/with Cecil Payne and Bud Powell — MGM 165 (1952) 10" **$100**; EP 1020 (1952) **$45**; MGM 165 (1952) 4 record 7" box set **$50**; *reissued* MGM 3274.

MY KINDA LOVE — MGM 3274 (1955) yellow label **$60**.

SINGS/with Bud Johnson and George Treadwell — MGM 544 (1954) 10" **$100**; MGM 71 (1953) 4 record 7" box set **$50**; *reissued* MGM 3274.

SARAH VAUGHAN/with Miles Davis, Bud Johnson and Benny Green — Columbia 6133 (1950) 10" **$100**; *reissued* Columbia 745 (Davis' name is not listed on 10", is on 12").

AFTER HOURS WITH/with Big Band — Columbia 660 (1955) red label with 3 black logos on each side **$60**; EP 1631 (1955) **$30**.

IN HI FI — Columbia 745 (1956) red label with 3 black logos on each side **$60**; *reissue* of Columbia 6133.

LINGER AWHILE/with Bill Butterfield — Columbia 914 (1957) red label with 3 black logos on each side **$50**; EP 9143 (1957) **$25**.

IMAGES — EmArcy 26005 (1954) 10" **$75**; EP 1-6000, EP 1-6001 (1954) **$35 ea.**; *reissued* EmArcy 36109.

SARAH VAUGHAN/with Clifford Brown, Paul Quinichette and Herbie Mann — EmArcy 36004 (1954) drummer logo **$65**.

IN THE LAND OF HI FI/with Cannonball Adderley and J.J. Johnson — EmArcy 36058 (1955) drummer logo **$65**.

SWINGIN' EASY — EmArcy 36109 (1957) **$40**; *reissue* of EmArcy 26005.

DIVINE SARAH — Mercury 25188 (1951) 10" **$75**.

AT MISTER KELLY'S — Mercury 20326 (1958) black label **$50**.

AFTER HOURS AT THE LONDON HOUSE/with Thad Jones and Frank Wess — Mercury 20383 (1958) black label **$50**.

NO COUNT SARAH/with Frank Wess, Frank Foster and Billy Mitchell — Mercury 20441 (1959) black label **$45**.

SASSY SWINGS THE TIVOLI/with Trio — Mercury 20831/60831 (1963) **$35**.

MANCINI SONGBOOK/with Frank Foster — Mercury 21009/61009 (1965) red label **$35**.

DREAMY/with Jimmy Jones and Harry Edison — Roulette 52046 (1960) **$30**; EP 1003 (1960) **$15**.

DIVINE ONE/with Harry Edison — Roulette 52060 (1960) **$30**; EP 1026, EP 1028 (1960) **$15 ea.**

COUNT BASIE/SARAH VAUGHAN — Roulette 52061 (1960) **$30**.

AFTER HOURS/with Mundell Lowe — Roulette 52070 (1961) **$30**.

SINGS SONGS OF BROADWAY/with George Treadwell — Rondo-Lette 35 (1959) **$45**.

---

*The only LP's within the scope of this book.

AL VEGA
piano

AL VEGA TRIO — Prestige 156 (1953) 10" **$40**.

CAROL VENTURA
vocals - born 1937

CAROL! — Prestige 7358 (1965) blue label with logo on right side **$15**.

I LOVE TO SING! — Prestige 7405 (1965) blue label with logo on right side **$15**.

CHARLIE VENTURA
saxes, leader - born 1916 Philadelphia, PA

Ventura played with many bop greats in addition to becoming well known through his work with Gene Krupa in the early 40's. By the late 40's, he had his own very popular combo playing in the modern style and featuring many unique vocalists as well as many fine musicians. He led groups of his own, owned night clubs and worked again with Krupa and other all star groups through the 50's and into the 60's.

CHARLIE VENTURA — Rendition EP 103 (1949) **$50**; *reissue* of 78 RPM National records.

AND HIS SEXTET/with Red Rodney — Imperial 3002 (1950) 10" **$100**.

STOMPING WITH THE SAX/with Barney Kessel — Crystalette 5000 10" **$80**.

F.Y.I. VENTURA/with Bill Harris — EmArcy 26028 (1954) 10" **$95**; EP 1-6046, EP 1-6047 (1954) **$45 ea.**; *reissued* Regent 6064.

JUMPING WITH VENTURA/with Kai Winding — EmArcy 36015 (1955) drummer logo **$45**.

QUARTET — Norgran 8 (1953) 10" **$100**; *reissued* Norgran 1075.

AN EVENING WITH/with Mary Ann McCall — Norgran 20 (1954) 10" **$100**; EP 33, EP 34 (1954) **$40**.

ANOTHER EVENING WITH/with Mary Ann McCall — Norgran 1013 (1954) **$80**; EP 76, EP 77, EP 78 (1954) **$40 ea.**; *reissued* Norgran 1053.

AN EVENING WITH/with Mary Ann McCall — Norgran 1053 (1955) **$70**; *reissued* Verve 8143 (1957) with Verve Records, Inc. on bottom of label **$60**.

COLLATES/with Conte Candoli — Mercury/Clef 117 (1951) **$125**; EP 127, EP 130 (1951) **$50 ea.**; *reissued* Norgran 1073.

IN A JAZZ MOOD — Norgran 1073 (1955) **$70**; *reissued* Verve 8163 (1957) with Verve Records, Inc. on bottom of label **$60**.

CARNEGIE HALL CONCERT — Norgran 1041 (1955) **$70**; *reissued* Verve 8132 (1957) with Verve Records, Inc. on bottom of label **$60**.

BLUE SAXOPHONE — Norgran 1075 (1955) **$70**; *reissued* Verve 8165 (1957) with Verve Records, Inc. on bottom of label **$60**; *reissue* of Norgran 8.

OPEN HOUSE — Coral 56067 (1954) 10" **$60**.

CHARLIE VENTURA CONCERT/with Conte Candoli — Decca 8046 (1953) black label with gold lettering **$85**.

HIGH ON AN OPEN MIKE/with Benny Green — RCA Victor 1135 (1955) dog on top **$55**.

HERE'S CHARLIE/with Jackie Cain — Brunswick 54025 (1957) black label with silver lettering **$55**.

NEW CHARLIE VENTURA IN HI FI — Baton 1202 (1957) **$50**.

ADVENTURE WITH CHARLIE/with Bill Bean — King 543 (1958) black label **$50**.

PLAYS HI FI JAZZ/with Dave McKenna and Bill Bean — Top 1528 (1958) **$45**; *reissued* Craftsman 8039.

THE CRAZY RHYTHMS OF/with Charlie Kennedy — Regent 6047 (1957) green label **$45**; one side only.

EAST OF SUEZ — Regent 6064 (1958) green label **$45**; *reissue* of EmArcy 26028.

PLAYS FOR THE PEOPLE — Craftsman 8039 (1960) **$35**; *reissue* of Top 1528.

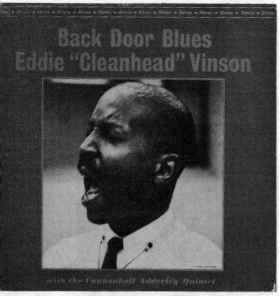

MILLI VERNON
vocals

INTRODUCING MILLI VERNON/with Jimmy Raney — Storyville 910 (1956) $65.

HAROLD VICK
tenor sax - born 1936 Rocky Mount, NC

STEPPIN' OUT/with Grant Green and Blue Mitchell — Blue Note 4138/84138 (1963) with NY on label $35; with A Division of Liberty on label $20.

LEROY VINNEGAR
bass - born 1928 Indianapolis, IN

Vinnegar became known early in his career as an outstanding rhythm player. He worked with some famous West Coast groups like Shelly Manne in the mid-50's, and Les McCann and Gerald Wilson into the 60's. In addition to being much in demand as a session player and in all star groups, Vinnegar made albums under his own name featuring his compositions and many examples of his fine solo capabilities.

LEROY WALKS/with Teddy Edwards and Carl Perkins — Contemporary 3542 (1957) yellow label $35; *reissued* Contemporary 7003 (1958) black label stereo $35.

LEROY WALKS AGAIN/with Teddy Edwards and Victor Feldman — Contemporary 3608/7608 (1963) yellow label mono; black label stereo $35.

JAZZ'S GREAT WALKER — Vee Jay 2502 (1965) black label $20.

EDDIE "CLEANHEAD" VINSON
alto sax, vocals - born 1917 Houston, TX

CLEANHEAD'S BACK IN TOWN/with Frank Foster and Paul Quinichette — Bethlehem 5005 (1957) maroon label $35; *reissued* Aamco 312; no date given, date on LP is that of the Bethlehem LP $25.

BATTLE OF THE BLUES - Vol 3/with Jimmy Witherspoon — King 634 (1959) $40; one side only.

BACK DOOR BLUES/with Nat and Cannonball Adderley — Riverside 3502/93502 (1962) blue label mono; black label stereo with Bill Grauer Pro. $35.

MAL WALDRON
piano, composer - born 1926 New York City, NY

Waldron first gained attention while working and recording with Charlie Mingus in the mid-50's and, in the late 50's, while performing as an accompanist with Billie Holiday. In addition, he worked with his own group in New York City night clubs when not working with Holiday. During the early 60's, Waldron worked with a group that included Eric Dolphy and Booker Little. They played extensively and were well recorded on LPs which subsequently have been issued with various members of the group listed as leader.

MAL 1/with Gigi Gryce — Prestige 7090 (1956) yellow label $60.

MAL 2/with John Coltrane — Prestige 7111 (1957) yellow label $60.

MAL 3/with Art Farmer — New Jazz 8201 (1958) $45.

MAL 4 — New Jazz 8208 (1958) $45.

IMPRESSIONS — New Jazz 8242 (1959) $45.

THE QUEST — New Jazz 8269 (1961) $35.

LEFT ALONE — Bethlehem 6045 (1960) maroon label $35.

GEORGE WALLINGTON
piano, songwriter - born 1924 Palermo, Sicily

Wallington was well known with many of the early bop groups around the New York City area during the 40's. He worked with Dizzy Gillespie, Charlie Parker and Red Rodney and was part of several recordings before starting his own group. Through the 50's, Wallington and his group produced recordings which demonstrated his impressive technique.

TRIO — Savoy 15037 (1954) 10" $50.

GEORGE WALLINGTON TRIO & SEXTET/with Brew Moore — Savoy 12081 (1956) maroon label $60; EP 8112, EP 8124, EP 8125 (1956) $20 ea.

JAZZ AT HOTCHKISS — Savoy 12122 (1957) maroon label $60.

TRIO — Prestige 136 (1952) 10" $50.

TRIO — Prestige 158 (1953) 10" $50.

JAZZ FOR THE CARRIAGE/with Phil Woods — Prestige 7032 (1956) yellow label $60.

SHOWCASE/with Frank Foster — Blue Note 5054 (1954) 10" $75.

TRIO — Progressive 3001 (1951) 10" $50.

AT THE BOHEMIA/with Jackie McLean — Progressive 1001 (1956) $55.

THE WORKSHOP OF — Norgran 24 (1954) 10" $50; EP 49, EP 50 (1954) $25 ea.

WITH STRINGS — Norgran 1010 (1955) $45; EP 66, EP 67, EP 68 (1955) $15 ea.

KNIGHT MUSIC — Atlantic 1275 (1956) black label $40.

THE PRESTIDIGITATOR — East-West 4004 (1957) $65.

THE NEW YORK SCENE/with Phil Woods — New Jazz 8207 (1958) $45.

WILBUR WARE
bass - born 1923 Chicago, IL

During the early 50's, Ware developed his reputation in the Chicago area and the Midwest through various collaborations. He worked and recorded with Thelonious Monk and groupings of his own in New York City in the late 50's. Ware was an extremely flexible player and contributed many examples of his excellent solos.

CHICAGO SOUND/with Johnny Griffin and John Jenkins — Riverside 12-252 (1957) blue label with Bill Grauer Pro. $45; *reissued* Jazzland 12.

CHICAGO COOKERS — Jazzland 12 (1960) $30.

*DINAH WASHINGTON
vocals - born 1924 Tuscaloosa, OK died 1963

Washington grew up singing gospel songs and playing piano in a church choir. She first came to prominence while working with Lionel Hampton's Band in the mid-40's and her subsequent recording career was very successful, producing hits in the blues, jazz and popular areas of music. Ms. Washington's voice was unmistakable and her style a unique and pleasing blend of her musical influences. She died in 1963 at the young age of 39 but has left behind her a legacy not to be taken lightly.

DINAH WASHINGTON, SONGS/with Cootie Williams — Mercury 25060 (1950) 10" $105.

DYNAMIC DINAH — Mercury 25138 (1951) 10" **$95.**

BLAZING BALLADS/with Paul Quinichette — Mercury 25140 (1951) 10" **$95.**

AFTER HOURS WITH MISS D/with Paul Quinichette and Eddie Davis — EmArcy 26032 (1954) 10" **$85**; EP 1-6054, EP 1-6055 (1954) **$40 ea.**; *reissued* EmArcy 36028 (1955) **$60.**

DINAH JAMS/with Clifford Brown — EmArcy 36000 (1954) **$75**; EP 1-6080, EP 1-6081, EP 1-6082 (1954) **$30 ea.**

FOR THOSE IN LOVE/with Jimmy Cleveland and Cecil Payne — EmArcy 36011 (1955) **$70**; EP 1-6118, EP 1-6119, EP 1-6020 (1955) **$30 ea.**

DINAH/with Herb Geller and Georgie Auld — EmArcy 36065 (1956) **$60.**

IN THE LAND OF HI FI/with Cannonball Adderley — EmArcy 36073 (1956) **$60.**

SINGS FATS WALLER — EmArcy 36119 (1957) **$55.**

SINGS BESSIE SMITH/with Eddie Chamblee and Charles Davis — EmArcy 36130 (1958) **$55.**

THE BEST IN BLUES/with Wardell Gray — Mercury 20247 (1957) black label **$50**; EP 1-3207 (1957) **$25.**

THE GOOD OLD DAYS — Mercury 20829/60829 (1963) black label **$35**; *reissue* of her 78 RPM days.

LATE LATE SHOW — Mercury/Wing 12140 (1960) **$25.**

The only LP's within the scope of this book.

EARL WASHINGTON
piano, composer - born Chicago, IL

ALL STAR JAZZ — Workshop 202 (1963) **$35.**

REFLECTIONS — Workshop 213 (1963) **$35.**

DOUG WATKINS
bass - born 1934 Detroit, MI died 1962

A Detroit jazz circle member of the early 50's, young Watkins' abilities soon led him to New York City and sessions with many name groups. Good examples of his work are the recordings he made with Horace Silver, Art Blakey, Kenny Burrell and Pepper Adams among others. Watkins died in an auto accident on the way to join Philly Joe Jones in 1962.

WATKINS AT LARGE/with Hank Mobley — Transition 20 (1956) **$65.**

SOULNIK/with Yusef Lateef — New Jazz 8238 (1960) **$40.**

JULIUS WATKINS
french horn, composer - born 1921 Detroit, MI

SEXTET/with Frank Foster — Blue Note 5053 (1954) 10" **$90.**

SEXTET - Vol 2 — Blue Note 5064 (1954) 10" **$90.**

BEN WEBSTER
tenor sax - born 1909 Kansas City, MO died 1973

Big-toned and aggressive on faster tempos while warm and expressive on ballads was Webster's style from his early work in the 30's with many swing bands. This style made him famous during his groupings with Duke Ellington in the early 40's. He continued to play with JATP and his own groups through the 50's moving to Europe in the 60's to stay and work until his death in 1973.

TENOR SAX/with Coleman Hawkins — Brunswick 58031 (1953) 10" **$85**; *reissued* Brunswick 54016.

BIG SOUNDS OF — Brunswick 54016 (1956) **$60**; *reissue* of Brunswick 58031.

BIG TENOR/with Benny Carter — EmArcy 26006 (1954) 10" **$95.**

CONSUMMATE ARTISTRY OF/with Barney Kessel — Norgran 1001 (1954) **$75**; EP 15, EP 16 (1954) **$35 ea.**; *reissued* Verve 8020.

MUSIC FOR LOVING/with Teddy Wilson — Norgran 1018 (1954) **$75**; EP 96, EP 97, EP 98 (1954) **$35 ea.**; *reissued* Verve 2026.

MUSIC WITH FEELING/with Ralph Burns — Norgran 1039 (1955) **$70**; *reissued* Verve 8130 (1957) with Verve Records, Inc. on bottom of label **$50.**

KING OF THE TENORS — Verve 8020 (1957) with Verve Records, Inc. on bottom of label **$50**; *reissue* of Norgran 1001.

SOPHISTICATED LADY — Verve 2026 (1956) with Verve Records, Inc. on bottom of label **$45**; *reissue* of Norgran 1018.

SOULVILLE/with Herb Ellis — Verve 8274 (1958) with Verve Records, Inc. on bottom of label **$45.**

AND ASSOCIATES/with Coleman Hawkins, Roy Eldridge and Budd Johnson — Verve 8318/6056 (1959) with Verve Records, Inc. on bottom of label **$40.**

COLEMAN HAWKINS ENCOUNTERS BEN WEBSTER — Verve 8327/6066 (1959) with Verve Records, Inc. on bottom of label **$45.**

GERRY MULLIGAN MEETS BEN WEBSTER — Verve 8343/6114 (1959) with Verve Records, Inc. on bottom of label **$50**; *reissued* Verve 8534/68534 (1964) with MGM on bottom of label **$30.**

BEN WEBSTER MEETS OSCAR PETERSON — Verve 8349/6114 (1959) with Verve Records, Inc. on bottom of label **$35.**

THE SOUL OF/with Art Farmer — Verve 8359/68359 (1960) with MGM on bottom of label **$35.**

BEN WEBSTER - SWEETS EDISON — Columbia 1891/8691 (1962) with 3 black logos on each side **$35.**

THE WARM MOODS/with Johnny Richards — Reprise 2001/92001 (1961) **$30.**

SEE YOU AT THE FAIR/with Hank Jones — Impulse 65 (1964) orange label **$30.**

SOULMATES/with Joe Zawinul and Thad Jones — Riverside 476/9476 (1964) blue label mono; black label stereo with Bill Grauer Pro. **$30.**

FRANK WESS
tenor sax, flute, composer - born 1922 Kansas City, MO

FRANK WESS QUINTET/with Oscar Pettiford — Commodore 20,031 (1950) 10" **$65**; *reissued* Mainstream 56033.

FRANK WESS/with Oscar Pettiford — Commodore 20,032 (1950) 10" **$65**; *reissued* Mainstream 56033.

NORTH, SOUTH, EAST, WESS/with Frank Foster — Savoy 12072 (1956) maroon label **$35**.

NO COUNT — Savoy 12078 (1956) maroon label **$35**.

OPUS IN SWING/with Kenny Burrell — Savoy 12085 (1956) maroon label **$35**.

TROMBONES AND FLUTE/with Jimmy Cleveland — Savoy 12086 (1956) maroon label **$35**.

JAZZ FOR PLAYBOYS/with Kenny Burrell and Joe Newman — Savoy 12095 (1956) **$35**.

OPUS THE BLUES/with Curtis Fuller — Savoy 12142 (1959) maroon label **$35**.

YO HO!/with Thad Jones — Prestige 7266 (1963) yellow label **$45**.

SOUTHERN COMFORT/with George Barrow — Prestige 7231 (1962) yellow label **$45**.

QUARTET/with Tommy Flanagan — Moodsville 8 (1960) **$35**.

AWARD WINNER — Mainstream 56033/6033 (1965) **$25**.

RANDY WESTON
piano, composer - born 1926 Brooklyn, NY

Weston was active in New York City clubs with his own groups from the mid-40's. His style was initially Monk-influenced but proved to be quite unique as he developed as a composer. He has served as a clinician and lecturer on blacks in America and on jazz history, traveling to Africa often since the late 50's. His music reflects much that he has absorbed in his travels and appears on many different labels.

PORTER IN A MODERN MOOD — Riverside 2508 (1954) 10" **$60**.

TRIO — Riverside 2515 (1955) 10" **$60**; *reissued* Riverside 12-227.

GET HAPPY — Riverside 12-203 (1955) white label **$50**.

WITH THESE HANDS/with Cecil Payne — Riverside 12-214 (1955) white label **$50**.

TRIO AND SOLO — Riverside 12-227 (1956) white label **$50**; *reissued* Jazzland 4; *reissue* of Riverside 2515.

JAZZ A LA BOHEMIA — Riverside 12-232 (1956) white label **$50**; *reissued* Jazzland 13.

MODERN ART OF JAZZ/with Cecil Payne — Dawn 1116 (1956) **$60**.

PIANO A LA MODE — Jubilee 1060 (1957) **$25**.

NEW FACES AT NEWPORT/with Lem Winchester — Metrojazz 1005 (1958) **$40**; one side only.

LITTLE NILES/with Johnny Griffin — United Artists 4011/5011 (1959) **$50**.

DESTRY RIDES AGAIN/with Slide Hampton — United Artists 4045/5045 (1959) **$50**.

LIVE AT THE FIVE SPOT/with Coleman Hawkins and Kenny Dorham — United Artists 4066/5066 (1960) **$45**.

UHURU AFRIKA — Roulette 65001 (1960) **$40**.

HIGHLIGHT/with Jimmy Cleveland — Colpix 456 (1963) gold label **$30**.

ZULU! — Jazzland 4 (1960) **$30**; *reissue* of Riverside 12-227.

GREENWICH VILLAGE JAZZ — Jazzland 13 (1960) **$30**; *reissue* of Riverside 12-232.

*GERALD "JERRY" WIGGINS
piano - born 1922 New York City, NY

WIGGIN' OUT/with Harold Land — Hi Fi Jazz 618 (1961) **$30**.

---

*The only LP's within the scope of this book.

JOE WILDER
trumpet - born 1922 Colwyn, PA

Wilder is an extremely talented musician who worked with many great bands during the 40's including Lionel Hampton and Lunceford and Millender. Beginning in the early 50's, except for a brief period with Count Basie, he worked in Broadway pit bands until he became a staff musician in 1957. Fortunately, Wilder continued to work occasionally and record in the jazz area throughout his years on Broadway and television.

WILDER & WILDER/with Hank Jones — Savoy 12063 (1956) maroon label **$35**.

JAZZ FROM PETER GUNN/with Hank Jones — Columbia 1319 (1959) red label with 3 black logos on each side **$40**.

THE PRETTY SOUND/with Hank Jones — Columbia 1372 (1959) red label with 3 black logos on each side **$35**.

DON WILKERSON
tenor sax - born 1932 Moreauville, LA

THE TEXAS TWISTER/with Nat Adderley — Riverside 12-336/1186 (1960) blue label mono; black label stereo with Bill Grauer Pro. **$35**.

PREACH BROTHER/with Sonny Clark — Blue Note 4107/84107 (1962) with NY on label **$40**; with A Division of Liberty on label **$15**.

ELDER DON — Blue Note 4121/84121 (1962) with NY on label **$40**; with A Division of Liberty on label **$15**.

SHOUTIN' — Blue Note 4145/84145 (1963) with NY on label **$35**; with A Division of Liberty on label **$15**.

BABY FACE WILLETTE
organ, composer - born 1933 New Orleans, LA

FACE TO FACE/with Fred Jackson — Blue Note 4068/84068 (1961) with NY address on label **$45**; with NY on label **$35**; with A Division of Liberty on label **$15**.

STOP AND LISTEN/with Grant Green — Blue Note 4084/84084 (1961) with NY on label **$35**; with A Division of Liberty on label **$15**.

NO ROCK — Argo 739 (1964) **$30**.

BEHIND THE 8 BALL — Argo 749 (1965) **$30**.

ANN WILLIAMS
vocals

FIRST TIME OUT/with Clark Terry — Charlie Parker 807 (1960) **$25**.

ANTHONY "TONY" WILLIAMS
drums, composer - born 1945 Chicago, IL

LIFE TIME/with Sam Rivers — Blue Note 4180/84180 (1964) with NY on label **$30**; with A Division of Liberty on label **$15**. Ⓐ

"COOTIE" WILLIAMS
trumpet, leader - born 1908 Mobile, AL

Williams enjoyed much success as a soloist with Duke Ellington from 1929-40, afterwhich he went with Benny Goodman for a year. He made many recordings in that era including Concerto for Cootie, written for him by Ellington. Through the 40's he led a band of his own which, due to changes in the music business, was down to a combo by the 50's and, eventually, he was working as a single with local rhythm sections. In 1962 he rejoined the Ellington Band.

IN HI FI/with Band — RCA Victor 1718 (1958) dog on top **$60**.

AROUND MIDNIGHT/with Wini Brown — Jaro 5001 (1959) **$60**.

DO NOTHING TILL YOU HEAR FROM ME — Warwick 2027 (1959) **$60**.

COOTIE & REX IN THE BIG CHALLENGE/with Rex Stewart, Coleman Hawkins, and Bud Freeman — Jazztone 1268 (1957) **$45**; *reissued* American Recording Society 448 (1958) **$50**.

THE SOLID TRUMPET OF — Moodsville 27 (1962) **$45**.

HERBIE WILLIAMS
soprano sax

THE SOUL AND SOUND OF — Workshop 216 (1963) **$35**.

JOE WILLIAMS
vocals - born 1918 Cordele, GA

Williams first achieved popularity with the Count Basie Band from 1954-61. During this period the combination of Basie's band and Williams' vocals proved to be very successful, resulting in many recordings and a considerable number of engagements. Williams went out on his own in 1961 and has continued to be successful but in recording more commercial tunes. Nonetheless, he has retained the admiration of jazz fans through continuing work in that area.

SINGS EVERYDAY EVERYDAY — Regent 6002 (1956) green label **$45**.

MAN AIN'T SUPPOSED TO CRY — Roulette 52005 (1958) white label with multicolored pinwheel, mono; light and dark orange checked roulette wheel label, stereo **$35**.

SINGS ABOUT YOU!/with Jimmy Jones — Roulette 52030 (1959) white label with multicolored pinwheel, mono; light and dark orange checked roulette wheel label, stereo **$35**.

THAT KIND OF WOMAN — Roulette 52039 (1959) white label with multicolored pinwheel, mono; light and dark orange checked roulette wheel, stereo **$35**.

SENTIMENTAL & MELANCHOLY — Roulette 52066 (1960) white label with multicolored pinwheel, mono; light and dark orange checked roulette wheel label, stereo **$30**.

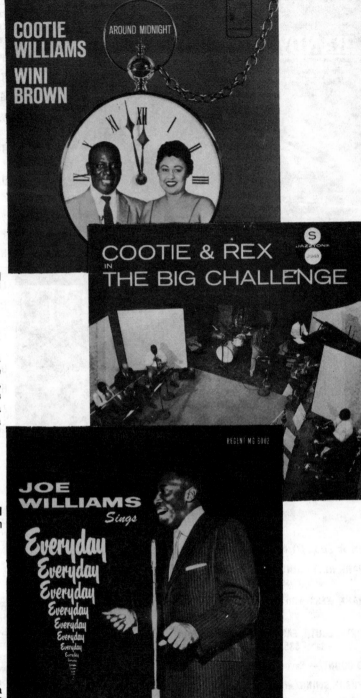

TOGETHER/with Harry "Sweets" Edison — Roulette 52069 (1961) white label with multicolored pinwheel, mono; light and dark orange checked roulette wheel label, stereo **$40**.

HAVE A GOOD TIME — Roulette 52071 (1961) white label with multicolored pinwheel, mono; light and dark orange checked roulette wheel label, stereo **$25**.

SWINGIN' NIGHT AT BIRDLAND — Roulette 52085 (1962) white label with multicolored pinwheel, mono; light and dark orange checked roulette wheel label, stereo **$35**.

ONE IS A LONESOME NUMBER — Roulette 52102 (1962) white label with multicolored pinwheel, mono; light and dark orange checked roulette wheel label, stereo **$25**.

JUMP FOR JOY — RCA Victor 2713 (1963) dog on top **$20**.

AT NEWPORT '63 — RCA Victor 2762 (1963) dog on top **$35**.

ME & THE BLUES — RCA Victor 2879 (1963) dog on top **$25**.

SONG IS YOU — RCA Victor 3343 (1965) dog on top **$20**.

JOHN WILLIAMS
piano, composer - born 1929 Windsor, VT

After gigs around Boston and in the Army, Williams teamed up with big name musicians such as Zoot Sims, Stan Getz and Charlie Barnet. An admitted admirer of Hank Jones, Williams possesses the ability to do justice to a rhythm section or a solo performance. He is an excellent sideman who has been recorded on several labels with other fine musicians.

JOHN WILLIAMS — EmArcy 26047 (1954) 10" **$50**; EP 1-6091, EP 1-6092 (1954) **$20 ea.**

TRIO — EmArcy 36061 (1955) **$45**.

*KEITH WILLIAMS
trumpet, arranger

BIG BAND JAZZ THEMES — Edison 501 (1960) **$15**.

The only LP's within the scope of this book.

MARY LOU WILLIAMS
piano, composer - born 1910 Pittsburgh, PA died 1981

A fine pianist, Ms. Williams first wrote for and then worked with the Andy Kirk Group from 1931-42. During that time, her composing and arranging abilities became well known. After leaving Kirk's group, she began writing and arranging for bands such as Benny Goodman and Duke Ellington while continuing to integrate the newer styles into her own playing. Ms. Williams worked in Europe for a couple of years in the mid-50's, retired for a couple of years and returned to music and renewed popularity and respect in the early 60's.

MARY LOU WILLIAMS/with Don Byas — Stinson 24 (1950) 10" **$100**.

JAZZ VARIATION/with Coleman Hawkins — Stinson 29 (1950) 10" **$100**.

PROGRESSIVE PIANO STYLINGS/with Mundell Lowe — King 295-85 (1953) 10" **$50**; EP 279, EP 280 (1953) **$25 ea.**

PIANO PANORAMA - Vol 2 — Atlantic 114 (1951) 10" **$50**; *reissued* Atlantic 1271.

LADIES IN JAZZ/with Barbara Carroll — Atlantic 1271 (1957) black label **$35**; EP 518 (1957) **$15**; one side only which is a *reissue* of Atlantic 114.

MARY LOU — EmArcy 26033 (1954) 10" **$50**.

PIANO CONTEMPO — Circle 412 (1951) 10" **$60**.

MARY LOU WILLIAMS: PIANO '53 — Contemporary 2507 (1953) 10" **$50**.

A KEYBOARD HISTORY — Jazztone 1206 (1956) **$45**.

RICHARD WILLIAMS
trumpet, composer - born 1931 Galveston, TX

NEW HORN IN TOWN/with Leo Wright — Candid 8003/9003 (1960) **$45**.

STU WILLIAMSON
trumpet - born 1933 Battleboro, VT

PLAYS/with Charlie Mariano — Bethlehem 1024 (1955) 10" **$80**; *reissued* Bethlehem 31 (1956) maroon label **$45**.

STU WILLIAMSON/with Charlie Mariano — Bethlehem 55 (1956) maroon label **$45**.

GERALD WILSON
composer, leader, trumpet - born 1918 Shelby, MA

BIG BAND MODERN — Audio Lab 1538 (1959) **$40**.

YOU BETTER BELIEVE IT — Pacific Jazz 34 (1961) **$25**.

MOMENT OF TRUTH — Pacific Jazz 61 (1962) **$25**.

PORTRAITS — Pacific Jazz 80 (1963) **$20**.

ON STAGE — Pacific Jazz 88 (1965) **$20**.

JACK WILSON
piano - born 1936 Chicago, IL

QUARTET/with Roy Ayers — Atlantic 1406 (1963) with logo on right side **$25**.

NANCY WILSON
vocals - born 1937 Chillicothe, OH

LIKE IN LOVE/with Billy May — Capitol 1319 (1959) black label with logo on left side **$35**; *reissued* Capitol 1319 (1963) black label with logo on top **$20**.

SOMETHING WONDERFUL/with Billy May — Capitol 1440 (1960) black label with logo on left side **$35**; *reissued* Capitol 1440 (1963) black label with logo on top **$20**.

SWINGIN'S MUTUAL/with George Shearing — Capitol 1524 (1961) black label with logo on left side **$40**; *reissued* Capitol 1524 (1964) black label with logo on top **$20**.

NANCY WILSON/CANNONBALL ADDERLEY — Capitol 1657 (1961) black label with logo on left side **$40**; *reissued* Capitol 1657 (1964) black label with logo on top **$25**.

HELLO YOUNG LOVERS/with George Shearing — Capitol 1767 (1962) black label with logo on top **$25**.

BROADWAY-MY WAY/with Jimmy Jones — Capitol 1828 (1963) black label with logo on top **$20**.

HOLLYWOOD-MY WAY/with Jimmy Jones — Capitol 1934 (1963) black label with logo on top **$20**.

YESTERDAY'S LOVE SONGS...TODAY'S BLUES/with Gerald Wilson — Capitol 2012 (1963) black label with logo on top **$15**.

TODAY, TOMORROW, FOREVER/with Kenny Dennis — Capitol 2082 (1964) black label with logo on top **$15**.

*TEDDY WILSON
piano, composer - born 1912 Austin, TX

TOWN HALL CONCERT/with Don Byas and Flip Phillips — Commodore 20,029 (1950) 10" **$75**.

TEDDY WILSON FEATURING BILLIE HOLIDAY — Columbia 6040 (1950) 10" **$75**; *reissued* Columbia 637 (1956) **$45**.

TEDDY WILSON ALL STARS/with Flip Phillips — Dial 213 (1950) 10" **$75**.

RUNNIN' WILD/with Buck Clayton and Ben Webster — MGM 129 (1951) 10" **$75**.

ALL STAR SEXTET/with Don Byas — Allegro 4031 (1954) 10" **$60**.

ALL STAR SEXTET/with Charlie Shavers — Allegro 4024 (1954) 10" **$60**.

*The only LP's within the scope of this book.

LEM WINCHESTER
vibes - born 1928 Philadelphia, PA

WINCHESTER SPECIAL/with Benny Golson — New Jazz 8223 (1959) **$40**.

LEM'S BEAT/with Oliver Nelson — New Jazz 8239 (1960) **$40**.

ANOTHER OPUS/with Frank Wess — New Jazz 8244 (1960) **$40**.

WITH FEELING — Moodsville 11 (1960) **$30**.

KAI WINDING
trombone, composer - born 1922 Aarhus, Denmark died 1983

NEW TRENDS OF JAZZ/with Shorty Rogers — Savoy 9017 (1953) 10" **$95**; EP 8114 (1953) **$45**.

ALL STARS/with Brew Moore — Roost 408 (1952) 10" **$100**; *reissued* Jazztone 1231.

EARLY MODERN/with Sonny Stitt — Jazztone 1231 (1956) **$45**; *reissued* Jazztone 1263 (1957) **$40**; *reissues* of Roost 408.

TROMBONE SOUND/with Carl Fontana — Columbia 936 (1956) red label with 3 black logos on each side **$45**.

TROMBONE PANORAMA/with Carl Fontana — Columbia 999 (1957) red label with 3 black logos on each side **$45**.

SWINGIN' STATE — Columbia 1264 (1958) red label with 3 black logos on each side **$45**.

DANCE TO THE CITY BEAT — Columbia 1329/8136 (1959) red label with 3 black logos on each side **$35**.

THE INCREDIBLE — Impulse 3 (1960) orange label **$35**.

KAI OLE/with Orchestra — Verve 8427/68427 (1961) with MGM on bottom of label **$25**.

SUSPENSE THEMES IN JAZZ — Verve 8493/68493 (1962) with MGM on bottom of label **$35**.

KAI WINDING SOLO — Verve 8525/68525 (1963) with MGM on bottom of label **$35**.

MORE — Verve 8551/68551 (1963) with MGM on bottom of label **$20**.

KAI WINDING — Verve 8556/68556 (1963) with MGM on bottom of label **$20**.

MONDO CANE — Verve 8573/68573 (1964) with MGM on bottom of label **$20**.

MODERN COUNTRY — Verve 8602/68602 (1964) with MGM on bottom of label **$20**.

TROMBONES: FEATURING THE AXIDENTALS — Pickwick 3004 (1965) silver label **$10**.

PAUL WINTER
alto sax, composer, leader - born 1939 Altoona, PA

JAZZ MEETS THE BOSSA NOVA — Columbia 1925/8725 (1962) red label with 1 white logo on each side **$20**.

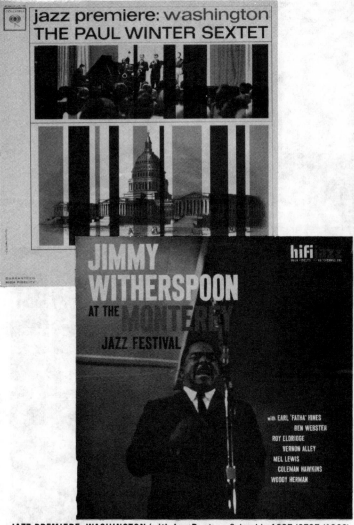

JAZZ PREMIERE: WASHINGTON/with Les Rout — Columbia 1997/8797 (1962) red label with 1 white logo on each side **$25**.

NEW JAZZ ON CAMPUS/with Jay Cameron — Columbia 2064/8864 (1963) red label with 1 white logo on each side **$25**.

JAZZ MEETS THE FOLK SONG/with Dick Whitsell — Columbia 2155/8955 (1963) red label with 1 white logo on each side **$20**.

THE SOUND OF IPANEMA/with Carlos Lyra — Columbia 2272/9072 (1965) red label with 1 white logo on each side **$15**.

RIO/with Luiz Bonfa — Columbia 2315/9115 (1965) red label with 1 white logo on each side **$15**.

*JIMMY WITHERSPOON
vocals - born 1923 Gurdon, AK

NEW ORLEANS BLUES/with Wilbur DeParis — Atlantic 1266 (1956) black label **$45**; EP 600 (1956) **$20**.

GOIN' TO KANSAS CITY BLUES/with Jay McShann and Seldon Powell — RCA Victor 1639 (1958) dog on top **$40**.

SINGIN' THE BLUES/with Teddy Edwards — World Pacific 1267 (1959) **$35**; *reissued* World Pacific 1402.

THERE'S GOOD ROCKIN' TONIGHT — World Pacific 1402 (1961) **$20**; *reissue* of World Pacific 1267.

AT THE MONTEREY JAZZ FESTIVAL/with Coleman Hawkins and Ben Webster — Hi Fi 421 (1959) **$35**.

AT THE RENAISSANCE/with Gerry Mulligan — Hi Fi 426 (1959) **$35**.

SPOON/with Teddy Edwards and Herbie Harper — Reprise 2008/92008 (1961) **$25**.

ROOTS/with Ben Webster — Reprise 6059/96059 (1962) **$25**.

BABY, BABY, BABY/with Leo Wright and Kenny Burrell — Prestige 7290 (1963) yellow label $35.

SOME OF MY BEST FRIENDS ARE THE BLUES/with Benny Golson — Prestige 7356 (1964) blue label with logo on right side $30.

BLUES FOR SPOON AND GROOVE/with Richard Groove Holmes — Surrey 1006 (1965) $20.

---

*The only LP's within the scope of this book.

JIMMY WOODS
alto, tenor saxes - born 1934 St. Louis, MO

AWAKENING/with Joe Gordon — Contemporary 3605/7605 (1962) yellow label $25.

CONFLICT/with Carmell Jones and Harold Land — Contemporary 3612/7612 (1963) yellow label $25.

PHIL WOODS
alto sax - born 1931 Springfield, MA

A Parker-inspired altoist who worked from the mid-50's on with the bands of Dizzy Gillespie, Gene Quill, Buddy Rich and Thad Jones. In the 60's, Woods worked with groupings of his own and with other prominent jazz artists and became involved in television, studio work and teaching. Woods is no copycat; his style is his own despite the obvious origins and he is an inspired soloist who is in command of his instrument.

PHIL WOODS/with Jon Eardley — New Jazz 1104 (1954) 10" $125; *reissued* Prestige 204.

PHIL WOODS NEW JAZZ QUINTET — Prestige 204 (1955) 10" $100, *reissued* New Jazz 8291.

WOODLORE — Prestige 7018 (1955) yellow label $75.

PAIRING OFF/with Donald Byrd — Prestige 7046 (1956) yellow label $70.

YOUNGBLOODS/with Donald Byrd — Prestige 7080 (1956) yellow label $70.

RIGHTS OF SWING — Candid 8016/9016 (1962) $45.

POT PIE — New Jazz 8291 (1963) $35; *reissue* of Prestige 204.

LARRY "WILD" WRICE

WILD — Pacific Jazz 24 (1961) $25.

JOHN WRIGHT
piano

SOUTH SIDE SOUL — Prestige 7190 (1960) yellow label $45.

NICE & NASTY — Prestige 7197 (1960) yellow label $45.

MAKIN' OUT — Prestige 7212 (1961) yellow label $40.

MR. SOUL — Prestige 7233 (1961) yellow label $40.

LEO WRIGHT
alto sax, clarinet, flute - born 1933 Wichita Falls, TX

Wright first recorded with Dizzy Gillespie in 1959 and worked with him until 1961 when he recorded his first LP as a leader. He performed in the New York City area, recording with many other artists before moving to Europe to live and continue working musically.

BLUES SHOUT/with Junior Mance — Atlantic 1358 (1960) with logo on right side $25.

SUDDENLY THE BLUES/with Kenny Burrell — Atlantic 1393 (1962) with logo on right side $20.

NAT WRIGHT
vocals

THE BIGGEST VOICE IN JAZZ/with Coleman Hawkins — Warwick 2040 (1960) $50.

ELDEE YOUNG
bass - born 1936 Chicago, IL

ELDEE YOUNG & CO.; JUST FOR KICKS/with Leo Wright — Argo 699 (1961) $45.

JOHN YOUNG
piano - born 1922 Little Rock, AK

YOUNG JOHN YOUNG/with Herbert Brown — Argo 612 (1958) $20.

THEMES AND THINGS/with William Yancey — Argo 692 (1961) $20.

A TOUCH OF PEPPER — Argo 713 (1962) $20.

LARRY YOUNG
organ, composer - born 1940 Newark, NJ died 1978

Originally known as a blues player in the late 50's, Young continued to evolve, working his way into the 60's with the groups of Donald Byrd, Grant Green, Tommy Turrentine and Hank Mobley. He played and recorded in a bop organ style that was undoubtedly unique in its flexibility. Young's first big recording hit was in 1960 and he continued to record intermittently throughout the 60's.

TESTIFYING/with Joe Holiday — New Jazz 8249 (1960) $35.

YOUNG BLUES/with Wendell Marshall — New Jazz 8264 (1960) $35.

GROOVE STREET/with Bill Leslie — Prestige 7237 (1962) yellow label $45.

INTO SOMETHIN' — Blue Note 4187 (1964) with NY on label $45.

LESTER "PREZ" YOUNG
tenor sax, composer - born 1909 Woodville, MS died 1959

As a child, Young played and traveled in a family band and by the late 20's was performing in bands in the Midwest and Southwest. This early experience led to better and better groupings, and the mid-30's found him in the company of such greats as Count Basie, Fletcher Henderson and Andy Kirk. With Basie in 1936, Young experienced the recordings that were to make him famous and start him on the road to becoming a powerful influence on other saxmen, in particular, and to jazz in general for the next 20 years. His influence was essentially that of an introspect or "cool" approach as contrasted with the more extroverted "hot" styles of the players who had gone before him. In the 40's, Young worked with groups of his own and big name groups such as JATP and, of course, we should all know of the great collaborations of Prez or Pres and Lady Day; the late, great Billie Holiday. Along with Coleman Hawkins, Young is considered to be a most significant influence on jazz via saxophone.

QUARTET — Mercury 25015 (1950) 10" **$250**; EP 1-3046 (1950) **$60**; *reissued* EmArcy 26021.

ALL STAR BE-BOP/with Jesse Drake — Savoy 9002 (1951) 10" **$150**; EP 8016, EP 8017 (1951) **$50 ea.**; *reissued* Savoy 12068.

BLUE LESTER — Savoy 12068 (1956) maroon label **$45**; *reissue* of Savoy 9002.

MASTER'S TOUCH — Savoy 12071 (1956) maroon label **$45**.

IMMORTAL — Savoy 12155 (1959) maroon label **$35**.

TRIO/with Nat King Cole — Aladdin 705 (1953) 10" **$125**; EP 502, EP 506, EP 507 (1953) **$45 ea.**; *reissued* Score 4019.

HIS TENOR SAX/with Red Callender — Aladdin 706 (1953) 10" **$125**; EP 503, EP 513 (1953) **$45 ea.**

AND HIS TENOR SAX - Vol 1/with Howard McGhee — Aladdin 801 (1956) **$95**.

AND HIS TENOR SAX - Vol 2/with Rodney Richardson — Aladdin 802 (1956) **$95**.

KANSAS CITY STYLE — Commodore 20,021 (1950) 10" **$175**; *reissued* Commodore 30014 (1959) **$55**.

PRES MEETS VICE-PRES/with Paul Quinichette — EmArcy 26021 (1954) 10" **$150**; EP 1-6002, EP 1-6006 (1954) **$60 ea.**

TRIO/with Buddy Rich — Clef 104 (1951) 10" **$150**; EP 177, EP 178 (1951) **$60 ea.**; *reissued* Norgran 1074.

TRIO #2 — Clef 135 (1953) 10" **$150**; EP 179, EP 180 (1953) **$60 ea.**; *reissued* Norgran 1074.

COLLATES/with Ray Brown — Clef 108 (1952) 10" **$120**; EP 122, EP 124 (1952) **$50 ea.**; *reissued* Norgran 1072.

COLLATES #2/with John Lewis — Clef 124 (1953) 10" **$120**, EP 174, EP 175 (1953) **$50 ea.**; *reissued* in part Norgran 1071.

WITH OSCAR PETERSON — Norgran 5 (1952) 10" **$100**; EP 8 (1952) **$45**; *reissued* Norgran 1054.

WITH OSCAR PETERSON — Norgran 6 (1952) 10" **$100**; EP 9 (1952) **$45**; *reissued* Norgran 1054.

THE PRESIDENT/with John Lewis — Norgran 1005 (1954) **$75**; EP 29 (1954) **$40**; *reissued* Norgran 1093.

LESTER YOUNG/with Connie Kay — Norgran 1022 (1954) **$75**; EP 111, EP 112, EP 113 (1954) **$30 ea.**; *reissued* Verve 8187.

PRES AND SWEETS/with Harry Edison — Norgran 1043 (1955) **$70**; *reissued* Verve 8134 (1957) with Verve Records, Inc. on bottom of label **$60**.

THE PRESIDENT PLAYS WITH THE OSCAR PETERSON TRIO — Norgran 1054 (1955) **$70**; *reissued* Verve 8144 (1957) with Verve Records, Inc. on bottom of label **$60**; *reissues of Norgran 5 and 6.*

LESTER'S HERE — Norgran 1071 (1955) **$70**; *reissued* Verve 8161 (1957) with Verve Records, Inc. on bottom of label **$60**; *reissue* in part of Clef 124.

PRES — Norgran 1072 (1955) **$70**; *reissued* Verve 8162 (1957) with Verve Records, Inc. on bottom of label **$60**; *reissue* of Clef 108.

LESTER YOUNG-BUDDY RICH TRIO — Norgran 1074 (1955) **$70**; *reissued* Verve 8164 (1957) with Verve Records, Inc. on bottom of label **$60**; *reissue* of Clef 104.

LESTER SWINGS AGAIN — Norgran 1093 (1956) **$65**; *reissued* Verve 8181 (1957) with Verve Records, Inc. on bottom of label **$60**; *reissue* of Norgran 1005.

IT DON'T MEAN A THING — Verve 8187 (1957) with Verve Records, Inc. on bottom of label **$55**; *reissue* of Norgran 1022.

PRES AND TEDDY/with Teddy Wilson — Verve 8205 (1957) with Verve Records, Inc. on bottom of label **$55**; American Recording Society 417 (1957) **$65**.

GOING FOR MYSELF/with Harry Edison — Verve 8298 (1959) with Verve Records, Inc. on bottom of label **$45**.

THE LESTER YOUNG STORY — Verve 8308 (1959) with Verve Records, Inc. on bottom of label **$45**.

LAUGHIN' TO KEEP FROM CRYING/with Roy Eldridge and Harry Edison — Verve 8316/6054 (1959) with Verve Records, Inc. on bottom of label **$50**.

IN PARIS/with Kenny Clarke — Verve 8378 (1959) with Verve Records, Inc. on bottom of label **$45** (recorded just before his death).

THE ESSENTIAL — Verve 8398 (1961) with MGM on bottom of label **$40**.

LESTER LEAPS IN/with Count Basie — Epic 3107 (1956) yellow label **$60**.

LET'S GO TO PREZ/with Count Basie — Epic 3168 (1956) yellow label **$60**.

MEMORIAL ALBUM — Epic 6031 (1959) 2 LPs **$65**.

MEMORIAL ALBUM - Vol 1 — Epic 3576 (1959) yellow label **$40**.

MEMORIAL ALBUM - Vol 2 — Epic 3577 (1959) yellow label **$40**.

GREATEST — Intro 603 (1957) **$55**; *reissued* Score 4029 (1958) **$45**.

SWINGING — Intro 602 (1957) **$55**; *reissued* Score 4028 (1958) **$45**.

LESTER YOUNG - NAT KING COLE TRIO — Score 4019 (1958) **$45**; *reissue* of Aladdin 705.

PREZ AND CHU/with Chu Berry — Jazztone 1218 (1956) **$45**; one side only.

PRES — Charlie Parker 402 (1962) **$30**.

PRES IS BLUE — Charlie Parker 405 (1962) **$30**.

PREZ — Mainstream 56012/6012 (1965) **$30**; *reissue* of Commodore matter.

WEBSTER YOUNG
trumpet - born 1932 Columbia, SC

FOR LADY/with Paul Quinichette — Prestige 7106 (1957) yellow label **$75**.

DENNY ZEITLIN
piano - born 1938 Chicago, IL

CATHEXIS — Columbia 2182/8982 (1963) red label with 1 white logo on each side **$25**.

CARNIVAL — Columbia 2340/9140 (1965) red label with 1 white logo on each side **$25**.

DO YOU KNOW IF YOUR RECORD COLLECTION IS ADEQUATELY PROTECTED AGAINST LOSS?

LIST YOUR RECORD COLLECTION UNDER A GENERAL HOMEOWNERS POLICY

If you do not have your record collection listed separately in your general homeowners policy, in the event of a loss, you would be paid only a fraction of your collection's actual value.

For example, if a record worth $300.00 in mint condition, is destroyed in a fire, the insurance company would only be able to give you 10% of the ORIGINAL COST of the Record. Since this record may have been released in 1955 and sold for 89¢, you would receive 9¢ for your record!

OBTAIN COMPLETE COVERAGE FOR YOUR COLLECTION

Getting FULL coverage for your record valuables is SIMPLE. It can be accomplished in two easy steps:

1. Make a list of your records. Using the O'Sullivan Woodside Price Guides for Collectible Records, Write down:

*
      1. Name of artist
      2. Title of record
      3. Label and number
      4. Price value

2. Call your insurance agent and tell him you have an itemized list of records that you want protected with your household goods on your homeowners or renters policy or highlight your record collection in the O'Sullivan Woodside Guide and turn the guide in to your agent.

* If you do not have all the information listed above, simply inform your insurance agent that you have records which need to be listed with your general household goods. Many insurance companies are currently using the Record Collector's Price Guides to appraise collections.

Pictures Really Do Say A Thousand Words . . .

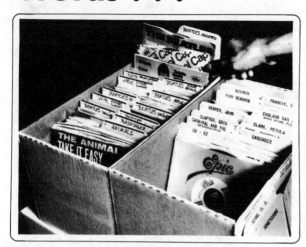

At **NOSTALGIA CORRUGATED** we sell *Organization!* These photographs say it best.

If your collection is in disarray or, if it takes you hours to find the record you want, then *you need us.* We were the first to design and produce the one product record collectors and retailers have been asking for all along — sturdy, inexpensive, lightweight, and great looking 45 and LP storage cases with custom fitting divider cards.

Although we've been imitated by box makers, our products have been consistently improved and upgraded to meet your highest standards. You see, we were collectors long before we ever made a box. We love records old and new and know their value to you.

Let **NOSTALGIA CORRUGATED** organize and protect your investment today.

THE NEW AND IMPROVED CARD.

- White in color, Plastic-coated for longer life.
- Designed to fit just about anywhere you keep records, even our competitors' boxes.
- Designed for easy scan. Won't bury your records.
- Easy to stagger. Glossy and flat surface on each.
- Grease, oil, fingerprint, and water resistant. Washable.
- Will accommodate standard office stick-on labels.
- Won't dog-ear or fray.
- The more you buy, the more you save!

THE BOX.

- Die recently upgraded for better fit and cleaner appearance.
- Strong enough to support a 200-lb. man.
- Stackable. Stack 3,4, or 5-up easy without risking collapse.
- Heat-tested in the desert Southwest, to withstand high outside temperatures while in transit.
- Attractive flat-white finish blends with any decor.
- Easy to assemble, no guesswork.
- Lightweight for easy transport.
- LP case holds 75 LPs, 45 case holds 150 singles.
- No gluing, stapling, or taping needed.
- The number-one most-requested corrugated record case in America.
- **NO CASH, CHECK, OR MONEY ORDER REQUIRED. USE YOUR VISA OR MASTERCHARGE FOR CONVENIENCE.**
- **SATISFACTION GUARANTEED, OR YOUR MONEY BACK!**

Merchandise Costs			
QTY		RATE	TOTAL
45 DIVIDER CARDS 7½" x 7¾"			
	1-100	17¢ ea.	
	100 min.	13¢	$13.00
	101-250	11¢	
	251-500	9¢	
	501-1000	7¢	
LP DIVIDER CARDS 12 3/16" x 13⅛"			
	1-100	22¢ ea.	
	100 min.	20¢	$20.00
	101-250	17¢	
	251-500	15¢	
	501-750	12¢	
45 BOXES (15" x 7¾" x 7¾")			
	1-5	$2.25 ea.	
	6-10	$2.10	
	11+	$1.95	
LP BOXES (12"x13"x13")			
	1-5	$2.75 ea.	
	6-10	$2.50	
	11+	$2.25	
TOTAL MDSE. COSTS			

Shipping Information			
DIVIDER CARDS	45s	LPs	RATE
100 or less	3.50	4.75	
101-250	4.50	7.50	
251-500	6.00	10.00	
501-1000	10.00	20.00	

Note: 100 card minimum when ordering cards only.

Box Customers: If ordering Divider Cards also, subtract $2.00 off applicable card shipping rates above.

45 BOX SHIPPING RATES*

*First Box: $2.75

Additional boxes: 35¢

*If ordering both 45 & LP boxes, use $3.95 only for first box rate.

LP BOX SHIPPING RATES*

*First Box: $3.95

Additional boxes: 50¢

TOTAL SHP. COSTS

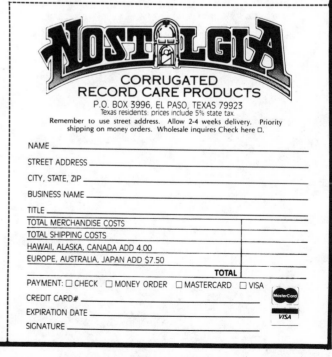